MODERN ASPECTS OF
# MASS SPECTROMETRY

# MODERN ASPECTS OF
# MASS SPECTROMETRY

Edited by

## Rowland I. Reed

*Department of Chemistry*
*The University of Glasgow*
*Glasgow, Scotland*

Proceedings of the Second NATO Advanced Study Institute
of Mass Spectrometry on Theory, Design, and Applications,
held July 1966 at the University of Glasgow, Glasgow, Scotland

℗ **PLENUM PRESS • NEW YORK • 1968**

Library of Congress Catalog Card Number 68-16994

© 1968 Plenum Press
A Division of Plenum Publishing Corporation
227 West 17 Street, New York, N. Y. 10011
All rights reserved

# FOREWORD

Recent major developments in the field of mass spectrometry, in particular, the great progress made in instrumentation in the last few years, are reflected in this volume, which is derived from the second NATO Advance Study Institute of Mass Spectrometry held at the University of Glasgow in July 1966.

While the NATO course was essentially a practical one, emphasis was placed, with the whole-hearted cooperation of the mass spectroscopists concerned, on a concurrent series of lectures and thus a comprehensive survey of the field was achieved. In this volume, which is based on the lectures, all aspects of instrumentation—a consideration of supreme importance to the subject—are surveyed by experts in the field. The volume also contains papers about metastable ions, some studies on organic mass spectrometry, physical problems related to the subject, including the difficult question of the existence of selection rules, as well as significant contributions to the theory of ion production. A paper about the collection of mass spectral data, a problem of international concern, is also included.

The papers included in the volume may be regarded as authoritative within the different branches of the discipline here reported and as such should be of much value to all those interested in the subject from beginning students to research workers already possessed of considerable experience.

I am extremely indebted to the instrument manufacturers for their cooperation; particularly A.E.I. Ltd., Manchester; E.A.I. Ltd., Palo Alto; 20th Century Electronics Ltd., Croydon; Bendix, Cincinnati; Field-Tech Ltd., London; Edwards Ltd., London; Fraser Electronics, Glasgow, for the loan of equipment and staff to explain it; and Varian Ltd., Zurich, for a last-minute contribution to the lectures.

I am also greatly indebted to I.C.I. Ltd., not only for providing lecturers, but also for the services of (the late) Dr. H. C. Hill and R. C. Coombes, both of whom provided instruction in the operation of mass spectrometers and in the complex problem of structure analysis.

The success of such a venture will necessarily depend upon the lecturers, the associated staff, and the publisher. In all three areas of endeavor, the response was remarkable and highly successful. For the most part, the lectures are here to be read while the efforts of Mr. R. Ubell and the Plenum Publishing Corporation may be recognized in this production.

I acknowledge the great assistance I have received from the University Court for permission to stage this Institute within the University, to the Head of the Department of Chemistry for permission to use its facilities, to the Finance Office for the accounting, to Miss H. Calder, Principal of the West of Scotland College of Domestic Science, for accommodation, and to Mr. J. Preston for the printing of the brochure.

Finally I must express my gratitude to NATO for the provision of the financial support necessary to stage this Institute and to Dr. J. C. Cade and his colleagues in the Science Affairs Division for their cheerful cooperation.

Rowland Ivor Reed

Glasgow
October 1967

# NATO INSTITUTE LECTURERS

| A. E. Banner | *Associated Electrical Industries Limited, Urmston, Manchester, England* |
| M. Barber | *Associated Electrical Industries Limited, Urmston, Manchester, England* |
| J. H. Beynon | *Imperial Chemical Industries Limited, Blackley, Manchester, England* |
| R. Brown | *Associated Electrical Industries Limited, Urmston, Manchester, England* |
| H. Budzikiewicz | *Institut für Organische Chemie, Technische Hochschule, Braunschweig, West Germany* |
| J. E. Collin | *Institut de Chimie, Université de Liège, Belgium* |
| R. D. Craig | *Associated Electrical Industries Limited, Urmston, Manchester, England* |
| J. A. Dadswell | *Edwards High Vacuum Limited, Crawley, Sussex, England* |
| D. C. Damoth | *Bendix Corporation, Cincinnati, Ohio, U.S.A.* |
| A. E. Fontaine | *Imperial Chemical Industries Limited, Blackley, Manchester, England* |
| I. Goldfinger | *Faculté de Sciences, Université Libre de Bruxelles, Belgium* |
| H. C. Hill[†] | *Imperial Chemical Industries Limited, Billingham, England* |
| G. R. Lester | *Imperial Chemical Industries Limited, Blackley, Manchester, England* |

A. Maccoll            *Department of Chemistry, University College, London, England*

M. T. Mason           *20th Century Electronics Limited, New Addington, Croydon, Surrey, England*

R. I. Reed            *Department of Chemistry, The University of Glasgow, Glasgow, Scotland*

R. G. Ridley          *United Kingdom Atomic Energy Authority, Aldermaston, Berkshire, England*

U. Scheidegger        *Varian A.G., Zurick 8, Switzerland*

R. C. Svedberg        *Department of Metallurgy, Imperial College of Science and Technology, London, England*

P. Swift              *Associated Electrical Industries Limited, Urmston, Manchester, England*

M. E. Wacks           *College of Engineering, The University of Arizona, Tucson, Arizona, U.S.A.*

A. E. Williams        *Imperial Chemical Industries Limited, Blackley, Manchester, England*

H. W. Wilson          *Scottish Reactor Centre, East Kilbride, Scotland*

# NATO INSTITUTE TECHNICAL STAFF

J. Ball | *20th Century Electronics Limited, Croydon, Surrey England*

J. Calvert | *Chemistry Department, The University of Glasgow, Glasgow, Scotland*

R. Coombes | *Imperial Chemical Industries Limited, Billingham, Durham, England*

J. A. Hardy | *Chemistry Deparment, The University of Glasgow, Glasgow, Scotland*

M. Harper | *Associated Electrical Industries Limited, Urmston, Manchester, England*

M. T. T. Lopes | *Chemistry Department, The University of Glasgow, Glasgow, Scotland*

J. W. W. MacLean | *Chemistry Department, The University of Glasgow, Glasgow, Scotland*

L. F. Monteiro | *Chemistry Department, The University of Glasgow, Glasgow, Scotland*

N. Morris | *Chemistry Department, The University of Glasgow, Glasgow, Scotland*

F. J. Preston | *Chemistry Department, The University of Glasgow, Glasgow, Scotland*

W. M. Scott | *Scottish Reactor Centre, East Kilbride, Scotland*

M. Slany | *Chemistry Department, The University of Glasgow, Scotland*

V. Takhistov | *Chemistry Department, The University of Glasgow, Scotland*

J. E. Williams | *FieldTech Limited, Heathrow Airport, London, England*

# CONTENTS

# THE DEVELOPMENT OF MASS SPECTROMETRY IN RELATION TO GAS-LIQUID CHROMATOGRAPHY

## Aubrey E. Banner

*Scientific Apparatus Department*
*Associated Electrical Industries Limited*
*Urmston, Lancashire, England*

## INTRODUCTION

The combination of a continuous sampling mass spectrometer and a gas chromatograph column provides an extremely powerful analytical technique, but there are certain stringent conditions which must be met in the design of a mass spectrometer for such applications.

### Mass Range

In most gas–liquid chromatography (g.l.c.) applications, the greatest sample molecular weight is not likely to exceed about 600. It is, therefore, necessary for the mass spectrometer, at maximum ion-accelerating voltage, to cover the mass range from $m/e$ 1 to a minimum of $m/e$ 600. The molecular ion peak must also be clearly distinguished from the adjacent peak, if present, and so the resolving power must be at least 600, using the definition in which two peaks of equal height are said to be resolved if the valley between them is 10% of the peak height.

### Sensitivity

#### Limit of Detection

It is clearly essential for the ion source sensitivity to be as high as possible in order that very small quantities of sample may be satisfactorily observed, but for any given source sensitivity the minimum limit of detection (i.e., the smallest usable sample size) is determined by the noise level of the mass spectrometer. This comprises electronic noise in the recording system,

1

ion noise at the collector input, and background noise due to residual gases in the vacuum system. The first of these effects can be minimized by careful design, but single stray ions will generally be observed if the collector system employs an electron multiplier, thus setting a fundamental minimum detection limit. If this limit is to be maintained, however, it is necessary to ensure extreme cleanliness in the source vacuum system, involving provision for baking it to high temperatures (approximately 350 °C).

### Dynamic Range

A typical g.l.c. sample will contain several components covering a very wide range of relative proportions (of the order of $10^4$ to 1); it is, therefore, important for the mass spectrometer to cover as wide a dynamic range as possible. One way of achieving this is to employ a multichannel recording system.

## Variation of Relative Sensitivity with Resolving Power and Scan Time

For general applications, frequently involving samples of molecular weights considerably greater than those encountered in normal g.l.c. work, a correspondingly higher resolving power is required. However, it is important to be able to adjust the resolving power easily to the appropriate value because of the considerable effect on the instrument sensitivity.

**Table I**

| Static resolving power | Relative static sensitivity, $S$ (arbitrary units) | |
|---|---|---|
| | Ultimate RP = 5000 | Ultimate RP = 2500 |
| 300 | 2.5 | 2.5 |
| 1000 | 1.0 | 0.45 |
| 2000 | 0.2 | 0.02 |
| 3000 | 0.05 | — |
| 4000 | 0.01 | — |

This is demonstrated approximately in Table I, in which an estimated comparison is made between two mass spectrometers of similar geometry, but having different ultimate resolving powers (RP). It is clear that the higher-resolution instrument also has significantly larger relative sensitivities at the higher values of resolving power.

## Fast Scanning and Recording

Since the sample peaks may be eluted from the chromatograph column in a few seconds, it is essential to be able to scan the desired mass range very rapidly and to record the resulting mass spectrum without any appreciable distortion of peak shape. The recording system must, therefore, have a high speed of response. A comparison of results [1] is given in Figs. 1 and 2, in which the variation of dynamic resolving power, $(RP)_D$, and relative peak height, respectively, are plotted against the ratio of the scan time per mass decade, $t_{10}$, to the recording system time constant, $\tau$, for various values of static resolving power, $(RP)_S$. The short vertical lines represent the experimental observations (the length of the line indicates the estimated error), and the continuous curves give the theoretical results. It will be seen that quite good agreement is obtained. From the theory, it is established that in order to prevent a loss of more than 7% in resolving power and 10% in peak height (or apparent sensitivity) on a 1-sec scan per mass decade, at $(RP)_S$ of 1000 [or a 10-sec scan at $(RP)_S$ of 10,000], then the bandwidth of the recording system must exceed 5 kcps.

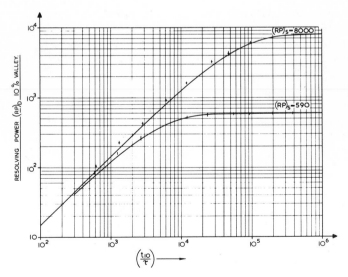

Fig. 1. Variation of resolving power. Comparison of theory with experimental observations.

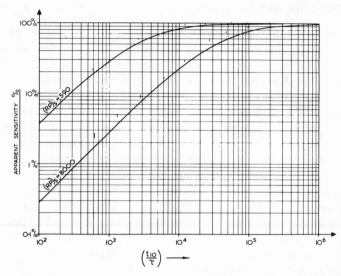

Fig. 2. Variation of apparent sensitivity. Comparison of theory with experimental observations.

Under fast scanning conditions, particularly when small sample quantities are involved, the significant parameter with regard to sample detection is the number of ions giving rise to a mass spectrum peak. This is proportional to $S \cdot t_{10}/(RP)_S$, where $S$ is the relative static sensitivity and $(RP)_S$ is the static resolving power. The minimum detection limit is clearly proportional to the inverse of this, and its estimated relative variation with static resolving

**Table II**

| Static resolving power | Relative minimum detection limit (arbitrary units) |
|---|---|
| 300 | 0.13 |
| 1000 | 1.0 |
| 2000 | 10 |
| 3000 | 60 |
| 4000 | 400 |

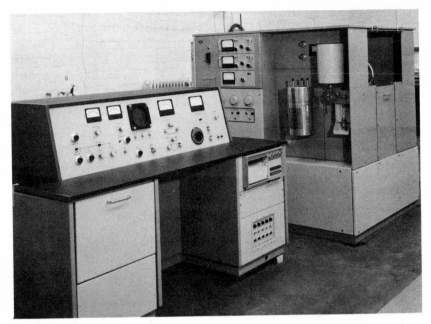

Fig. 3. Single-focusing mass spectrometer, model AEI MS12.

power is shown in Table II for an instrument having an ultimate resolving power of 5000.

## THE MASS SPECTROMETER

### Instrumental

The AEI MS12* is a single-focusing mass spectrometer employing a 90° magnetic sector and an ion path radius of 12 in. The instrument is shown in Fig. 3; it consists of two units, the "tube unit" on the right, which houses the vacuum system, and the electronics console.

The tube unit is shown schematically in Fig. 4. The vacuum system is constructed almost entirely of stainless steel; gold gaskets are used in the source region in order to permit baking to 350°C. Low source pressures (approximately $5 \times 10^{-8}$ torr) are, therefore, attainable and the resulting background spectra have very low intensities.

* Associated Electrical Industries Limited, Urmston, Lancashire, England.

Four inlet ports are provided for the admission of samples, although only two appear in the figure. Typical uses of these ports would be for (1) a capillary gas chromatograph column and a flow splitter, (2) a packed chromatograph column and a Biemann separator, (3) a common heated glass line from a heated inlet system or gallium system, and a room-temperature inlet system, and (4) a direct sample insertion lock, through which solid or involatile liquid samples may be very rapidly introduced into the source without loss of vacuum.

The electron bombardment ion source, which in general follows the original design of Nier [2], can be completely isolated from the rest of the vacuum system to facilitate very rapid changing of the source (approximately 30 min) should this be necessary for any reason. The MS12 also employs differential pumping of the source and analyzer regions; it is, therefore, possible to operate the instrument with relatively high sample pressures (of the order of $10^{-4}$ torr) in the ionization chamber without loss of performance due to sample entering the analyzer tube (high pressures in the tube would produce "tails" on the ion beam due to gas scattering effects).

Continuously variable source and collector slits allow the resolving power of the MS12 to be very easily controlled from outside the vacuum

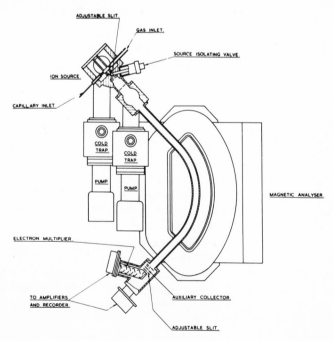

Fig. 4.   Tube assembly of mass spectrometer, model AEI MS12.

system. The minimum slit width in both cases is 0.00005 in., and the maximum widths are 0.010 in. (source) and 0.030 in. (collector).

Electrical detection of the ion beam is employed, and an 11-stage electron multiplier is provided as standard in order to attain the highest sensitivity and speed of response. The bandwidth of the recording system is 10 kcps when a tape recorder is connected. Otherwise, it is limited to about 4 kcps by the galvanometers in the ultraviolet recorder.

A total ion current monitor is fitted, intercepting about 20% of the ion beam, and it is extremely useful both in g.l.c. work, when it may be used as a chromatograph detector, and in conventional operation of the instrument.

The mass spectrum may be scanned by means of either the magnetic field or the accelerating voltage, the fastest scan speed in both cases being adequate for use of the instrument with a chromatograph column (2 sec per mass decade, magnetic scan, and 0.5 sec per mass decade, voltage scan). The accelerating voltage scan is repetitive and the resulting spectrum may be observed on a medium persistence oscilloscope. Permanent recording of mass spectra is obtained by means of an ultraviolet recorder with provision for up to five galvanometers, covering a useful intensity range of $10^4$ to 1; the electron-multiplier gain can be readily adjusted for g.l.c. peaks giving spectra outside this range.

## Performance

### Mass Range

The maximum mass that can be recorded at an accelerating voltage of 8 kV is $m/e$ 900, and the minimum is $m/e$ 1. At 2 kV the mass range is from $m/e$ 3600 to $m/e$ 4.

### Resolving Power

The guaranteed resolving power of the MS12, on the 10% valley definition and at 8 kV, is 3000. That this performance is easily attained is illustrated by the spectrum of the triplet CO, $N_2$, $C_2H_4$ at $m/e$ 28 shown in Fig. 5, in which the CO peak is on the left. The relative mass difference between CO and $N_2$ is 1/2540, and thus it is seen that the slow scan resolving power exhibited is greater than 4000.

### Sensitivity

The sensitivity of the MS12 is greater than $3 \times 10^{-5}$ A/torr. Spectra suitable for identification, covering a factor of 10 in mass, with a signal-to-noise ratio of the order of 100 to 1 can be obtained from less than 1 ng of sample of molecular weight 300, uniformly evaporated in the source during the time of a scan, the resolving power being 1000 (cf., section on capillary column).

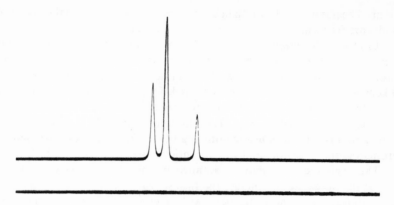

Fig. 5.  Triplet at *m/e* 28, showing RP > 4000.

### Fast Scanning

The fastest magnet scan is 2 sec per mass decade (limited by the inductance of the magnet), and the associated RP is 800. With a 5 sec per mass decade scan, the $(RP)_D$ is 1600, and 3000 for a 30-sec scan.

With voltage scanning, the $(RP)_D$ is 800 for a factor of 2 in mass in 0.5 sec.

## THE COMBINED SYSTEM

### Continuous Sample Inlet Systems

A special inlet system is required to connect the gas chromatograph column to the mass spectrometer, and it must permit continuous, direct sampling from the column effluent. Several different types have been devised, but they fall into two basic categories: (1) simple leak inlet systems and (2) molecular separators. The function of the inlet system is to transfer the sample from the column to the mass spectrometer ion source as efficiently as possible, consistent with limitations on permissible carrier gas flow into the ion source set by considerations such as loss of resolving power due to space charge and gas scattering effects, and in the limit, breakdown of the ion accelerating voltage.

On all these counts, the preferred carrier gas is helium, and the maximum permissible helium flow rate into the MS12 source is approximately 0.15 ml/min.

### Simple Leak Systems

A very simple, glass g.l.c. inlet system, which has been previously described [3], drops the pressure from atmospheric to source pressure without the need for any additional pumps. A similar system which has been used successfully on the MS12 is shown in Fig. 6. Essentially, it consists of a length of about 1 cm of 0.001-in. ID glass capillary tube, mounted on a glass re-entrant tube which is heated right up to the ionization chamber. The connection between the g.l.c. column and the glass leak consists of a length of stainless steel capillary tube of approximately 0.020 in. ID. It is essential to avoid cold spots and an auxiliary heater is fitted over the end of the glass tube to prevent those which might otherwise be formed.

The stainless steel connecting tube is heated by passing through it an electric current from a low-voltage transformer. The temperatures of the system are increased until the g.l.c. sample enters the mass spectrometer with no appreciable distortion of the g.l.c. peak shape as observed on the total ion current monitor.

This simple type of inlet leak is more suitable for use with capillary g.l.c. columns, with which it gives a higher sample transfer efficiency than with packed columns.

Consider a typical capillary column with a carrier gas flow rate of 1 ml/min. Since the inlet leak is arranged to pass 0.15 ml/min into the mass spectrometer, the transfer efficiency is 15%. Clearly, if the simple leak is used with a packed column, for which the flow rate might well be 30 ml/min, then the transfer efficiency is 0.5%. If a packed column is to be used, therefore, it is desirable to use a more efficient inlet system, such as a molecular separator, various types of which will be discussed later.

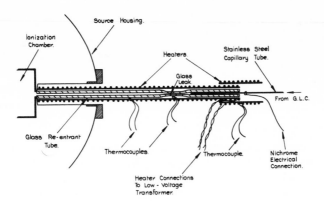

Fig. 6. Prototype g.l.c. inlet system for MS12.

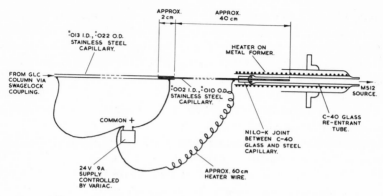

Fig. 7.   Improved inlet leak for use with capillary columns.

Again, considering the simple glass leak in use with a capillary column, it is clear that the sample transfer efficiency could be increased by reducing the carrier gas flow rate through the column. However, with low flow rates of 1 ml/min or less, difficulties arise because of air leaking into the mass spectrometer together with the sample and carrier gas. This variable leak interferes with the recording of the chromatogram.

An improved inlet leak for use with capillary columns is shown in Fig. 7 and consists of a length of about 16 in. of stainless steel capillary tube of inner diameter 0.002 in. and outer diameter 0.010 in., mounted on the end of a glass re-entrant tube. The required pressure drop is obtained simply by this narrow capillary tube, which again is heated by means of an electric current. No additional pumps are required.

In this case, a helium flow rate of 1 ml/min is quite enough to prevent leakage of air into the mass spectrometer, so enabling the detection of small g.l.c. peaks to be made much more easily.

Both of the simple leak systems just described employ metal parts; they are, therefore, suitable only for use with thermally stable compounds.

### Molecular Separators

There are four main types of molecular separator, all of which work, basically, by preferentially pumping away the helium carrier gas and admitting as much sample as possible into the mass spectrometer ion source.

It is important to notice that although very high *concentrations* of sample with respect to the carrier gas may be obtained, the significant parameter is the *efficiency of sample transfer* from the chromatograph column to the mass spectrometer. It is useless to produce an extremely high concentration, if in the process most of the sample is pumped away together with the carrier.

One form of the Biemann separator [4, 5] is shown in Fig. 8. It employs a fritted glass tube, through which the output of the g.l.c. column is passed, situated in a vacuum jacket.

Restrictions to gas flow are required at the input and output ends of the fritted tube and are provided by suitable glass leaks. A significant fraction of the sample passes into the ion source, but the bulk of the helium diffuses through the porous walls and is pumped away. Watson and Biemann report sample transfer efficiencies of between 10 and 50% with this device.

In Fig. 8, a metal adaptor is shown for the connection to the chromatograph column. However, this can be replaced by a glass connection right up to the column. The inlet system then consists entirely of glass, and this confers the major advantage of reducing to a minimum the risk of decomposition of thermally unstable samples (cf., use of glass g.l.c. columns at higher temperatures).

In addition, the Biemann separator has little tendency to block, owing to the very large number of pores in the fritted tube. It can also be used at high temperatures (up to 300 °C) and gives a good, clean vacuum.

The Lipsky separator [6] is similar in principle but uses a length of thin-walled Teflon tubing instead of a fritted glass tube. It is thus possible to make it in a compact form by suitably winding the tube into a ball; connections to the Teflon tube are made of stainless steel.

Sample transfer efficiencies of between 40 and 65% are claimed.

In the Ryhage type [7, 8] of separator, no frits or semipermeable membranes are used. Instead, the output from the chromatograph column passes successively through a system of narrow stainless steel jets, the interspaces

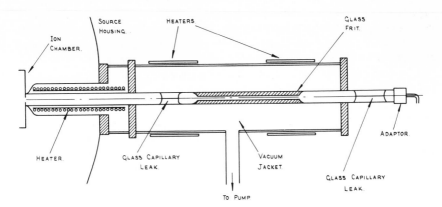

Fig. 8. Biemann separator.

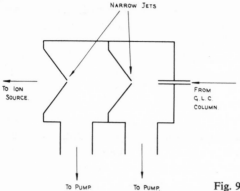

To Pump      To Pump          Fig. 9.   Principle of Ryhage separator.

between the jet assemblies being pumped. The helium carrier gas is preferentially removed and up to 90% efficiency is reported. It is a very robust and clean device, being constructed entirely of metal; two rotary pumps are required, compared with only one in the other cases. A schematic arrangement of the Ryhage type separator is shown in Fig. 9.

Another type of separator, due to Llewelyn, has also been developed, and works by transmission of samples through a pair of thin silicon rubber diaphragms. Helium is again pumped away. Exceptionally high performances are claimed.

## Detection of the Chromatograph Peaks

The use of conventional g.l.c. detectors, such as the flame ionization detector or the katharometer, is not sufficient for a combined m.s.–g.l.c. system. Because of the delay between the response of the column detector and the arrival of the sample in the mass spectrometer ion source, the operator would not know when to scan the spectrum. It is, therefore, necessary to provide a g.l.c. peak detector within the mass spectrometer, and one method is to employ a total ion current monitor. Since the relative amounts of sample may be very small compared with the helium carrier gas (of the order of $1/10^6$ on the column), suppression of the ion current due to helium is essential. It is not enough simply to back off this current by means of a suitably adjusted potential, because of variations in the helium flow rate (typically 1%). One method is to operate the ion source electron beam at an energy of 20 eV, below the ionization potential of helium, but above those of most organic samples. The output of the total ion current monitor may be used to operate a pen recorder. In the MS12, the electron beam energy is automatically switched to 70 eV when the mass spectrum is scanned, thus increasing the sensitivity and operating the source under the usual conditions to facilitate recognition of the sample cracking pattern.

The same switch also automatically operates the chart paper drive in the ultraviolet recorder.

An alternative method of providing a g.l.c. detector within the mass spectrometer is to use a sensitive ionization gauge, permanently operated at 20 eV, the output again being connected to a pen recorder.

## RESULTS OBTAINED
## FROM THE COMBINED MASS SPECTROMETER–GAS
## CHROMATOGRAPH SYSTEM

In general, at optimum performance with a capillary column and simple flow splitter, or with a packed column and a molecular separator, satisfactory spectra are obtainable with the MS12 from less than 3 ng of sample on the column, at a molecular weight of 300.

The chromatographs used in conjunction with the MS12, from which the results discussed in this section were obtained, were the Perkin-Elmer F11 (capillary column) and the Pye 104 (packed column).

### Capillary Column

In order to detect g.l.c. sample peaks in the source of the MS12, the electron beam was operated at 20 eV and switched to 70 eV when a spectrum was scanned, as has previously been indicated, with a pen recorder connected

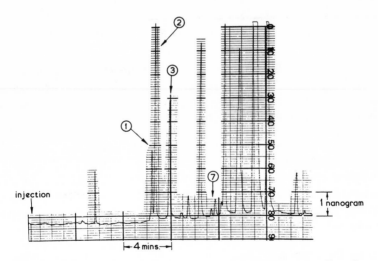

Fig. 10. Part chromatogram of 3 $\mu$l red thyme oil. Column split ratio is 1:300, i.e., 0.01 $\mu$l on column. Capillary column; polypropylene glycol; 50 m × ½ mm.

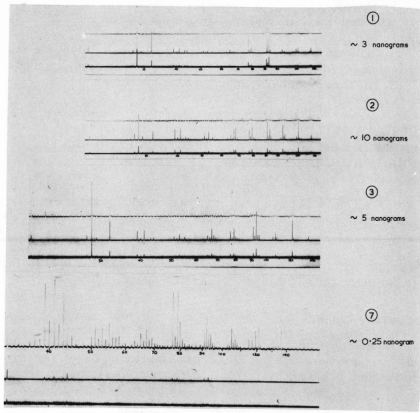

Fig. 11.   Mass spectra taken with 70-eV electron beam energy.

to the monitor amplifier output. In this way, the chromatogram shown in Fig. 10 was obtained from a capillary column, the inlet system being the stainless steel capillary leak type. On a second run, mass spectra were taken with the electron beam energy switched to 70 eV, and some are shown in Fig. 11, the g.l.c. peaks and the associated spectra being indicated by the respective reference numbers. The spectrum labelled (7) was obtained from 0.25 ng of sample in the ion source.

This work is typical of a flavor problem, when a manufacturer may be interested in synthesizing a particular flavor extract, rather than continue the relatively costly extraction from natural sources. In such cases, it is frequently the trace components which are of great importance.

## Packed Column

A chromatogram of a steroid mixture, recorded by the conventional flame ionization detector, is shown in Fig. 12. A simple glass leak was used for the m.s.–g.l.c. interface, and the associated magnetically scanned mass spectra, taken at 5 sec per mass decade, are shown in Figs. 13–15.

Problems involving steroids are of considerable biological importance, a mixture frequently being extracted which is easily separated by the chromatograph column. The mass spectrometer readily provides identification of the components.

A second flame ionization detector chromatogram is shown in Fig. 16, and it was obtained from a tobacco leaf wax. Magnet scans of the $C_{30}$ and $C_{32}$ peaks are given in Figs. 17 and 18, but the $C_{31}$ g.l.c. peak was an unresolved doublet. In order to obtain identifications of its components, it was necessary to employ the very fast 0.5-sec accelerating voltage scan of the MS12.

Figures 19 and 20 show the high mass regions of the spectrum ($m/e$ 300–450). The significant feature of these is the very intense peak at $m/e$ 393 in Fig. 19, showing this compound to have a branching point at $C_2$, whereas the other component of the g.l.c. peak is a straight-chain compound.

The tobacco leaf wax is typical of a complex mixture of components similar in chemical nature. The mass spectrometer provides, in each case, the molecular weight and the branching points.

SOLVENT

Fig. 12.   Chromatogram of a steroid mixture.

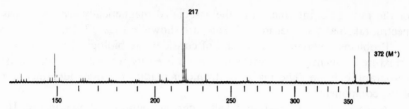

Fig. 13.   Magnet scan at 5 sec per mass decade. Peak 1 identified as cholestane.

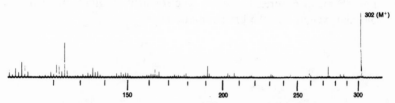

Fig. 14.   Magnet scan at 5 sec per mass decade. Peak 2 identified as androstan-3, 11, 17-trione.

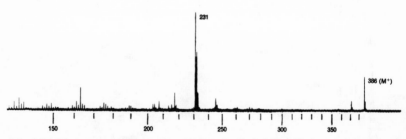

Fig. 15.   Magnet scan at 5 sec per mass decade. Peak 3 identified as cholestan-3-one.

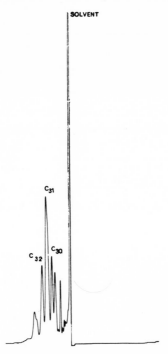

Fig. 16. Chromatogram of mixtures of straight and branched-chain hydrocarbons from tobacco leaf wax, M.W. $\simeq$ 450.

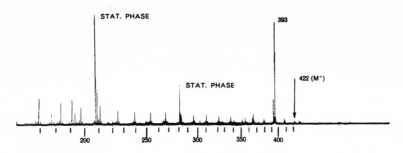

Fig. 17. Magnet scan at 8 sec per mass decade. Sample admitted from chromatograph and identified as $C_2H_5CH$—$C_{26}H_{53}$.
$|$
$CH_3$

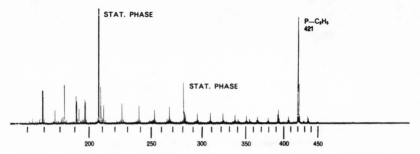

Fig. 18. Magnet scan at 8 sec per mass decade. Sample admitted from chromatograph and identified as $C_2H_5 \cdot CH\!-\!C_{28}H_{57}$.

$$\overset{\displaystyle |}{CH_3}$$

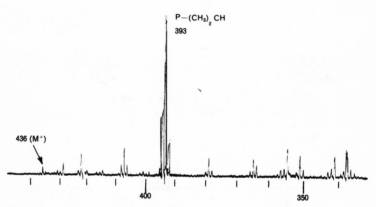

Fig. 19. A 0.5-sec voltage scan of tobacco leaf wax component identified as

$$\begin{matrix} CH_3 \\ CH_3 \end{matrix}\!\!>\!\!CH \cdot C_{28}H_{57}.$$

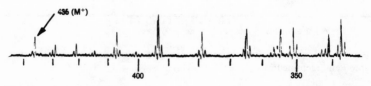

Fig. 20. A 0.5-sec voltage scan of tobacco leaf wax component $C_{31}H_{64}$.

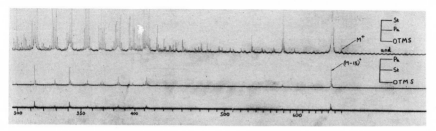

Fig. 21.   Magnet scan at 5 sec per mass decade taken during a composite g.l.c. peak as it emerged from the column.

## Packed Column with Biemann Separator

Figure 21 shows a 5 sec per mass decade magnet scan taken during a composite g.l.c. peak as it emerged from the column; the two components of the peak are

$$CH_2OCO(CH_2)_{16}CH_3 \qquad\qquad CH_2OCO(CH_2)_{14}CH_3$$
$$CHOCO(CH_2)_{14}CH_3 \quad\text{and}\quad CHOCO(CH_2)_{16}CH_3$$
$$CH_2OSi(CH_3)_3 \qquad\qquad CH_2OSi(CH_3)_3$$

As these have the same molecular weight and very similar gross structure, they are not separated by the g.l.c. column. Similarly, their individual mass spectra differ very little.

A 15-in. glass g.l.c. column and $1\frac{1}{2}\%$ XE60 stationary phase were used, the helium flow rate being 45 ml/min and the column temperature about 260 °C. Initial attempts were made with a stainless steel connection between the column and the Biemann separator, but they were unsuccessful due to decomposition of the sample. Satisfactory results were achieved only when a glass connection was used.

## CONCLUSION

Various aspects of mass spectrometer design imposed by g.l.c. considerations have been discussed, and a description of an instrument intended for on-line, continuous sampling from a gas chromatograph column was given. Several types of inlet system were compared, and results obtained from a combined m.s.–g.l.c. system were presented.

## ACKNOWLEDGMENTS

The writer wishes to thank his colleagues in the Scientific Apparatus Department of Associated Electrical Industries Limited for their much appreciated help and encouragement. In particular, he is indebted to Dr. J. R. Chapman and Mr. W. A. Wolstenholme, as a result of whose considerable efforts Figs. 7, 10, 11, and 21 are presented. In addition, the cooperation of Dr. M. Barber in the work on the steroids and tobacco leaf wax is gratefully acknowledged. This chapter is presented with the approval of the Management of the A.E.I. Electronics Group.

## REFERENCES

1. A. E. Banner, *J. Sci. Instr.* **43**:138–140, 1966.
2. A. O. Nier, *Rev. Sci. Instr.* **18**:398, 1947.
3. A. E. Banner, R. M. Elliott, and W. Kelly, *Gas Chromatography*, Institute of Petroleum, London, 1964, pp. 180–189.
4. J. T. Watson and K. Biemann, *Anal. Chem.* **36**:1135–1137, 1964.
5. J. T. Watson and K. Biemann, *Anal. Chem.* **37**:844–851, 1965.
6. S. R. Lipsky, C. G. Hovarth, and W. J. McMurray, *Anal. Chem.* **38**:1585–1587, 1966.
7. R. Ryhage, *Anal. Chem.* **36**:759, 1964.
8. R. Ryhage, G. R. Walter, and S. Wilkstrom, *Anal. Chem.* **37**:435–436, 1965.

# APPLICATIONS OF LOW-COST MASS SPECTROSCOPY

### R. D. Craig

*Associated Electrical Industries*
*Manchester, England*

---

The smaller type of mass spectrometer, developed over the past few years, has a very different concept from the large installation of the previous decade. These small instruments notably do not require (1) a large capital outlay, (2) a room set aside as a mass spectroscopy laboratory, and (3) a specialized operator. Indeed, for many applications the instrument is built right into the experimental apparatus and used to give precise and instantaneous information on the gases and vapors present in the system.

Recently several types of small mass spectrometer have been introduced. These include models based on RF linear acceleration, time of flight, mass filtering (quadrupole and monopole), cyclotron orbital (omegatron), cycloidal path, and, finally, either sector or 180° deflection in a magnetic field. This last type of instrument, namely, 180° deflection in a magnetic field, is the one that has been used by the author, and a description of the model he is most familiar with, the AEI MS10,* is given in the next section.

Advantages of the 180° geometry are that it gives very good reproducibility of spectra and sensitivities, both relative and absolute. This characteristic is attributed to the ion source being immersed in the main magnetic field so that the ionizing electrons are tightly collimated and confined to predetermined paths, so minimizing spurious defocusing surface potentials.

## DESCRIPTION OF MS10

Any mass spectrometer does three things: it produces ions, it separates them according to their mass, and it records the relative intensity of the ions of different mass to form a mass spectrum.

---

\* Associated Electrical Industries, Manchester, England.

In the MS10 (Fig. 1) ions representative of gas or vapor molecules present in the ion-source region are formed by bombardment in an electron beam. For most analytical purposes, the electrons are given 70-V energy, but for special applications the electron energy can be reduced to as little as 5 V or increased to 300 V.

The ions are accelerated in the ion gun to a voltage which is adjustable between 2000 and 20 V. The whole instrument is immersed in a magnetic field so that the ions follow circular paths and reach a refocus after turning through 180°. Ions of different mass follow paths of different radii, but the radius of any particular mass may be altered either by varying the accelerating voltage (called electrostatic or voltage scanning) or by varying the magnetic field (called magnetic scanning).

In the simpler forms of MS10, a small permanent magnet is used and the ions of different mass are swept across the collector by varying the accelerator voltage, so recording the intensity of the ion beams of each mass in turn. The collector slit is spaced 10 cm from the source slit so that only ions with a 5-cm radius of curvature will reach the detector. The standard small permanent magnet has a field of 1850 G, which means that ions have the required 5-cm curvature only if the product of mass and voltage is 4000. Tuning for a particular mass is by varying the ion voltage between 2000 and 20 V, thus covering the mass range 2 to 200 with this magnet.

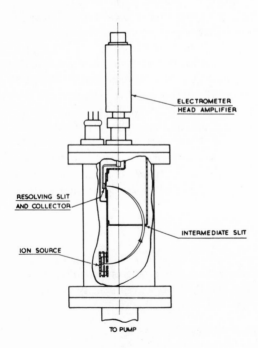

Fig. 1.   The MS10 analyzer tube.

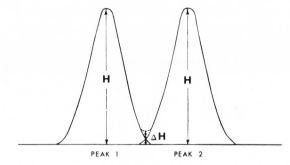

Fig. 2. Definition of 10% valley ($\Delta H = 10\% H$).

The resolving power obtained depends both on the magnet and on the width of collector slit. With the small permanent magnet and a 0.25-mm collector slit, 10% valley resolution (see Fig. 2) can be obtained up to mass 100 and peaks at adjacent mass numbers can be distinguished up to mass 150.

The mass range and resolving power may be extended by using either a larger permanent magnet (4 kG) or an electromagnet (9 kG). With the electromagnet the mass range is extended to 800, the 10% valley resolution can be almost 400 (see Fig. 3), and peaks at adjacent mass numbers can be distinguished up to mass 600.

Controls for the MS10 (see Fig. 4) are particularly simple compared with those for larger instruments. The mass number required may be selected by turning the mass dial to the appropriate number. Alternatively, motor drive of the mass dial can be switched on giving an automatic scan of 50 sec, $3\frac{1}{2}$ min, or 13 min, dependent on the motor fitted.

Another facility is the "narrow scan," which on the flick of a switch provides a scan of 16% of the particular mass dial setting. This facility may be adapted for repetitive scanning such as is required in isotope ratio measurements.

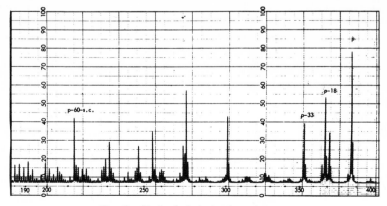

Fig. 3. Part of cholesterol spectrum.

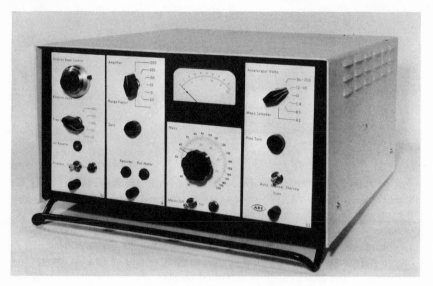

Fig. 4.    The front panel of the MS10 control unit.

The ion beam intensity is measurable either on the meter or on a plug-in recorder of the potentiometer, pen type, or of the galvanometer, ultraviolet type. Switched ranges provide a signal measurement range of $10^5:1$, but by changing the plug-in preamplifier the overall measurement range may be extended to $10^9:1$, corresponding approximately to the partial pressure range from $5 \times 10^{-4}$ torr down to $5 \times 10^{-13}$ torr.

For higher sensitivities an electron-multiplier detector is used. This increases the current to the electrometer amplifier by a factor of $10^6$, but because of the "statistical noise" associated with the arrival of individual ions at the multiplier the effective gain in sensitivity is more usually about $10^3$. Thus, the lower limit of detection becomes $5 \times 10^{-16}$ torr. However, in many applications a more useful advantage of the electron multiplier is that the same sensitivity as before can be maintained at scanning speeds 1000 times greater. This means that a complete spectrum at standard sensitivity can now be taken in 1 sec.

The ionizing electron current and voltage are variable. Generally the highest values (300 $\mu$A and 300 V) are used when maximum sensitivity is required, for example, when measuring partial pressures in the $10^{-13}$ torr range; intermediate values (for example, 50 $\mu$A and 70 V) are used for standard analysis and general work where reproducibility is most important, and the lowest values (10 $\mu$A and 5 to 20 V) are used for fundamental studies of ionization and dissociation processes. For these studies very fine adjustment of the electron voltage is essential and for this reason a resolution of 0.01 V is provided on the voltage adjustor.

## INTERPRETATION OF MASS SPECTRA

A mass spectrum is a unique means of identification. Consider, for example, the carbon monoxide spectrum shown in Fig. 5.

When carbon monoxide molecules are bombarded with electrons, the molecular, or parent, ions $CO^+$, the fragment ions $C^+$ and $O^+$, and the doubly charged ions $CO^{++}$ are formed according to definite probabilities, giving a characteristic spectrum with primary peaks at mass numbers 28, 12, 16, and 14, the relative intensity of which for a particular mass spectrometer should always be the same. Such a "fingerprint" spectrum serves to identify the compound and is conveniently tabulated as a "cracking pattern" in which the peak mass numbers are listed in one column and the relative

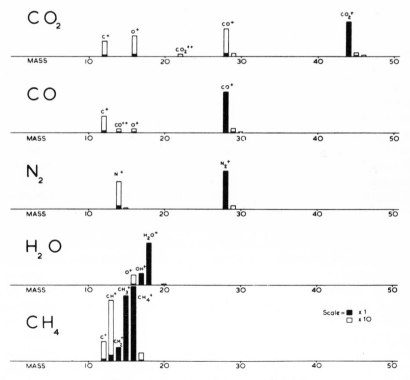

Fig. 5.   Mass spectra of some simple gases.

intensities are set opposite them, as in Table I. Conventionally the largest peak is scaled 100 and called the "base" peak.

### Table I.   Cracking Pattern of Carbon Monoxide

| $m/e$ | Relative intensity |
|-------|--------------------|
| 12    | 4.49               |
| 13    | 0.048              |
| 14    | 0.61               |
| 14.5  | 0.007              |
| 15    | 0.001              |
| 16    | 0.95               |
| 28    | 100.0              |
| 29    | 1.13               |
| 30    | 0.21               |

In addition to the primary peaks referred to above, there will generally be secondary peaks due to the minor isotopes, for example, at mass 29 a peak due to $^{13}C\,^{16}O^+$ and $^{12}C\,^{17}O^+$ and at mass 30 one due to $^{12}C\,^{18}O^+$.

Analysis of mixtures of gases having overlapping spectra, for example, carbon monoxide and nitrogen, depends on differences in their cracking patterns. Consider, as a more general case, a mixture of $CO_2$, $O_2$, CO, and $N_2$ (Fig. 6).

In making such an analysis the contribution of the higher-mass components, $CO_2$ and $O_2$, would first be subtracted from the measured 12, 14, 16, and 28 peaks. This is possible since the 44 peak is uniquely representative of $CO_2$ and the 32 peak is uniquely representative of $O_2$. Simultaneous equations based on the 12, 14, 16, or 28 peaks can then be solved to determine the relative contributions of CO and $N_2$ at mass 28. The method of analysis of other and more complex mixtures is broadly similar and a useful discussion of the principles involved is given by Barnard [1].

The above treatment is, however, only step 1 in making a full quantitative analysis of the gases or vapor present in a system. Thus, in this step, cracking-pattern data positively identify the components present and enable their relative proportions in terms of ion current to be measured. Step 2 is the calculation of the true proportion of each component in the total and requires a knowledge of the relative sensitivity of the instrument to the various gases present. Step 3 is the calculation of the actual partial pressure of each gas or vapor in the system and requires a knowledge of the absolute sensitivity of the instrument to one of the gases.

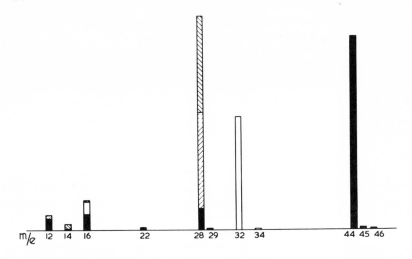

■ CO₂ CRACKING PATTERN.     ▨ C O CRACKING PATTERN.

☐ O₂ CRACKING PATTERN.     ▧ N₂ CRACKING PATTERN.

Fig. 6. Spectrum of a mixture of $CO_2$, $O_2$, CO, and $N_2$ (2:2:1:1).

Information on relative sensitivities can best be obtained by admitting a known mixture or known quantities of each calibration gas into the mass spectrometer system at the time of the analysis. However, where this is not practicable, data from a previous calibration experiment or from manu-facturer's tables (see Table II) may be used.

### Table II. MS10 Sensitivity to Common Gases

| $m/e$ | Gas | Sensitivity relative to $N_2$ |
|---|---|---|
| 2 | $H_2$ | 1.50 |
| 4 | He | 0.35 |
| 16 | $CH_4$ | 1.10 |
| 20 | Ne | 0.29 |
| 28 | CO | 1.10 |
| 32 | $O_2$ | 0.58 |
| 40 | A | 1.20 |
| 44 | $CO_2$ | 0.88 |
| 84 | Kr | 0.83 |
| | | Absolute sensitivity |
| 28 | $N_2$ | 48 μA per torr |

Information on absolute sensitivity is obtainable by calibration against a pressure standard (for example, McLeod gauge) or from manufacturer's data (Table II).

The amount of calibration data necessary and the precision with which they must be known depend on the problem. Some examples are considered below.

## Identification

For the identification of unknown compounds it is only necessary to have cracking-pattern data. Patterns for more than 2000 compounds have now been catalogued (see Reference 2) and most of these relate to spectra taken with 70-V electron bombardment on conventional magnetic deflection instruments. Such data are directly applicable to spectra run on an MS10.

Where the spectrum has not previously been catalogued, identification is still possible in many cases by consideration of the general rules governing bond dissociation, fragmentation, and metastable ion formation, as discussed in the works of Beynon [3].

## Quantitative Analysis of a Mixture

In making the chemical analysis of a mixture, only the percentage composition is required so it is not necessary to know the absolute sensitivity of the instrument. However, both cracking patterns and relative sensitivities are needed and, as these can change slowly with time, it is usual to check the calibrations about once per week for the most accurate work. With such precautions, an accuracy of 2 or 3% of the component concentration will generally be maintained, that is, a 10% component will be determined to within $\pm 0.2$ or 0.3%.

## Determination of Impurity Levels

The major limitation in impurity determinations is often imposed by the blank spectrum or by the contribution from a peak of the main constituent; each case has therefore to be considered individually. A typical result would be the determination of a 10-ppm component to $\pm 20$%. However, in favorable cases, for example, impurities in hydrogen or helium, the level of detection might be dropped one or two orders of magnitude, if a sample of pure gas is available for calibration.

## Partial Pressure Measurement

Determination of the partial pressure of the different gases or vapors in a system requires calibration data on all three quantities, namely, cracking patterns, relative sensitivities, and absolute sensitivity. Often in this type of measurement an accuracy of $\pm 20\%$ is acceptable and with the MS10 this accuracy should be obtainable by using published data [4]. If greater accuracy (down to 5%) is required, the individual spectrometer in use should be calibrated in a separate experiment.

### Isotopic Ratio Analysis

Isotopic ratio measurements are always made with reference to a standard sample and results are expressed as an enrichment relative to this standard. The important measure of accuracy is therefore the reproducibility of ratio measurements on repeat analysis of the same sample. With a standard single-collector arrangement, the reproducibility of the isotope ratio measurement is generally better than 0.5% for ratios of 100:1, or less. However, with a special double-collector system, enabling simultaneous ratio recording of the two isotope beams, reproducibilities of better than 0.005% have been obtained [5].

## METHODS OF SAMPLING

The four basic methods of sampling are (1) direct sampling, (2) continuous sampling, (3) batch sampling, (4) direct inlet.

### Direct Sampling

As the name implies, direct sampling involves connecting the mass spectrometer directly to the system under investigation (see Fig. 7). Obviously the method is applicable only if the system pressure is less than the maximum operating pressure of the mass spectrometer, namely, $10^{-3}$ torr. For higher pressure systems, the mass spectrometer must have its own vacuum system as discussed below.

Fig. 7.   Direct sampling (pressure range, $10^{-4}$ to $10^{-12}$ torr).

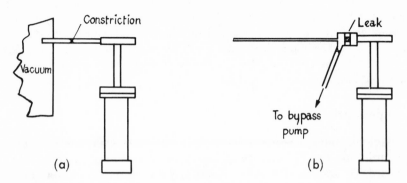

Fig. 8. Continuous sampling. (a) With constriction (pressure range, $10^{-5}$ to $10^2$ torr). (b) With bypass (pressure range, 0.1 to 100 atm).

## Continuous Sampling

Continuous sampling is used where the gas or vapor to be monitored is at too high a pressure for direct connection of the spectrometer. If the system has a partial vacuum (pressure range, $10^{-5}$ to 100 torr), a simple restricted flow tube or capillary connection to the mass spectrometer will be sufficient to drop the pressure to within the working range [see Fig. 8(a)]. However, for high-pressure systems (0.1 to 100 atm) it is usually preferable to supplement the restricted flow tube with a bypass pump and leak arrangement as shown in Fig. 8(b).

In both arrangements the spectrometer requires its own high-vacuum system which may be based on either a diffusion or an ion pump. Advantages of the ion pump are that it requires no cold trap, no cooling water, no rotary pump (except for starting), it can be orientated in any direction, and it is generally more portable. However, there are limitations regarding the gas handling characteristics of ion pumps [6] which may make them unsuitable for some applications.

## Batch Sampling

Batch sampling is used when a discrete amount of gas, liquid, or solid is to be analyzed for chemical composition.

The optimum amount of gas is about 1 cm³ at NTP (or 1 mg of a liquid or solid). The sample is expanded into a reservoir of about 1 liter at a pressure of about 1 torr, from whence it "leaks" at a rate of approximately 5% per hour into the mass spectrometer and out through the pumping system (see Fig. 9). A continuous flow condition is thus created with the reservoir pressure falling by a negligible amount during the time of the analysis, which is usually between 5 and 15 min.

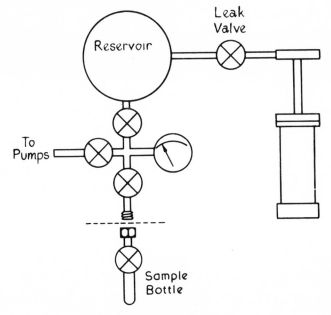

Fig. 9.   Single inlet batch-sampling system.

Smaller samples, down to $5 \times 10^{-6}$ cm$^3$ of gas, can also be analyzed this way by using greater leak rates and accepting some loss in sensitivity and mass range.

For the less volatile liquid samples, and for solids, it is generally necessary to heat the whole inlet system to produce the necessary evaporation. It may also be necessary to heat the mass spectrometer.

For isotopic analysis a pair of identical batch-sampling systems is used, the unknown sample being introduced into one system and the standard reference sample into the other. An important component of such systems is the leak valve, shown diagrammatically in Fig. 10. This valve enables the flow of sample from reservoir to mass spectrometer to be cut off or readmitted

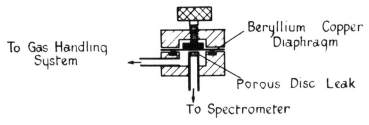

Fig. 10.   Leak valve.

within a few seconds, thus permitting rapid interchange between the sample to be measured and the standard reference sample.

### Direct Inlet

Direct inlet is the name given to arrangements where the sample is evaporated directly into the mass spectrometer without there being any "leak" or capillary restricting the flow of vapor. The rate of evaporation is controlled by adjusting the temperature of the sample container.

This method is used mainly for analyses to identify unknown organic liquid or solid samples, and it has the advantage that only small amounts of sample are required, typically 1 $\mu$g with the standard spectrometer and 0.001 $\mu$g when using an electron multiplier.

## FIELDS OF APPLICATION

The diverse fields of application of the small mass spectrometer may be appreciated from the range of the headings of the following 14 subsections. This section is by no means intended as a complete review, but rather as an indication of the variety of problems that can be tackled with the small mass spectrometer, and is also intended as an introduction to those applications with which the author is most familiar.

### Residual Gas Analysis

Analysis of the residual gases in any vacuum system operating in the pressure range $10^{-3}$ to $10^{-12}$ torr can be made by connecting a small mass spectrometer, such as the MS10, directly to the system. The mass spectrometer will identify all the gases and vapors present and tell the partial pressure of each.

Residual gas analysis is increasingly being used on systems where it is necessary to have a *clean*, rather than just a high, vacuum. Electron microscopy is an example where relatively high pressures of the constituents of air and water vapor are acceptable but even small amounts of hydrocarbon are troublesome. This is because hydrocarbons break down under electron bombardment and cause growth of carbonaceous deposits on the specimen under examination. Residual gas analysis can identify the source of the hydrocarbons and indicate corrective steps to reduce them.

Another important application of residual gas analysis is in thin film research to assess the importance of different contaminants during film preparation. Caswell [7] has shown that oxygen present during the evaporation of a tin film has a pronounced effect on the superconducting properties

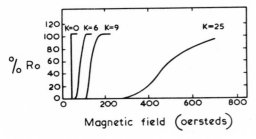

Fig. 11. The effect of oxygen pressure during preparation on the magnetic characteristics of a tin film.

of the final product, as is shown in Fig. 11. This figure shows the results obtained for different values of $K$, the percentage ratio of $O_2$ molecules to tin atoms striking the surface. On the other hand, similar experiments in the presence of $H_2$, $CH_4$, $N_2$, CO, A, and $CO_2$ showed no effect on the final product. This emphasizes the increasing need in vacuum work to know not just total pressure but the identity and partial pressure of all the gases and vapors present.

## Chemical Analysis

The range of problems in chemical analysis that can be handled by a small mass spectrometer, such as the MS10, is very wide indeed and includes such fields as small-sample analysis, accurate quantitative analysis of mixtures, and identification of unknown organic compounds.

The analysis of small amounts of the common gases as may be found in bubbles in glass, or encapsulated electronic devices, has been described by Hazelby [8]. He showed that by using simple sample cracking arrangements it was possible to make good analyses with as little as $5 \times 10^{-6}$ standard $cm^3$ of gas using a basic MS10 without an electron multiplier.

For the quantitative analysis of mixtures, it is essential to have a batch inlet system in which the sample to be analyzed is stored in a reservoir operated at a sufficient temperature to maintain all components of the mixture in the vapor phase. Common operating temperatures for reservoir inlet systems are 20 °C (room temperature), 150 °C (maximum convenient temperature for Viton valves), and 350 °C (rapid decomposition of most organic compounds occurs above this temperature). These temperatures are suitable for the analysis of $C_1$–$C_5$, $C_1$–$C_{20}$, and $C_1$–$C_{40}$ hydrocarbons, respectively.

The identification of unknown organic compounds can be made using the simplest of sample introduction methods, namely, direct evaporation into the spectrometer using temperature to control the rate. With this method very high sensitivities are possible and a sample of molecular weight 400 should be identifiable using as little as a nanogram ($10^{-9}$ g) of material in a spectrometer fitted with an electron multiplier.

## Reaction Kinetics

Because of its low sample consumption, the mass spectrometer is particularly convenient for continuously monitoring the products of gas phase or heterogeneous reactions by direct sampling from the reaction vessel. Furthermore, its ability to identify specific compounds shows up any unsuspected intermediate products. Small mass spectrometers are usually quite adequate and they have been extensively used in studies of gaseous reactions and of the role of the catalyst.

Hartog [9] has reported on systems involving deuterated benzene and has shown that the calculations in this case can be greatly simplified by working at reduced electron voltages which prevent the formation of the benzene fragment peaks.

Other problems studied include the cracking of saturated hydrocarbons on a metal surface, and Roberts [10], using an ultrahigh-vacuum ion pumped system to prepare his metal surfaces at $10^{-9}$ torr, has shown that freedom from surface contamination can have a profound effect on catalytic reaction. Thus, the addition of oxygen to a clean rhodium film greatly inhibits the subsequent cracking of ethane to methane and, if the film is completely oxygenated, the major reaction product is water. This is to be contrasted with the reaction for the clean surface at 27°C as shown in Fig. 12, where the overall decomposition is given by

$$C_2H_6 \text{ (gas)} \xrightarrow[\text{rhodium}]{\text{clean}} 1.2 \, CH_4 \text{ (gas)} + 0.8 \, CH_{1.5} \text{ (residue on film)}$$

In many reaction studies it is necessary to avoid the use of any metal parts in the reaction chamber, which itself will be made of glass. For such cases, a special form of silicon carbide sintered leak, manufactured by AEI

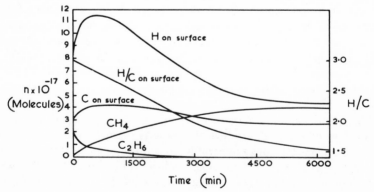

Fig. 12.   Rate of decomposition of ethane on clean rhodium at 27°C.

under the trade name Metrosil, and suitable for sealing directly into a glass tube, may conveniently be used to isolate the mass spectrometer from the reaction chamber.

## Process Monitoring

The efficiency of many industrial chemical reactions depends on keeping close control of the vapor composition in one or more supply lines and small mass spectrometers are increasingly being used as process monitors in such applications. Usually these supply lines are operating at about atmospheric pressure and there is no problem in bleeding off, say, 0.5 standard $cm^3$/sec through a conventional type of continuous sampling system as has been described. However, many of the components of importance are likely to be rather strongly absorbed at room temperature, and it may therefore be necessary to operate both the inlet system and the mass spectrometer analyzer tube at elevated temperature.

One such system has been described by Bokhoven and Theeuwen [11] in which a mixture of ammonia, carbon dioxide, and water vapor is continuously monitored on a production urea plant using an MS10 mass spectrometer. In this case, satisfactory performance over several years operating experience has been achieved with the sampling system and mass spectrometer run at 150°C and using a conventional vacuum system based on an air-cooled diffusion pump surmounted by a cold trap with solid $CO_2$ refrigerant.

However, the advantages of ion pumps, as mentioned earlier, are of particular relevance to process monitoring and should always be considered on new installations. The simplicity of such an arrangement is illustrated in Fig. 13.

## Respiratory Analysis

The small mass spectrometer may be used to advantage in respiratory analysis. Special instrumental features are however required if meaningful traces are to be obtained. The overall response of the system to a change in the composition of the gas at the patient's mouth must be 0.1 sec or less, and thus the individual response times of the gas flow system and of the amplifier–recorder system must each be better than 0.1 sec. In addition, special precautions must be taken to eliminate errors arising from variations in the amount of water vapor present in the sample. This means that in general the sampling capillary would be operated at a temperature in the region of 100°C.

In most respiratory analysis applications, it is necessary to study at least two and often as many as four gases simultaneously and thus a multi-

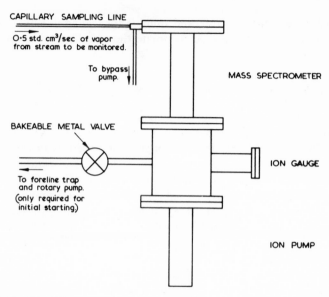

Fig. 13.  Diagrammatic arrangement of ion pumped mass spectrometer for process monitoring applications.

channel detection system must be used. Such systems may take one of the
following forms, all of which have been used sucessfully:

1. Single analyzer tube with fast scanning and preset channels.
2. Single analyzer tube with multiple preset collectors.
3. Multiple analyzer tubes, each preset to a different peak.

   The gases of most common interest in respiratory analyses are water
vapor (mass 18), nitrogen (mass 28), oxygen (mass 32), argon (mass 40), and
carbon dioxide (mass 44). For these gases an instrument having a resolving
power of 20 is adequate, but for experiments on solubility it is of interest to
use a series of "artificial air" mixtures. These are made by replacing atmospheric nitrogen with one of the rare gases, helium (mass 4), neon (masses 20
and 22), argon (mass 40), krypton (masses 78–86), or xenon (masses 124–136).
A mass spectrometer with a mass range extending to 200 is therefore more
generally useful, particularly since the study of anesthetic gases, such as
halothane ($C_2F_3HBrCl_2$), can also be undertaken.

   Fowler and Hugh-Jones [12] have used a small mass spectrometer with
fast scanning to determine the degree of inequality of gas distribution in the
lungs by "washing out" the nitrogen with successive breaths of an oxygen–
argon mixture. The mass spectrometer was preset to record the concentration
of argon and nitrogen at the lips. Figure 14 illustrates the "washing out"
process.

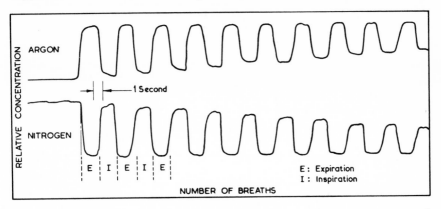

Fig. 14. The assessment of uneven ventilation in the lungs by the gas "wash-out" technique.

Although the small mass spectrometer provides useful information on "wash-out" measurements, it will give much more useful information, which cannot be obtained by other methods, from analyses of the gases contained in a single deep breath.

## Measurement of Atmospheric Pollution

Small mass spectrometers have been used on many occasions to study atmosphere pollution. Problems investigated have included:

1. The purity of mine gases.
2. The presence of corrosive components, especially sulfur compounds, in flue gases.
3. The effect of different additives on the efficiency of electrostatic precipitation.
4. The presence of nitric oxide in automobile exhaust gases.

Each application, of course, has its own special requirements but Fig. 15, which is similar to results obtained by Campau and Neerman [13], illustrates the type of result that can be obtained in the study of automobile exhaust gases. This example shows the variation of nitric oxide level in the exhaust gas from a car engine run at different speeds. It also shows that the speed of response of the overall system, including the sampling arrangement, was sufficiently rapid to follow momentary changes in NO concentrations occurring during changing of gears on the engine. In a separate experiment, the overall response time was measured as 95% of full scale in 2 sec.

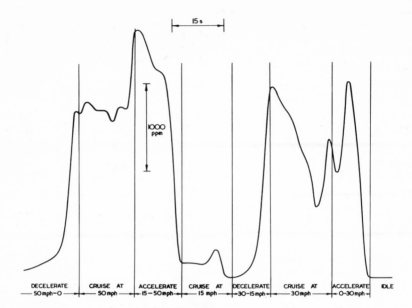

Fig. 15. Variation of nitric oxide in automobile exhaust gases during a seven-mode cycle.

## Purity Determinations

The wide range of partial pressure measurement of the small mass spectrometer, from $10^{-3}$ to $10^{-12}$ torr and less, offers possibilities of impurity determinations to the 0.001-ppm level with favorable gases. However, in practice for any particular sample gas this full range of impurity sensitivity in unlikely to be realizable for all impurities. Nevertheless a sensitivity of the order of 1 ppm should be possible for the majority of impurities in most simple gases.

There are three basic reasons for the impurity detection level at a particular mass number being less than the theoretical value. First, there may be present a peak due to a system gas as distinct from the sample gas. This can occur either as a result of the base pressure in the apparatus being worse than $10^{-12}$ torr, or through the presence of the sample at $10^{-3}$ or $10^{-4}$ torr causing desorption from the walls of the spectrometer or of the inlet system. Second, a low-level background continuum from the major peak of the sample gas may necessitate a high blank correction for the impurity peak. Third, the sample gas itself may have a peak at the particular mass number of interest, completely overlapping the impurity peak.

An example where spectral overlap would limit the detection level to the order of 100 ppm is $H_2S$ in air. In this case there will be a 800-ppm peak at mass 34 due to the $^{16}O^{18}O^+$ ion. A more typical case where background factors are the limitation is shown in Fig. 16, which illustrates the determination of nitrogen impurity in a high-quality argon intended for welding purposes. Here it can be seen that the "blank" contribution at mass 28 is 19 ppm compared with a measured amount of 27.7 ppm with the sample admitted. Thus, 8.7 ppm is the amount of nitrogen in the argon and the limit of error put on this measurement to allow for variation in "blank" and "tail" contributions is $\pm 2$ ppm.

Finally, in more favorable cases, such as the determination of impurities in helium, where the peaks of the impurities and of the major component are well separated, the detection level for the majority of gases should be 1 ppm or less.

## Diffusion Through Plastic Membranes

The storage life of foodstuffs, pharmaceuticals, and other perishable products in plastic containers and packages depends on the rate of diffusion of atmospheric oxygen through the plastic material.

For the experimental arrangement shown in Fig. 17, Harden and Cooper [14] calculated a detection sensitivity of $10^{-8}$ standard $cm^3/sec/cm^2$ and showed that good reproducibility could be obtained provided the pressures on the two sides of the foil were maintained equal, so that the membrane was not stretched. However, when this condition was not met the results were variable, the apparent diffusion rate generally being many times the value obtained for the unstretched foil.

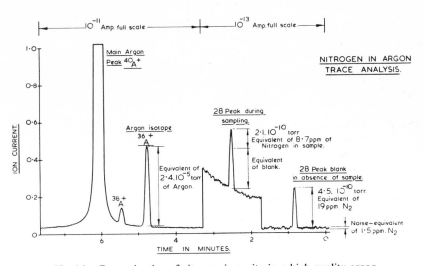

Fig. 16.   Determination of nitrogen impurity in a high-quality argon.

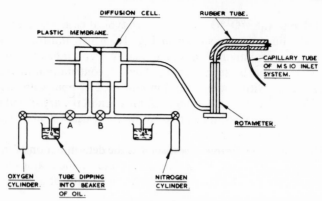

Fig. 17. Apparatus for measurement of diffusion rate through a plastic membrane.

This application is given as an illustration of how varied are the uses of mass spectrometric analysis in industrial research problems.

## Vacuum Troubleshooting

Leaks on vacuum systems are of two types, either "real" or "virtual." A real leak is one where the external atmosphere enters the system through a crack, faulty joint, or other defect in the vacuum wall; a virtual leak is one where the gas or vapor comes either from diffusion out of the wall material or from some other source within the vacuum envelope. In either case a small mass spectrometer, connected directly to the system and used as a partial pressure gauge, will identify the source of trouble and indicate a corrective procedure.

Detailed consideration of this application of partial pressure gauges has been given elsewhere [15] but as an illustration three typical cases are given below.

*Case 1: Partial Pressure Gauge Indicates that Main Components Limiting the Vacuum are the Constituents of Air; Peaks at Masses 28, 32, and 40 are in Correct Ratio for the Mass Spectrum of Air*

This is usually a clear indication of a real leak and the corrective procedure is to select a convenient probe gas, for example, town gas; tune into the appropriate mass number (in this case, mass 15) and start either to probe or bag the walls of the vessel until a positive response is obtained. In this way the exact position of the leak can be located.

*Case 2: Partial Pressure Gauge Indicates that Main Components Limiting the Vacuum are the Constituents of Air but Peaks at Mass 28, 32, and 40 are in Wrong Ratio for Air; 28:32 Ratio is Approximately 4:1 Rather than 8:1*

This indicates a diffusion phenomenon, most probably through a rubber or plastic gasket. The corrective procedure is first to identify the source, and one means of doing this is to use lumps of solid $CO_2$ to chill preferentially suspected components; if these have been guessed correctly, the virtual leak will be greatly reduced.

*Case 3: Partial Pressure Gauge Indicates that Main Component Limiting the Vacuum is Water Vapor; Largest Peak in Spectrum is at Mass 18*

The corrective procedures are one or more of the following :

1. Bake entire system to as high a temperature as possible, preferably to at least 100 to 250 °C.
2. Prolong the pumping; this in itself however is likely to have only a slow effect.
3. Fit a larger pump; this will produce a *pro rata* improvement only if the effective speed is not conductance-limited.
4. Fit a liquid-nitrogen cold trap or Meissener coil.

These three cases show how a small mass spectrometer (partial pressure gauge) can simplify vacuum troubleshooting. In practice there are of course many more than three alternatives, but in each case the mass spectrometer will give a direct indication of the cause and will show whether the corrective steps are effective.

## Analysis of Gas in Metals

The rapid advance in purification of metals through the use of vacuum metallurgy has demanded a similar advance in the analysis of gases in metals at the ppm level and below. In 1966 Aspinal [16] described a system based on melting the sample under vacuum and using a small mass spectrometer to detect the gases evolved. This method has a number of important advantages over previous techniques.

First, the sensitivity is high. For example, Aspinal quotes figures of 0.01 ppm for hydrogen and 0.1 ppm for nitrogen and oxygen. However, the results of the oxygen in copper analysis shown in Fig. 18 indicate that a sensitivity of 0.05 ppm should be comfortably achieved.

Second, the identification is positive. The mass spectrometer positively

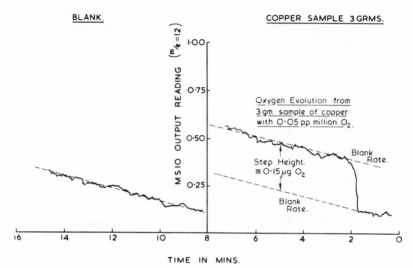

BLANK.                                                    COPPER SAMPLE 3 GRMS.

Oxygen Evolution from
3 gm. sample of copper
with 0·05 pp million $O_2$.

Blank
Rate.

Step Height.
≡ 0·15 μg $O_2$

Blank
Rate.

TIME IN MINS.

Fig. 18.    The evolution of oxygen from a sample of copper.

identifies each gas present, in contrast with other methods [17] where nitrogen is usually determined as the difference between the total gas evolution and the hydrogen and oxygen content. This positive identification can be an important consideration as regards accuracy in cases where methane and carbon dioxide may also be present.

Third, the gas evolution can be monitored. This is illustrated in Fig. 18 where the oxygen evolution is plotted against time. Monitoring is particularly important in certain nitrogen analyses, for example, with transition elements, such as titanium and zirconium, where the decomposition of the nitrides can be slow and careful study is required to ensure that the reaction has reached completion.

More recently Aspinal and Hazelby [18] have described a commercial instrument for routine analysis. This instrument features an automatic doser arrangement for calibration purposes and a combined 18-sample magazine and vacuum lock to permit successive analyses at 5-min intervals.

### Isotopic Analysis

Isotopic ratio measurements are valuable, first, because the determination of small variations in isotope abundance in naturally occurring specimens tells something about conditions in prehistoric times and, second, because measurements using stable isotopes as tracers make possible investigations into biological processes in present times. One of the most important applications in the first category is the measurement of $^{16}O/^{18}O$ ratios to

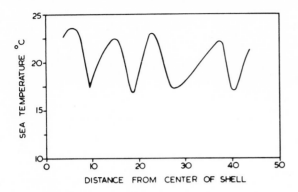

Fig. 19. Plot of sea temperature against distance from the center of the shell of a Jurassic belimnite.

determine palaeotemperatures. A good example, shown in Fig. 19, is the determination of the seasonal variations in sea temperature over a 4-year period, for a specimen taken from about 120 million years ago. These measurements were made by Epstein[19] by analyzing $^{16}O/^{18}O$ ratios of calcium carbonate from successive layers of a marine shell.

Measurement of temperature by this method requires the very accurate determination of the unknown isotopic ratio relative to that of standard oxygen, an error of 0.016% in ratio being equivalent to 1 °C. Thorley *et al.* [5] have studied the problem of errors arising in the mass spectrometer and in the gas preparation plant and have shown it possible to measure the isotopic ratios with a 95% confidence ($2\sigma$) limit of better than 0.005% and the overall temperature to better than 0.5 °C with 95% confidence. This work was done with a small mass spectrometer specially adapted with double collectors for simultaneous ratio recording of the $^{12}C^{16}O^{16}O^+$ and $^{12}C^{16}O^{18}O^+$ ion beams using a dual viscous inlet system for sample introduction.

In the second category perhaps the most important isotope is $^{15}N$ which is widely used as a tracer in studying the metabolism of human, animal, and plant systems. With the advent of the small inexpensive mass spectrometer this very powerful technique is becoming more widely used and applications include investigations into yeast for brewing, nitrogen in eggs, and abnormal protein conversion in very sick patients. For such tracer studies the instrumental requirements are much less exacting than considered above and generally a precision of 0.5% is adequate. Such accuracy is readily obtained by the single-collector technique, as is shown in Fig. 20.

A third application is in chemical analysis using the isotope dilution technique, a comprehensive description of which is given by Beynon [3]. This rather specialized method is useful in single element determinations under conditions where other methods fail either because of lack of accuracy or because of insufficient sensitivity. Among other problems it has been used for determinations of H, C, N, O, and S in organic compounds.

NITROGEN
Series of 10 repeat scans through peaks 28 and 29
having a standard deviation of only 0.18% in measured $^{14}N_2/^{14}N^{15}N$ ratio
with a maximum peak-peak scatter of only 0.5%.

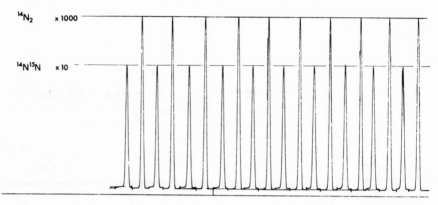

Fig. 20.   Determination of the isotopic ratio $^{14}N_2/^{14}N^{15}N$.

## Age Determination of Rocks

The use of small mass spectrometers in the age determination of rocks by the potassium–argon decay method is now well established. The pioneering work by York *et al.* [20] showed that indeed a small, low-voltage instrument, such as the MS10, could have certain advantages over previous larger instruments with respect to reduced memory effects. The half-life of the potassium–argon transition is 1300 million years which makes it suitable for determining ages from 1 million years right up to 4500 million years, the age of the earliest known rocks. The measurement required is the concentration of radiogenic $^{40}A$ in the rock. A known quantity of argon enriched in $^{38}A$ is added to the argon extracted from a weighed amount of rock. Measurement of the 38:40 isotope ratio in the mass spectrometer then gives the amount of $^{40}A$ present. Measurement of the $^{36}A$ concentration gives a correction for atmospheric argon contamination (see Fig. 21).

For the older rocks there is plenty of gas and straightforward determinations of the 36:38:40 ratios to 0.5% are sufficient. For younger rocks it is usual to increase the sensitivity of the method by using a static system where the spectrometer is completely shut off from the pumps during the analysis, and this extends the method to ages as low as 1 million years [20].

## Gas Chromatography

Mass spectrometry and gas chromatography share the ability to handle minute traces of sample, as little as 1 ng ($10^{-9}$ g) being detectable by both

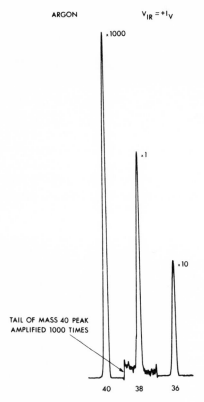

Fig. 21. Mass spectrum of an atmospheric argon sample.

techniques. However, whereas chromatography is a very able separator of mixtures into pure components, mass spectrometry is the most powerful known method for the identification of these separated components. In this respect the two techniques are complementary.

The three methods of coupling mass spectrometry and chromatography are: (1) sample collection, (2) continuous direct sampling, and (3) interrupted elution.

Sample collection from the chromatograph and subsequent transfer to the mass spectrometer, as has been described by Beynon [3], has the advantages of being inexpensive and of not restricting the method to one particular chromatograph user. It also enables the operator of the mass spectrometer to select the scan conditions most appropriate to the particular problem. However, where a large amount of routine data is required there are economies in using one of the other two methods.

When the mass spectrometer is coupled directly to the chromatograph the mass spectrometer must scan rapidly so that the spectrum is taken

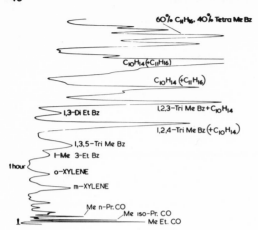

Fig. 22.   Identification of chromatogram by mass and infrared spectrometry.

during the passage of the chromatograph peak. This normally takes between a few seconds and several minutes; thus, mass spectrometric scans down to 1 sec are required. Generally, this requires an instrument fitted with an electron-multiplier detector.

Use of an interrupted elution chromatograph in combination with a small inexpensive mass spectrometer and infrared spectrometer has been described by Scott et al.[21] as a means of harnessing the complementary advantages of mass and infrared spectroscopy in the identification of the separated components. Application of the method is shown in Fig. 22 where Elliott and Richardson[22] have used the MS/IR combination to identify a number of the more difficult peaks in the chromatogram of an industrial oil where, in general, identification would not have been possible using either technique on its own. In the same work the identification of the separate components of unresolved chromatogram peaks was shown to be possible by taking MS/IR scans at different points in time throughout the elution of the peak.

Apart from the advantages of combining mass and infrared spectroscopy and of allowing sufficient time for selection of the optimum mass scan conditions, the interrupted elution system can be set to work completely automatically and unattended for long periods. Thus, by running overnight and at weekends, a high overall rate of component identification has been achieved with relatively inexpensive equipment.

## Applications in Teaching

The small mass spectrometer opens up a number of important and basic teaching possibilities covering a wide range of disciplines. However, even the briefest consideration of these would require a chapter in itself; therefore, all that will be given here is the following, by no means complete, list of topic headings compiled by Allenden [23]:

1. Verification of mass, voltage, field relationship. *
2. Measurement of resolving power and its dependence on geometry. *
3. Measurement of ion-source characteristics. *
4. Ionization potential measurement: single and multiple ionization. *
5. Comparison of ionization cross sections. *
6. Collision cross sections. *
7. Ion–molecule reactions. *
8. Plotting of peak shape: dependence on kinetic energy. *
9. Plotting appearance potential curves. *
10. Cracking patterns. *
11. Isotope identification: measurement of isotope ratios. *
12. Analysis of flame combustion gases. *
13. Analysis of the breath. *
14. Free-radical studies.
15. Simple structural determinations. *
16. Detection of impurities in gases. *
17. Analysis of nitrogen and carbon monoxide. *
18. Detection and localization of leaks, using probe gas. *
19. Measurement of leak rate. *
20. Analysis of gases in rocks.
21. Age determinations by $^{40}K$–$^{40}A$ method.
22. Analysis of gases in metals.
23. Analysis of gases in small sealed devices (lamps, tubes, and transistors).
24. Desorption and outgassing studies. *
25. Operation of an ion pump. *
26. Measurement of pumping speeds for different gases. *
27. Characteristics of ion * and diffusion pumps.
28. Effects of baffles, cold traps, and pump fluids in diffusion pumped systems.
29. Reaction studies using labelled gases. *
30. Residual gases in a vacuum system. *
31. Estimation of hydrocarbon partial pressure. *
32. Evolution of gases from experiments, plants, and organisms. *

In considering these experiments, Allenden has suggested that those marked with an asterisk could be done with a single basic unit, while the others would in general require some additional equipment. A small 180° type of mass spectrometer is particularly good for such experiments because it is simple in conception and design and can therefore be operated and maintained by inexperienced users.

---

* Can be accomplished with a single basic unit.

## REFERENCES

1. G. P. Barnard, *Modern Mass Spectrometry*, The Institute of Physics, London, 1953.
2. American Petroleum Institute, *Mass Spectral Data*, Carnegie Institute, Pittsburgh.
3. J. H. Beynon, *Mass Spectrometry and Its Applications to Organic Chemistry*, Elsevier, Amsterdam, 1960.
4. R. D. Craig and E. H. Harden, "The Interpretation of Mass Spectra," *Vacuum* **16**(2): 67, 1966.
5. N. Thorley, J. Smethurst, and D. L. Ralph, "The Measurement of Carbonate Palaeotemperatures," *Proc. Univ. Newcastle-upon-Tyne Phil. Soc.* **1** (6), 1965.
6. R. D. Craig and U. R. Bance, "Some Characteristics of Triode Ion Pumps," *Vacuum* **16** (12): 647, 1966.
7. H. L. Caswell, "The Effect of Residual Gases on the Superconducting Properties of Tin Films," *J. Appl. Phys.* **32**: 105, 1961.
8. D. Hazelby, "A Versatile Gas Analysis Apparatus Incorporating a Small Mass Spectrometer," *J. Sci. Instr.* **42**: 486, 1965.
9. F. Hartog, "The Analysis of Deuterated Hydrocarbons with the MS10 Mass Spectrometer," *Mass Spectrometry Symposium (1965)*, Associated Electrical Industries Limited, Manchester, England, 1965.
10. R. W. Roberts, "The Reaction of Ethane with a Clean Rhodium Film," *Trans. Faraday Soc.* **58**: 1159, 1962.
11. C. Bokhoven and H. J. Theeuwen, "The Application of the MS10 for Continuous Monitoring of Ammonia, Carbon Dioxide and Water on a Process Stream," *Mass Spectrometry Symposium (1965)*, Associated Electrical Industries Limited, Manchester, England, 1965.
12. K. T. Fowler and P. Hugh-Jones, "Mass Spectrometry Applied to Clinical Research and Practice," *Brit. Med. J.*, May 25, 1957.
13. R. M. Campau and J. C. Neerman, "Continual Mass Spectrometric Determination of Nitric Oxide in Automatic Exhaust," *Proceedings of the S. A. E. Automotive Engineering Congress*, Held in Detroit, January 10–14, 1966, S.A.E., New York.
14. E. H. Harden and M. C. Cooper, "Use of the MS10 Mass Spectrometer to Measure the Diffusion Rate of Oxygen Through Plastic Membranes," T. I. Sheet A510, Associated Electrical Industries Limited, Manchester, England, 1966.
15. "The Partial Pressure Gauge at Work," No. 1 in a series, Associated Electrical Industries Limited, Manchester, England, 1967.
16. M. L. Aspinal, *Analyst* **91**: 1078, 1966.
17. J. A. James, *Met. Rev.* **9**: 93, 1964.
18. M. L. Aspinal and D. Hazelby, *Proceedings of the International Vacuum Metallurgy Congress*, New York, 1967.
19. S. Epstein, *Nat. Bur. Std. (U.S.) Circ.* **522**: 153, 1953.
20. E. Farrar, R. M. Macintyre, and D. York, "A Simple Mass Spectrometer for the Analysis of Argon," *Proceedings of the A. S. T. M. Committee E14 12th Annual Conference on Mass Spectrometry*, Montreal, 1964.
21. R. P. W. Scott, I. A. Fowlis, D. Welti, and T. Wilkins, "Interrupted Electron Chromatography," *Proceedings of the International Symposium on Gas Chromatography, Rome, 1966*, Butterworth, London.
22. R. M. Elliott and W. R. Richardson, "Mass Spectrometric Identification of Eluents from an Interrupted Electron Chromatograph," *Proceedings of the A. S. T. M. Committee E.14 15th Annual Conference on Mass Spectrometry*, Denver, 1967.
23. D. Allenden, Picker Nuclear, Inc., White Plains, New York (private communication).

# LASER MICROPROBE SAMPLING AND OTHER NEW TOF MASS SPECTROMETER DEVELOPMENTS

## D. C. Damoth

*The Bendix Corporation*
*Cincinnati, Ohio*

This paper summarizes and discusses recent developments in sampling techniques and readout modes used in conjunction with the time-of-flight mass spectrometer. The sampling techniques include laser microprobe sampling, a direct inlet probe for high-temperature studies, thermal (surface) ionization capability, and a maximum sensitivity gas chromatograph hookup. The readout techniques include a total output integrator and a stepped raster oscilloscope display.

The most startling and far-reaching development in mass spectrometer sampling or ionization techniques to arise recently has been developed and described by Professors Bruce Knox and Frank Vastola of Pennsylvania State University. This technique is the use of a laser of about 0.1 J per pulse power to vaporize minute samples directly into the ion source of the time-of-flight mass spectrometer. Researchers had used lasers to vaporize samples in other types of mass spectrometers and others had used the general technique in conjunction with time-of-flight (TOF) instruments.

Those who tried to use lasers on other types of mass spectrometers rapidly discovered one of the most important fundamental properties of the TOF instruments, that is, it delivers essentially all of the ions to the detector each cycle of operation (usually 10,000 to 100,000 spectra/sec). Other instruments, such as geometric separation types (notably magnetic deflection) and filter types (represented by the quadrupole and other radio-frequency instruments), can only monitor a single mass peak at one time. The only exception is the tandem magnet instrument of Mattauch–Herzog geometry with photoplate readout, but the sensitivity of this type of ion detection is too low to be of value in this instance. The TOF instrument, thus, is the only type capable of sufficiently rapid operation to analyze the species vaporized in a laser, because the burst of gas, which is caused by the intense laser heat, lasts about 2 msec. The collection of all the ions by the detector on each cycle of the instrument also means that the sensitivity is much greater for those applications where the spectrum is composed of more than one mass peak.

Professors Knox and Vastola recognized an important aspect of lasers which made such devices unique in their capabilities for mass spectrometer sampling, that is, the capability to deliver a large amount of energy at a selected time to very small, previously chosen spots. In other words, they recognized the potential of lasers to sample small domains in heterogeneous samples. This capability is also realized without heating sample supports, crucibles, or extraneous devices inside the vacuum system of the mass spectrometer, thereby avoiding problems caused by degassing, or background as it is generally known.

They set about coupling a 0.1-J laser to the TOF mass spectrometer and, by an ingenious, but simple, arrangement of the optics, achieved a very handy arrangement which permits them to vaporize a spot as small as $10^{-3}$ cm in diameter. Sampling from such small regions is beyond the capability of any other mass spectrometric technique and, for that matter, beyond most analytical techniques. Only the electron microprobe has the capability to probe such small regions. However, electron microprobes are very expensive and have one major drawback compared to the laser–TOF microprobe: the dynamic range is small because the specific sensitivity is not as high as that of the laser–TOF combination. The reasons for this become evident after several simple calculations. A region $10^{-3}$ cm in diameter and about $10^{-4}$ cm deep has a volume of about $10^{-10}$ cm$^3$. With a density of 10, that region would be $10^{-9}$ g. On typical analyses with the laser–TOF microprobe, traces of $10^{-3}$ concentration can readily be seen on any given spectrum. Thus, a sensitivity of $10^{-12}$ g is obtained.

Figure 1 is a line drawing of the laser coupled to the mass spectrometer. The optical well in the top of the source cross permits the optical probe to be lowered to within 1 cm of the ion source. A vertical illumination system beams light on the surface of the sample through the optical probe. A cross-hair sighting system permits exact location of the area to be sampled. The energy delivered to the surface of the sample can be varied by changing the power input or by means of different-size collimating apertures between the laser and the prism. A movable silvered microscope slide permits viewing of the sample, and it must be moved out of the optical path before the laser can be fired in order to protect the operator's sight.

It is, of course, the prerogative of Professors Knox and Vastola to describe the results which they have obtained; at the American Chemical Society meeting in Pittsburgh in March 1966, they have already announced work which they did on coal samples. In May, they described work on selenium in conjunction with the description of their system in a paper presented at the ASTM E-14 meeting in Dallas. In their analysis of selenium, they found that

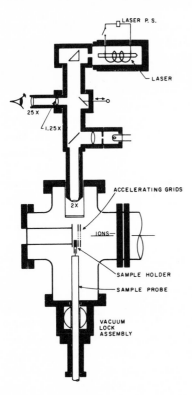

Fig. 1. Schematic of system.

the vapors arising from the sample immediately after the laser burst (that is, within the first few hundred microseconds) indicate temperatures very much higher than those produced by conventional vaporization. As the time after the laser pulse increases, the spectrum gradually assumes the same ratios of polymers normally observed by other techniques.

Another interesting fact which they have noted is the specific time after the laser pulse during which ions produced by the laser energy, rather than by electron impact, are observed. Ions produced by electron impact are observed on every cycle of the mass spectrometer operation from the time of the laser pulse until the sample leaves the ion source, about 1 msec later. The ions produced by the laser energy directly, observed by turning the ionizing electron beam off, are observed only during a short time interval about 200 $\mu$sec after the laser pulse.

Recently, they have successfully analyzed the composition of areas as small as the emitter-base region in microelectronic circuits. The potential for analyses of such miniature devices is sorely needed with the present state-of-the-art of research and production of these devices. The applications for analysis in thin film work are also promising.

The extent of the analysis which this system offers is actually unknown at this time, but will unfold in the coming years. It is interesting to contemplate the potential of applying this technique to sampling inclusions in biomedical samples for trace analysis of elements, analyzing metallurgical samples for the nature of slight inclusions, or examining known materials for new states when vaporized by this technique.

The commercial development of the laser microprobe system for the TOF mass spectrometer is now under way. The 0.1-J laser will not vaporize highly reflective samples unless they are coated with light-absorbing materials, so a 1-J laser will be used in the commercial version. The design features of the commercial version will parallel those of the Knox–Vastola apparatus.

Another device developed by Dr. Knox is the 1700°C direct inlet probe. The direct inlet probe, now commonly copied on most mass spectrometry equipment, was first developed for use on the TOF mass spectrometer. The original design was a simple ribbon filament with a dimple in which the sample rested. Dr. K. Biemann of the Massachusetts Institute of Technology suggested a change which led to the present standard direct inlet system shown in Fig. 2. The simple heat shields permit a maximum operating temperature of about 700°C. Dr. Knox needed temperatures to at least 1500°C for studies of silicon-based compounds. He developed a water-cooled version of the direct inlet system which uses crucibles formed from tubular platinum. The crucibles are heated by passing current directly through the crucible body instead of being heated by an auxiliary heater outside the crucible. This method achieves the desired temperature with lower power, simplifying the problem of heat dissipation.

In the standard direct inlet system, the quartz crucible rests on the tip of a coaxial thermocouple. This provides accurate temperature measurement in the sample region. In the higher-temperature version designed by Dr. Knox, the temperature is measured with an optical pyrometer which sights through a viewing port, through the ion source, directly into the sample crucible. The temperature can be measured accurately with the pyrometer because the length-to-depth ratio of the crucible is about 4. This system can be used to study free evaporation phenomena of many species to 1700°C. It offers greater sensitivity than the Knudsen cell system in the temperature range up to 1700°C. The Knudsen cell furnace operates to 2500°C. The sample is about 2 cm from the ionization region with the high-temperature direct inlet probe, while it is about 4 cm away with the Knudsen cell. The high-temperature direct inlet and the standard direct inlet fit the same vacuum lock, and the two different types of probes may be used interchangeably.

It is rapidly being recognized that the most valid mass spectrometric sampling techniques involve a means for the sample vapor species to travel directly from the source of the sample through the ionization region without

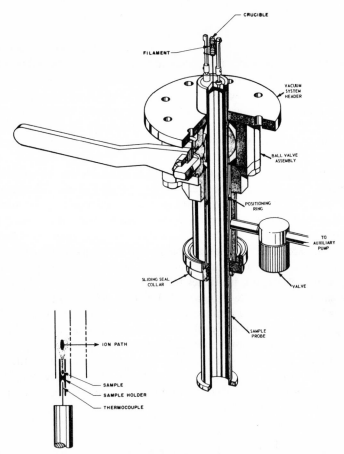

Fig. 2.    Direct inlet system Model 843A.

contacting any surfaces, particularly metal surfaces at temperatures dissimilar to that of the sample. In some cases, all contact with any surface must be avoided. This technique is commonly known as line-of-sight sampling. The laser microprobe and the versions of the direct inlet just discussed both utilize this principle. Another similar sampling means uses line-of-sight sampling in a secondary sense, but relies on contact with a hot metal surface for ionization. This is the technique of thermal or surface ionization.

Thermal ionization sampling is useful for alkali-metal and radioactive-element analysis. The specific sensitivity of thermal ionization is greater because as much as 10% or more of the sample vaporized may be ionized, while electron bombardment ionization will usually ionize only about

$10^{-6}$ of the ions vaporized. Consequently, specific sensitivities of $10^{-15}$ g are readily obtained by thermal ionization.

From the first use of the technique until 1961, thermal ionization was used only on magnetic deflection mass spectrometers. In 1961, Dr. Martin Studier of Argonne National Laboratory showed that many discrepancies in thermal ionization analyses were being caused by the occurrence of reduction of samples in the oxide form while they were being vaporized from the filament. He was aided materially in this discovery by the oscilloscope output of the TOF mass spectrometer which permits continuous observation of the whole mass spectrum.

Now the thermal ionization capability is available for any TOF mass spectrometer. The multiple-channel analog output system will make fast, accurate isotope ratio measurements possible, because the variations in sample evaporation rate are recorded and averaged out simultaneously for each isotope measured.

The commercial thermal ionization system is patterned after the system developed by Dr. Studier. Figure 3 is a line drawing of the device on the mass spectrometer. Again, it utilizes the ball valve vacuum lock system to facilitate sample entry. The standard direct inlet probe is fitted with a top assembly which supports a dual filament configuration. The inset in Fig. 3 shows the relationship of the two filaments. The filament assembly plugs into four connectors and is simply removed to change samples.

The upper filament is the sample-bearing filament and the lower filament is the ionizing filament. The sample can be ready for analysis about 1 min after entry is started. The ionizing filament is operated at about

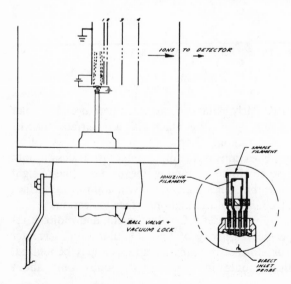

Fig. 3. Thermal (surface) ionization probe in the TOF mass spectrometer.

2000 °K. The upper-filament temperature is raised to a value sufficient to vaporize the sample. Much of the sample hits the ionizing filament and, if the work function is low, becomes ionized. Proper biases on the two filaments with respect to each other and to the source region direct the ions upward into the conventional source region.

Figure 4 shows a "dirty" background with the surface ionization probe in place, but with electron beam ionization. Figure 5 shows the spectrum, shortly afterward, with surface ionization, but without electron beam ionization. The background is gone and the very small sample is easily detected and measured, showing the high specific sensitivity of the system.

In the field of general analytical chemistry, the most popular instrument is unquestionably the gas chromatograph. The combination of gas chromatographs with mass spectrometers results in the most powerful research and analytical tool known. Several techniques are available to couple gas chromatographs to mass spectrometers. The simplest is the familiar splitter valve, whereby a fraction of the gas chromatograph effluent is introduced into the mass spectrometer. This technique is flexible and may be used with any gas chromatograph or mass spectrometer. It has two principal shortcomings; first, the carrier gas predominates in the mass spectrometer and limits the sensitivity, and, second, the time scale is determined by the gas chromatograph (G.C.), so the mass spectrometer must complete a scan in less time than the time-width of a G.C. peak.

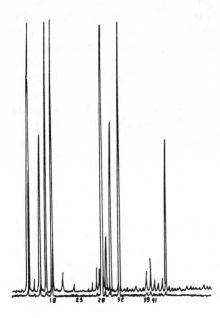

Fig. 4.   Typical background spectrum with thermal ionization probe in place.

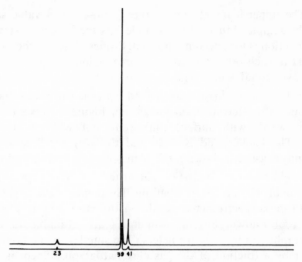

Fig. 5.   Thermal ionization spectrum of sodium and potassium.

A popular means for coupling gas chromatographs to mass spectrometers is the use of enrichment devices. These are similar to the splitter
valve, except that they preferentially pass higher-molecular-weight compounds, while shunting off lower-molecular-weight compounds to be
pumped away. If helium is used as a carrier gas, an enrichment ratio of
10 may be obtained, with some loss of lower-molecular-weight sample. Some
carrier gas is still delivered to the mass spectrometer and will probably
still be the main limitation on sensitivity. The second principal shortcoming
of the simple splitter valve is still inherent in these enrichment devices, that is,
the mass spectrometer must still scan as fast as the peaks are eluted from the
gas chromatograph.

A. A. Ebert of DuPont Company described a gas chromatograph
manifold system [1]. This manifold system traps all of a selected gas chromatograph effluent fraction. The sample gas can be condensed at cryogenic
temperatures, the carrier gas pumped away, and the sample introduced into
the mass spectrometer under chosen conditions. Thus, essentially all of the
carrier gas is eliminated so it is not the primary limit of sensitivity. The
fact that the sample is trapped in a small volume means that it can be introduced into the mass spectrometer as rapidly or slowly as desired. Thus,
if slow scans are required, they can be obtained. Most mass spectrometers
without fast scan capabilities can do excellent G.C. effluent identification
with this device. This technique should not be confused with the cumbersome
method of trapping G.C. effluent in a separate container, then introducing
it into the mass spectrometer; the volumes, physical arrangement, and the

fact that there is no possibility of sample contamination make the manifold a very powerful tool.

Two previous disadvantages of the G.C. manifold were that it could not be used with capillary column gas chromatographs and it could not be temperature-cycled. The first disadvantage was due to the internal volume of the trapped volume of the manifold "legs." The trapped-leg volume is 2.5 cm$^3$. Capillary gas chromatographs typically have a flow rate of about 0.1 cm$^3$/sec, so such a trap would sample a G.C. effluent fraction which would contain many separate compounds. The people at DuPont overcame this difficulty by putting a T-fitting in the line between the capillary gas chromatograph and the manifold, locating it as close to the G.C. detector as possible. The carrier gas flow from the G.C. is amplified by putting in additional carrier gas at the "T," so the flow rate to the manifold is increased to 2.5 cm$^3$/sec or more and the manifold traps take a fraction of only about 1-sec duration. A restriction between the G.C. detector and the introduction point of the extra carrier gas eliminates problems from any variation in pressure of the extra carrier gas supply. The extra carrier gas can be dry nitrogen as well as helium.

The temperature cycling problem was caused by the differential expansion of the valve elements and the problem was solved by the use of bimetallic compensating elements so the system remains leak-tight from ambient temperature to 200 °C.

Because the manifold system delivers all the G.C. fraction to the mass spectrometer and the mass spectrometer scan speed can be chosen, the sensitivity of the system is such that G.C. fractions of $10^{-11}$ to $10^{-12}$ g can be identified with a good mass spectrometer, well baked out, with an electron multiplier detector. This is about 1000 times better than the results that simple enrichment techniques provide.

Some of the most productive work using the gas chromatograph–mass spectrometer combination is being done with the simplest coupling system of all. A capillary gas chromatograph column is coupled directly into the TOF ion source region without any detector or other devices in between. Thus, the complete gas chromatograph effluent goes to the mass spectrometer with no possibility of remixing, contamination, or loss.

An essential adjunct to the use of this system is the total output integrator module for the TOF. This device permits the TOF to function as a sensitive, linear ionization detector for the G.C. operation, while scanning the mass spectrum on the oscilloscope and recording the spectrum on a strip chart recorder. R. Gohlke of the Dow Chemical Company described a simple version of such a device at the ASTM E-14 meeting in New Orleans in 1962.

The concept is best illustrated in Fig. 6. The row of digits in boxes at the top of the figure represents individual complete mass spectra developed

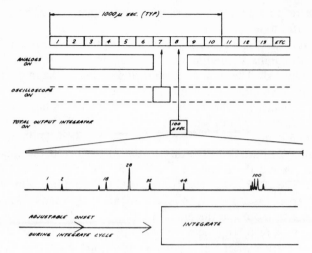

Fig. 6.   Total output integrator time sequence.

on each cycle of operation of the TOF. The cycle of operation of the TOF is normally repeated 10,000 times each second, so each cycle takes 100 $\mu$sec. The total output integrator has a built-in binary scalar (counter) which counts up to eight, with each count triggered by the start of each cycle of the TOF-principle electronics. Starting at some initial point chosen by chance, the binary scalar and associated circuitry cause the analog output system to function on each of the first six of the eight cycles in each series. This means that the analog output scans of the TOF will be reduced in intensity by a constant 25%. This is a small enough reduction to be classed as insignificant, and it does not affect the accuracy of measurement because all peaks are reduced by the same factor.

On the seventh cycle of each series, the counting system turns off the analog scanning system by suppressing the final gate pulse amplifier stage on each analog and triggers the oscilloscope on, providing the familiar oscilloscope spectrum at the rate of 1250 spectra/sec. This is $\frac{1}{8}$ of the normal number, but since optical response is approximately logarithmic the trace appears only slightly dimmer and a slight adjustment of the CRT brightness control easily makes up the difference. A significant functional improvement in the observed oscilloscope spectrum results from this mode of operation.

Normally, when the analog scanning system is employed while observing the spectrum on the oscilloscope, the high-frequency oscillation set up by analog gates (gate pulse ringing) obscures mass peaks in the immediate vicinity (e.g., 3–10 amu) of the peak being scanned at any given instant. Because the analog gate pulses are suppressed on the oscilloscope cycles, only a modest residual ringing remains and the complete mass spectrum is readily observed.

On the eighth cycle of each series, the counter triggers on the gating circuit of the total output integrator. There is an adjustable time-delay circuit which allows the integration of the mass peaks to be started at any mass number from 1 to 250. All the mass peaks from that mass number to the end of the cycle ($m/q = 1300$) are consequently integrated. The output of the total output integrator, then, is proportional to the combined amplitudes of those peaks.

Thus, the total output integrator allows the TOF mass spectrometer to detect the gas chromatograph effluent by ionization of the output, and the maxima of the G.C. output coincide exactly with the maxima of the regular mass spectra. This eliminates any ambiguity of the correlation between a mass spectral scan and the gas chromatogram.

The total output integrator function differs from the total-ion-current monitors sometimes used on geometric separation mass spectrometers in that the TOF does not collect the low-mass-number peaks, so the standard ionizing voltages of 50 and 70 V may be used in G.C. work.

In very fast analyses, such as in the laser–TOF microprobe sampling, the information is presented on the oscilloscope readout. The maximum frequency response of the analog output is 1000 cps, so events which occur in less than 0.1 sec must be presented on the oscilloscope.

The early fast-response recordings of the TOF output on the oscilloscope were made utilizing drum cameras which move film past a focused image of the oscilloscope pattern at a rapid rate. This technique is still used, but is cumbersome and costly.

Simpler methods are the Z-axis gating and time-resolved raster techniques described by Lincoln [2]. These techniques are straightforward and are commonly used. The Z-axis gating gives the abundance of two mass peaks on each cycle of the spectrometer, and the time-resolved raster gives qualitative information about the presence or absence of each mass peak over the chosen time interval. The combination of these two techniques requires two oscilloscopes and two Polaroid cameras.

The drum camera has the basic advantage, however, that it gives quantitative information on each peak during the recording time interval. A new technique has been evolved which gives the general capability of the drum camera, yet has the ease of use of still cameras, as in the Z-axis and time-resolved raster technique. This easier general technique is called the stepped raster technique. The basic idea of the stepped raster technique was described by Moulton and Michael [3]. The idea of the technique is to move the electron beam of the oscilloscope CRT between successive cycles of the mass spectrometer, while the photographic film remains fixed. Thus, five successive mass spectra can be spaced 1 cm apart on a 6-cm-high raster.

To increase the number of spectra and thus the time period that can be covered with a given oscilloscope and camera, the electronic chassis which regulates the raster stepping can be set to overlay one, two, four, or eight spectra at each position before moving the electron beam to a new vertical elevation. Thus, with five vertical positions, up to 40 successive spectra can be recorded.

To prevent large peaks from extending up past the base line of the next spectrum higher in the vertically spaced display and coinciding with the same peak in that spectrum, thus obscuring the top of the peak and preventing amplitude measurement, the horizontal position of each series of spectra at a given vertical position is offset slightly. This prevents large peaks from overlapping each other. All these capabilities have been incorporated into a single electronic chassis called the oscilloscope stepped raster chassis.

The foregoing has been a review of some of the significant instrumental developments associated with the TOF mass spectrometer in the last year.

## REFERENCES

1. A.A. Ebert, *Anal. Chem.* **33**:1865, 1961.
2. K.A. Lincoln, *Rev. Sci. Instr.* **35**:1688, 1964.
3. D.McL. Moulton and J.V. Michael, *Rev. Sci. Instr.* **36**:226, 1965.

# THE QUADRUPOLE
# MASS SPECTROMETER
# AND SOME RECENT APPLICATIONS

## Martin T. Mason*

*Chartered Consulting Engineer*
*London, England*

## THEORY OF OPERATION

The quadrupole mass filter was first developed by Paul and co-workers [1] in Germany. In this instrument, ions are injected along the axis of a quadrupole radio-frequency electric field. This type of field is produced between four parallel rods of hyperbolic section to which a radio-frequency potential and a superimposed DC potential are applied. In practice, however, it is sufficient to approximate the field by the use of cylindrical rods.

Mathematical analysis of the equations of motion of an ion injected axially into one end of the quadrupole field shows that the system acts as a mass filter. Depending on the values of certain parameters, only ions within a particular mass range perform oscillations of constant amplitude ("stable" ions) and can be collected at the far end of the analyzer. All ions outside this range perform oscillations of increasing amplitude ("unstable" ions) and do not reach the collector.

One typical form of quadrupole mass analyzer head is illustrated in Fig. 1 and shown schematically in Fig. 2. This head comprises three principal components, which are a simple thermionic ionizer, a precision quadrupole rod section, and an ion collector. The substance which is to be analyzed is introduced into the ionizer as a gas or vapor at low pressure. A small percentage of the atoms or molecules which comprise the substance is ionized by electron bombardment, and the ions so formed are then accel-

---

* Formerly with 20th Century Electronics Limited, New Addington, Croydon, Surrey, England.

Fig. 1.   Quadrupole mass analyzer head, with ionizer and electron multiplier section.

erated and focused into the quadrupole section. Filtering of the ion beam
results from the fact that only those ions within a specific range of mass-
to-charge ratios are permitted to pass through the quadrupole. Ions which
are able to pass through the filter are collected by the ion detector which is
generally an electron multiplier or a Faraday cup.

The ion detector output current provides an indication of the number of
atoms or molecules in the substance which, when ionized, have a particular
mass-to-charge ratio. The mass-to-charge ratio detected is determined
from the values of the DC and RF voltages which are applied to the poles of
the quadrupole section. As most of the ions which are produced in the

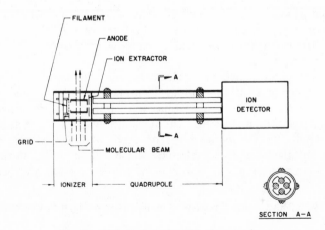

Fig. 2.   EAI quadrupole residual gas analyzer.

ionizer are singly charged, the mass of the atoms or molecules may be determined directly. Quantitative abundance, as a function of atomic mass, can be conveniently presented on display instruments such as an oscilloscope, an $x$-$y$ plotter, or a strip chart recorder. However, when precise abundance ratio measurements are to be made on samples of varying atomic numbers, it is necessary to calibrate the system using mixtures of known composition, which approximate the composition of the sample. An abundance ratio measurement of the isotopes of one atom does not require the use of standards, but, if an electron multiplier is used, a correction by the inverse-square-root relation should be made because of the nonlinear response of the electron multiplier.

The most critical part of the quadrupole mass analyzer is the pole assembly. This assembly comprises four stainless steel rods, each of which is approximately 125 mm (5 in.) long and 6 mm ($\frac{1}{4}$ in.) in diameter, held in the four corners of a square array of ceramic insulators. The DC voltage and superimposed RF voltage are applied to the rods, as shown in Fig. 3, and an electrostatic field is thereby generated in the space between the rods. If the rods were of hyperbolic sections (Fig. 4) rather than cylinders, the potential of this electrostatic field would be

$$\phi = (V_1 + V_0 \cos t)\frac{x^2 - y^2}{r_0^2} \tag{1}$$

This potential is very nearly achieved with cylindrical rods. From this

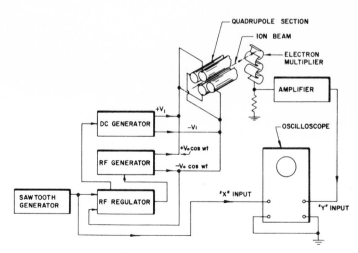

Fig. 3.   Quadrupole voltages.

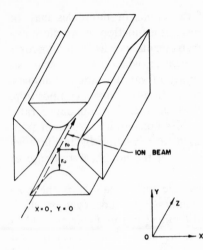

Fig. 4.  Hyperbolic quadrupole rods.

equation the electrostatic force applied to a singly charged ion while traveling between the quadrupole rods is given by

$$m\ddot{x} = F_x = -e\frac{\partial\phi}{\partial x} = -e(V_1 + V_0\cos\omega t)\frac{2x}{r_0^2} \qquad (2)$$

$$m\ddot{y} = F_y = -e\frac{\partial\phi}{\partial x} = +e(V_1 + V_0\cos\omega t)\frac{2y}{r_0^2} \qquad (3)$$

$$m\ddot{z} = F_z = -e\frac{\partial\phi}{\partial z} = 0 \qquad (4)$$

where $e$ is the electronic charge. Therefore, the equations of motion of a singly charged ion of mass, $m$, are

$$m\ddot{x} + \left(\frac{2e}{r_0^2}\right)(V_1 + V_0\cos\omega t)\,x = 0 \qquad (5)$$

$$m\ddot{y} - \left(\frac{2e}{r_0^2}\right)(V_1 + V_0\cos\omega t)\,y = 0 \qquad (6)$$

$$m\ddot{z} = 0 \qquad (7)$$

Equation (7) may be immediately integrated to determine the axial motion of the ion,

$$\dot{z} = \dot{z}_0 = \text{constant} \qquad (8)$$

Thus, the axial velocity of any ion is its value at the entrance to the filter through the quadrupole. This velocity is constant and is independent of the voltages applied to the rods of the quadrupole filter. The ionizer and ion extraction system thereby govern the time required for an ion to pass through the filter.

The filtering action of the quadrupole results from the trajectory characteristics of equations (5) and (6). Under certain conditions, there is an unlimited increase in amplitude of the trajectory, in which case the ion collides with one of the rods and is removed from the ion beam. The characteristics of these Mathieu equations have been analyzed by a number of investigators [2] and, for the particular case of the RF quadrupole mass spectrometer, stability diagrams have been developed by Paul *et al.* [3], Stanford Research Institute [4], and Electronic Associates, Inc.

Typical stable and unstable trajectories of an ion are shown in Fig. 5. (A PACE analog computer was used to obtain these solutions of the equations of motion.) In the upper left corner is a typical trajectory of an ion stable in the $x$-direction and below is the trajectory of an ion unstable in the $y$-direction. The upper right-hand corner shows trajectories of ions unstable in the $x$-direction and stable in the $y$-direction. On the bottom is an ion trajectory transformed to an ion stable in $x^2 + y^2$. The significant point here is that ions instable in $x$ will oscillate in an undamped oscillation. Ions unstable in the $y$-direction move outward from the axis.

The Paul and Stanford Research Institute stability diagrams are shown in Fig. 6. In this, and in Fig. 7, certain nondimensional groupings have been introduced into the equations of motion. These parameters are

$$\theta = \omega t \tag{9}$$

$$\alpha = \frac{(2\,eV_0)}{(mr_0{}^2\,\omega^2)} \tag{10}$$

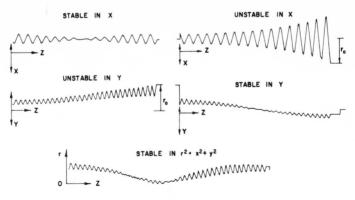

Fig. 5. Typical ion trajectories.

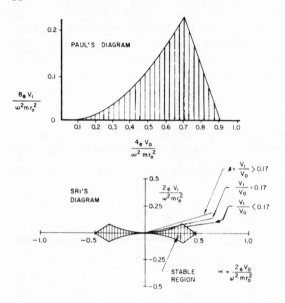

Fig. 6.  Stability  diagrams.

$$\beta = \frac{V_1}{V_0} \tag{11}$$

The transformed equations of motion are

$$\ddot{x} + \alpha(\beta + \cos\theta)\,x = 0 \tag{12}$$

$$\ddot{y} - \alpha(\beta + \cos\theta)\,y = 0 \tag{13}$$

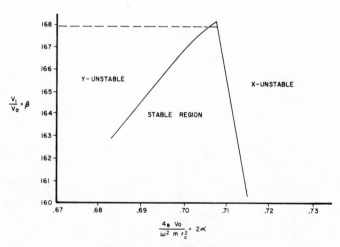

Fig. 7.  EAI stability diagram.

For a given value of the parameter $\alpha$, there exists a value of the parameter $\beta$ which divides a region of stability from a region of instability. The locus of points which form this division is plotted in Fig. 6 for equations (12) and (13). It may be seen that, of all possible values these parameters may take, only a small portion will result in the stability of both equations. An alternative form of the stability diagram has been developed at Electronic Associates, Inc., and is given in Fig. 7. The RF-to-DC ratio is referred to as $\beta$ on the ordinate; a $2\alpha$ term on the abscissa includes the parameters which will determine stability. Three regions of the stability diagram which are of interest are:

1. Stability in $y$-direction and instability in the $x$-direction. This is the area to the left of the stability envelope. These ions will be unstable in $r = x^2 + y^2$.
2. Stability in the $x$-direction and instability in the $y$-direction. This is the area to the right of the stability envelope. These ions will also be unstable in $r = x^2 + y^2$.
3. Stability in the $x$-direction and in the $y$-direction. This is the area enclosed by the stability envelope. Ions whose trajectories are included within the stability envelope will be stable in $r$. These ions will traverse the mass filter and strike the detector.

By varying the RF-to-DC ratio, one can increase or decrease the area of the stable region available to ions (the area enclosed by the stability envelope, and above the $\beta$ line). Since resolution is defined by $M/\Delta M$, and $\Delta M$ is a result of the width of the operating portion of the stability diagram, it is obvious that by increasing $\beta$, $\Delta M$ is decreased and resolution is increased.

It should be noted that if the parameter, $\beta = V_1/V_0$, is constant at a value of approximately 0.168, there is a very small range of values of the parameter $\alpha$, which will result in stable solutions. Physically, this implies that only ions within a very small range of mass-to-charge ratios will have trajectories which will allow them to traverse the quadrupole structure. Ions having mass-to-charge ratios outside this range will have trajectories which will result in collisions with the poles.

Furthermore, if either the voltage $V_0$ or the frequency $\omega$, or both, are varied in such a manner that the ratio of voltages, $V_1/V_0$, remains constant at about the 0.168 level, the value of the transmitted and detected mass-to-charge ratios will vary in a known manner. That is, the mass-to-charge ratios of the ions which reach the detector will be that value necessary for $\alpha$ to have the value of 0.354. Therefore, this ratio may be determined from the relation

$$e/m = 0.354 \frac{(r_0^2 \, \omega^2)}{(2 \, V_0)} \tag{14}$$

Under the assumption that the ions are singly charged, the mass of the ion which reaches the detector is

$$m = \frac{0.136 \, V_0}{(r_0^2 f^2)} \, \text{amu} \qquad (15)$$

where $V_0$ is in volts, $r_0$ is in cm, and $f$ is in mcps.

## APPARATUS

A number of experimental quadrupole mass spectrometers have been produced and, in addition, commercially made equipment is now available. The instruments to be described are those first evolved at the Stanford Research Institute, Stanford, California, and further developed and manufactured by Electronic Associates, Incorporated, of Palo Alto, California.

### Ionizers

While the ionizer of the quadrupole can be of the field ion and field emission type, the most commonly used ionizer is the thermionic electron impact type. Two forms of ionizer of the latter type are shown in Fig. 8. On the left is an ionizer designed to accept a molecular beam transverse to the quadrupole axis. This is known as a cross-beam ionizer. The ions are formed when the atoms or molecules in the system are bombarded with thermionically emitted electrons in a small ionization chamber. The ions so formed are focused and drawn out to the left where the quadrupole would be located. On the right is an ionizer designed to accept a molecular beam axially with

Fig. 8.   Two simple thermionic ionizers for use with the quadrupole mass analyzer.

respect to the quadrupole axis. While this is referred to as an axial-beam ionizer, the unit can also be used for transverse molecular beams. In the cross-beam ionizer, the electron beam travels axially with respect to the quadrupole and is collected internally at appropriate electrodes. In the axial-beam ionizer, the electron beam is formed as a ribbon and travels perpendicularly to the axis of the quadrupole. The axial-beam ionizer is now the more generally used, because the focusing and control of both electrons and ions are more closely monitored. However, the cross-beam ionizer is to be recommended where molecular beams are to be analyzed, as these can be directed straight through the ionizer, thereby avoiding prior surface reactions. Figure 9 shows diagrammatically a cross-beam ionizer. This consists of a filament, a grid, an ionizing chamber, and three electrodes, all of which are enclosed. Atoms and molecules enter the ionizing chamber via holes in the tube and are ionized by low-energy electrons emitted by the filament.

Electrons produced at the filament are accelerated by a controllable voltage between the filament and grid. Those electrons passing through the grid and into the ionizing chamber encounter neutral atoms and molecules. If the resulting transfer of energy through electron interaction is adequate, a positive ion is produced. In this manner, one electron may produce several ions before it loses its energy and is collected.

The ions are extracted from the ion chamber by a starting electrode which is operated at a positive potential (Fig. 9) slightly less than the potential of the chamber itself. After passing through the starting aperture, the ions are accelerated by a focusing aperture which is set at a negative potential, $V_f$. The approximate energy of the ions then becomes

$$(eV_c - eV_s) + (eV_s - eV_f)$$

Finally, in going from the focusing aperture to the grounded exit aperture, the ions lose energy $eV_f$. The net ion energy is then calculated as follows:

$$\text{Ion energy} = (eV_c - eV_s) + (eV_s - eV_f) + eV_f = eV_c \qquad (16)$$

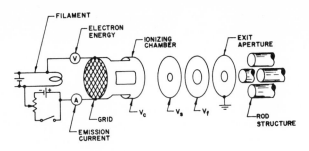

Fig. 9.   Ionizer schematic.

Therefore, the energy with which the ion enters the quadrupole structure is determined by the potential on the ionizing chamber. The lens system serves the dual purpose of extracting the ions from the chamber and giving them optimum entrance conditions with respect to velocity and position when they enter the quadrupole structure.

The ionizer and lens system is made of tungsten, alumina, and a stainless steel. It is well suited to applications in the high to ultrahigh vacuum range ($10^{-5} - 10^{-15}$ torr).

## Quadrupole Section

As has been stated earlier, the quadrupole section is composed of four stainless steel rods which are attached to alumina insulators. This assembly is enclosed in a stainless steel cylinder. The ionizer is attached to one end of the cylinder and the ion detector is fitted to the other end. The critical parts are machined to a tolerance of better than 0.005 mm (0.0002 in.). Apart from performance demands for high mechanical accuracy, the very close matching of quadrupole head components makes possible the complete interchange of parts for maintenance purposes without resort to recalibration of the heads. Complete interchange of heads also is possible, so that any number of quadrupoles can be operated with only one control unit. If care is taken, the assembly can be dismantled, cleaned, and reassembled without difficulty. The filter is designed for baking to 400 °C and has actually withstood a 900 °C bakeout. However, the latter high temperature resulted in a deterioration of resolution.

A complete quadrupole mass analyzer head is illustrated in Fig. 10. The assembly is mounted on a standard ultrahigh vacuum flange. This particular assembly has an axial-beam ionizer at the top, the quadrupole filter immediately below it, and the ion detector housing mounted directly on the vacuum flange. Below the vacuum flange are mounted demountable cable terminations to permit simple connection and disconnection of the electrical leads. Two external ceramics are shown, one above the ion detector housing and one immediately below the ionizer, which serve to position the electrical leads and provide electrical insulation from surrounding metal walls. The head can be used without the vacuum flange for mounting right inside the vacuum system.

## RF/DC Generator

The RF/DC generator supplies the RF and DC voltages to the poles and regulates the ratio of the voltages to the desired level. Three RF frequencies are employed to provide a mass range of 1 to 500 amu. These frequencies correspond to 1–50, 10–150, and 50–500 amu, or 50–1000 amu if desired.

Fig. 10.   A complete quadrupole mass analyzer head mounted on an ultrahigh vacuum type flange.

Mass unit measurement is accomplished by varying the RF and DC voltages, and variation may be either manual or automatic. During automatic operation, the full range of mass units for the given frequency is scanned in times as short as 10 msec. This is accomplished by sweeping the voltage in the form of a sawtooth while holding the RF/DC voltage amplitude-ratio constant. A resolution control is provided to change the RF/DC amplitude-ratio manually. A typical control panel is shown in Fig. 11.

The maximum RF voltage is about 1000 V. As required by the stability diagram, the maximum DC voltage is about 170 V. The RF/DC generator is designed so that its frequency is stabilized to better than 1 part in 5000, and through the use of feedback techniques, the RF and DC amplitudes are stabilized to better than 1 part in 100,000. These stability levels are required for satisfactory operation of the analyzer, as can be deduced from the stability diagrams (Figs. 6 and 7).

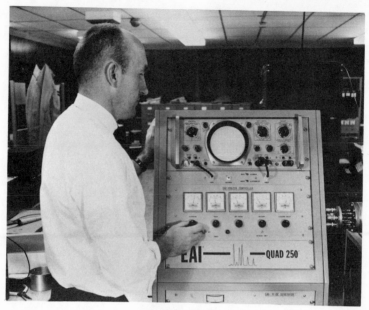

Fig. 11.   The controls of the quadrupole mass analyzer showing the cathode ray tube display.

## Detectors

Collection of the ions at the output end of the quadrupole is accomplished by the use of a Faraday cup or an electron multiplier. The Faraday cup detects singly charged particles on a one-to-one input-to-output ratio regardless of their energy, mass, or cross section. Unfortunately, it lacks the sensitivity required for measuring low partial pressures at reasonable scan rates.

The electron multiplier which is used in the equipment described is bakeable to 400°C together with its internal vacuum-sealed resistors and beryllium–copper dynodes. Positive ions striking the first dynode produce secondary electrons which, in turn, strike the second dynode, starting an electron cascade. The secondary emission ratio for properly activated Be–Cu dynodes varies from 2.3 at 1000 V per stage to 5.5 at 400 V per stage [4]. While this ratio is considerably lower than the ratio of several other common dynode materials, it appears to give the best long-term gain stability. Silver-magnesium (with a secondary emission ratio of 9.5 at 400 V per stage) is also used.

The electron multiplier allows sweep times as low as 10 msec to be used. It is also used to make ion current measurements in the quadrupole system corresponding to a partial pressure of $10^{-14}$ torr and lower. The limitations of the electron multiplier are its susceptibility to contamination and its nonlinearity of response over the mass spectrum.

Normally, the output of the electron multiplier is amplified by a DC amplifier and displayed on an oscilloscope or recorder. An electrometer amplifier may also be used.

## PERFORMANCE

The following results are obtainable from the quadrupole mass analyzer.

### Resolution

Two peaks of equal height are said to be resolved when the valley between them is 10% of the height of either peak. For example, the spectrometer would be said to have a resolution of 100 if the valley between two peaks corresponding to isotopic masses 100 and 101 were 10% of the peak height of either.

Based on this definition, resolutions of approximately 200 have been obtained as shown in Fig. 12. For a radio-frequency quadrupole mass spectrometer, resolution is hightly dependent upon the stability of the

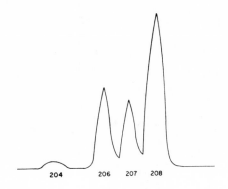

| AMU | ACTUAL ABUNDANCE RATIO (%) | OBSERVED ABUNDANCE RATIO (%) |
|-----|-----|-----|
| 204 | 1.37 | 1.40 |
| 206 | 26.26 | 25.50 |
| 207 | 20.82 | 21.20 |
| 208 | 51.55 | 51.80 |

Fig. 12.  Lead spectrum.

RF/DC generator, the alignment of the filter rods, the length of the quadrupole structure, the frequency of the RF/DC generator, and the injection
energy of the ion.

### Sensitivity and Linearity

The sensitivity of a clean spectrometer system using a freshly activated
electron multiplier is $10^{-15}$ torr. A partial pressure measurement of
$4 \times 10^{-11}$ torr is presented in Fig. 13. This recording was taken without the
aid of an electrometer amplifier.

Sensitivity can be enhanced by decreasing the scanning frequency and
noise filtering. With a scan time of 50 msec, partial pressures of $10^{-11}$ torr
are readily observed on a good oscilloscope.

Two general types of system nonlinearities are possible. The first type
is a nonlinearity in the mass number, dispersion observed at the beginning
of the sweep where the RF/DC voltage ratio is not preserved. Throughout
each quoted mass range, the dispersion is virtually constant, however. The
second type of nonlinearity is a quantitative nonlinearity resulting in abundance ratio errors. This nonlinearity is primarily produced by a combination
of effects in the ionizer and the electron multiplier.

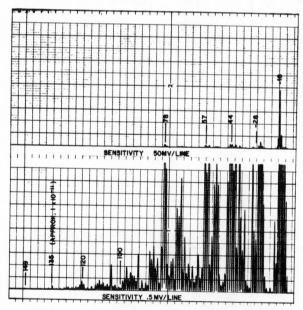

Fig. 13.   Partial pressure sensitivity. Total pressure =
$4 \times 10^{-8}$ torr.

The response of the electron multiplier is dependent not only upon the charge of the ion, but also upon its mass and cross section. That is, equal currents of He and Ce ions reaching the multiplier will not produce signals of equal magnitude. Ions of the same mass and charge (i.e., hafnium and anthracene) also may produce different numbers of secondary electrons in striking the first dynode.

### Speed of Response

One of the assets of the EAI quadrupole mass spectrometer is its ability to scan one mass range of the spectrum in 10 msec or less. Beyond a certain minimum sweep rate, both intensity and resolution decrease. This is caused by ion "flight times" becoming relatively short with respect to sweep time. In general, it is not recommended that sweep times less than 50 msec be used for precision analysis.

### Long-Term Stability of the System

Long-term instabilities are caused primarily by electron multiplier gain changes and focusing system contamination when the spectrometer is operated for extended periods at pressures greater than $10^{-6}$ torr. The gain of an EAI silver–magnesium multiplier deteriorates after several days of use from $5 \times 10^6$ to about $10^5$. Upon reaching a gain of about $10^5$, the multiplier appears to restabilize itself. The gain loss of 50 is due to a combination of hydrocarbon contamination and activated surface deterioration.

### Spectra

Figure 14 shows a typical mass spectrum from the quadrupole of the low mass range, i.e., 1 to 50 amu including mass 12 on the left through to mass 44 on the right. Significant is the linear mass dispersion (constant separation) between mass peaks which is one of many advantages of the quadrupole.

## APPLICATIONS
## OF THE QUADRUPOLE MASS SPECTROMETER

Although the quadrupole mass spectrometer was largely used at first as a residual gas analyzer for high and ultrahigh vacuum systems, more recent uses include chemical kinetics and surface chemistry studies, gas chromatography, the study of free radicals, and ion–neutral collision investigations.

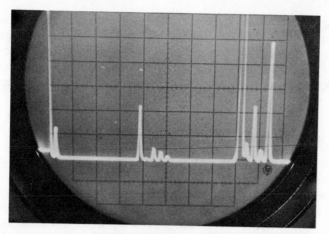

Fig. 14.   Quadrupole mass spectrum resulting from filament at 1000 °K in presence of hydrazine at $2 \times 10^{-5}$ torr.

## Simple Residual Gas Analysis

Figure 14 shows a simple application of the quadrupole where it was used to analyze residual gases in an ultrahigh vacuum system. In this case, the scan was from right to left in which mass 44 was continually observed during a vacuum system bakeout. The points at which the heaters were turned on and off can be noted and the evolution of gas during the bakeout and the subsequent pumping after the heaters were turned off are clearly shown. (Mass 44 of course represents carbon dioxide in the system.) This figure also demonstrates one use of the manual mode of operation of the quadrupole. The manual mode of operation means that the sawtooth voltage is not used. Instead, the quadrupole is operated at a fixed voltage to monitor only one mass peak. Any mass peak which can be dealt with by the quadrupole can be so monitored.

## Low-Energy Electron Diffraction

The relatively old technique (1927) of low-energy electron diffraction (LEED) is now undergoing great advances as a means of studying surface reactions and of determining the structure of single-crystal surfaces.

With the use of the post-acceleration method, the diffraction pattern is displayed visibly on a fluorescent screen, and changes in surface structure can be observed by noting changes in the corresponding diffraction pattern.

The small penetration of electrons in the energy range of 5 to 500 eV results in the LEED technique being very sensitive to surface conditions.

LEED makes it possible to determine the structure of a small fraction of a monolayer of gas adsorbed on an otherwise atomically clean single-crystal surface. Experiments have, in the main, been limited to the determination of the surface structures of clean metals, semiconductors, and insulators, or of the structures of gases adsorbed on these surfaces. To obtain good patterns, initial contamination must be reduced to one monolayer. Obviously, it is better to remove all contamination, but this is very difficult.

Contamination cannot be detected with a LEED system alone and the result is an unsuccessful experiment. Furthermore, LEED does not indicate what contaminant may be present and effective removal of the contaminant may be dependent upon identification. Both these problems have been solved by using the LEED in conjunction with a quadrupole mass analyzer.

In Fig. 15 the quadrupole can be seen in operation on LEED equipment. The head is mounted on the right of the glass viewing port and the electronics console is in the right foreground.

The value of the LEED–QRGA* combination is illustrated by the following technique used in Georgia Institue of Technology. A contaminated sample of tungsten was to be examined. Heating alone causes $C^{12}$ to diffuse to the surface and this is not identified in a LEED pattern. The tungsten is therefore flash-heated to 2000 °C and the increase of $C^{12}$ evolution is observed

* Quadrupole residual gas analyzer.

Fig. 15. A quadrupole mass analyzer installation coupled up to LEED equipment.

by a change in system pressure from $10^{-11}$ to $10^{-10}$ torr. When degassing (other than $C^{12}$) decreases, oxygen is admitted, which combines with the $C^{12}$ to form $CO_2$. The sample is then heated to 1000°C in an atmosphere of oxygen at $10^{-18}$ torr followed by flash heating to 1700°C. During the latter heating, maximum desorption of carbon monoxide (mass 28) is observed without any great increase in $C^{12}$. This experiment is carried out with the aid of a quadrupole mass analyzer.

Other surfaces, such as chromium and titanium, which cannot be heated as can tungsten, can be cleaned with ionic bombardment in an inert gas, such as argon. Here the quadrupole mass analyzer can be used to determine the purity of the ion beam and to sense the degree of contamination of the specimen.

The general requirements for a quadrupole mass analyzer for use with LEED are as follows:

| | |
|---|---|
| Sensitivity | 1 to 100 amu |
| Resolution | Unit throughout the range |
| Pressure | $10^{-7}$ to $10^{-11}$ torr |
| Magnetic field | None permissible |
| Specimen–ion source distance | As small as possible (a few inches) |
| Sweep time | 1 sec full range for monitoring a flash heating time of 3 sec |
| Bakeout temperature | 250 to 400°C |
| Single mass scan facility | Very fast response needed in order to monitor single mass peaks during adsorption |
| Gas control | Instrument must be able to control up to four gases simultaneously |

## The Use of the Quadrupole Mass Analyzer with a Gas Chromatograph

One of the most useful applications of the quadrupole to date has been its association with a gas chromatograph. This is shown schematically in Fig. 16.

To prevent condensation, the effluent from the chromatograph to the quadrupole inlet is heated. Various types of inlets can be used from a simple needle valve to more sophisticated systems, which reduce the carrier gas content. These include sintered glass diffusion-type inlets, capillary inlets, and the Ryhage system, which employs an orifice differentially pumped diffusion jet as a molecular "splitter."

In view of the high sensitivity of the quadrupole, some useful work can be done with a single inlet, but obviously the sensitivity of detection can be

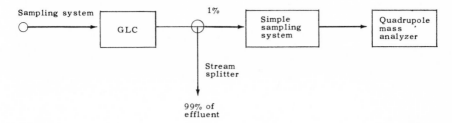

Fig. 16. Schematic of gas chromatograph–quadrupole mass analyzer combination.

increased considerably by reducing the proportion of carrier gas which is admitted into the mass spectrometer.

Gas chromatograph peaks can be identified by observing and recording the mass spectrum taken from the quadrupole as each peak is plotted on the gas chromatograph. It is desirable to try to scan the quadrupole mass range at least five times during each chromatograph plot of a peak.

The general requirements of a quadrupole mass analyzer for use with a gas chromatograph are

| | |
|---|---|
| Mass range | 1–500 amu |
| Resolution | Unit to 500 |
| Sensitivity | $10^{-14}$ torr M.D.P.P. (corresponding to 1 ppm throughout the range) |
| Sweep time | 0.5 sec/mass range |
| Temperature | Must operate with inlet gas at 250°C |
| Contamination sensitivity | Must be insensitive to both carrier gas and hydrocarbons |

Applications of the mass spectrometer–gas chromatograph combination include investigations into pesticides, food flavors, and plastics development.

## Analysis of Motor Car Exhaust Gases

The following *ad hoc* tests were carried out using a quadrupole mass spectrometer in a car park to test the exhaust from two cars.

The cars were backed up to the unit and a probe inserted into the exhaust pipe of one car at a time.

The probe consisted of a Pyrex funnel containing a fritted-glass filter disk of fine porosity to remove solid particles. Approximately 9 ft of $\frac{1}{4}$-in. copper tubing conducted the sample from the exhaust pipe probe to the inlet system of the mass spectrometer. A schematic of the inlet system is shown in Fig. 17. The pressure was reduced from 1 atm to approximately 250 $\mu$ by the meter valve. The high-vacuum pump produced $2 \times 10^{-6}$ torr and higher during operations.

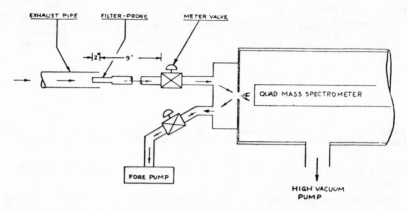

Fig. 17.   Automobile exhaust system.

The chemical reaction for burning petroleum fractions is as shown by the example for octane:

$$2\,C_8H_{18} + 25\,O_2 \rightarrow 16\,CO_2 + 18\,H_2O$$

Complete combustion in an engine represents, to a first approximation, conversion of all hydrocarbons to carbon dioxide and water. Therefore, one can obtain relative efficiencies of engines by plotting the ratio (carbon dioxide + water)/hydrocarbons. This ratio will increase as the efficiency of the engine increases. Neither car had been tuned for some time prior to the test, and they were probably representative of average private cars.

The results of four typical spectra are given in Table I. The peaks represent argon (40), water (18), carbon dioxide (44), and hydrocarbons (27). The peak height at $m/e = 27$ represents the hydrocarbon content. This

### Table I.   Tabulation of Mass Peaks in Automobile Exhaust

|  | Peak height (mV) | | | |
| --- | --- | --- | --- | --- |
| Description | $m/e$ 40 (argon) | $m/e$ 18 (water) | $m/e$ 44 (carbon dioxide) | $m/e$ 27 (hydrocarbons) |
| Car "M" at idle, choke out | 39.6 | 27.6 | 101.0 | 21.9 |
| Car "M" 2850 rpm, choke in | 21.4 | 30.9 | 68.0 | 9.1 |
| Car "D" at idle, choke in | 146.0 | 28.4 | 700.0 | 21.6 |
| Car "D" 2850 rpm, choke in | 120.0 | 160.0 | 470.0 | 26.1 |

peak is common to all light hydrocarbons and is used (cautiously) as a measure of total hydrocarbon content. No estimate was made of the absolute quantities of these gases; only relative measurements were made. No attempt was made to measure nitrogen or carbon monoxide quantities although this could have been done. The condition of the cars is noted in the table.

For the comparison of combustion efficiencies, the following ratio was used:

$$\frac{PH_{44}+PH_{18}}{PH_{27}}$$

where PH denotes peak height. Therefore, from the combustion equation, it is obvious that the ratio will increase as combustion efficiency increases. Table II lists the ratio as a function of car and condition. The higher combustion ratio emitted from Car "D" relative to Car "M" can be observed, and also the increased combustion ratio as the choke of Car "M" is pushed in and the engine speed increased from idle to 2850 rpm. A sample spectrum is included in Fig. 18. The mass peaks between 56 and 95 are probably due to heavier hydrocarbons. The negative pulse following the mass 29 peak is not normal and is the result of overloading the recorder amplifier. This negative pulse is not due to a pressure transient or to the desensitized condition of the electron multiplier.

While this simple experiment was carried out successfully to demonstrate feasibility, more accurate results could be obtained under more closely controlled conditions. However, the results proved the suitability of the quadrupole for this type of investigation.

**Table II. Tabulation of Combustion Ratios**

| Description | $\dfrac{PH_{18}+PH_{44}}{PH_{27}}$ |
|---|---|
| Car "M" at idle, choke out | 5.9 |
| Car "M" 2850 rpm, choke in | 10.9 |
| Car "D" at idle, choke in | 45.5 |
| Car "D" 2850 rpm, choke in | 24.1 |

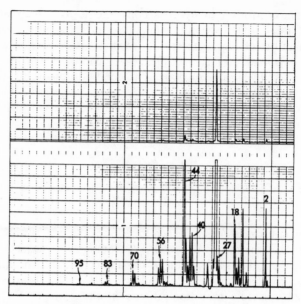

Fig. 18.   Typical mass spectrum from car exhaust gas. (Lower spectrum is 20 times as sensitive as upper spectrum.)

## Mass Spectrometric Detection of $N_2H_2$ Produced by the Catalytic Decomposition of $N_2H_4$ on Heated Platinum

The first work on the study of free radicals evaporating from a heated filament placed inside the ion source of a mass spectrometer was carried out in 1949 by Robertson [7]. The quadrupole spectrometer with a nude ion source is suitable for work of this kind. The rapid response of the instrument and the oscillographic presentation are very convenient when transient effects are being investigated. In a series of investigations, Le Goff [8] has obtained oscillographic results with sector spectrometers.

E. M. A. Willhoft and A. J. B. Robertson in 1967 examined the decomposition of hydrazine on platinum at pressures of about $10^{-5}$ torr by joining their reaction vessel (containing the catalyst) to a Centronic EAI quadrupole mass spectrometer (quad 250). The effect of heating the platinum in hydrazine was to increase the peak at $m/e = 30$ in the spectrum, although peaks at $m/e = 31$ and 32 decreased. In experiments at low electron energies (nominal value 7 eV) peak 30 was increased by a factor of 2. Thus, by the ordinary principles of mass spectrometry, the formation of diimide, $N_2H_2$, can be deduced. Further evidence for the formation of diimide was obtained from the appearance potential of the 30 peak which was reduced by well over 1 eV when hydrazine was passed over the hot platinum.

The synthesis of nitric oxide from hydrazine and residual water in these experiments was negligible. Effects of residual gases were also investigated. If the platinum after heating was left for 10 min, subsequent heating gave a very transient 27 peak, lasting a fraction of a second. A further period of 10 min of exposure of the cold platinum to the gas mixture was required before this peak was again produced on heating the platinum. It seems likely that 10 min is the time needed to build up a layer of hydrocarbon (from residual gases) on the platinum.

## SUMMARY

Separation of gaseous ions according to their mass-to-charge ratio is accomplished in the quadrupole mass analyzer by an electric filtering arrangement. This filter employs four accurately made and accurately spaced rods which are energized with RF and DC potentials. The high sensitivity obtainable, together with fast response, absence of all magnets, and relative insensitivity to contamination, has enabled this unique instrument to be applied to a number of interesting problems. The operating principles of the quadrupole mass spectrometer and some of its applications were described.

## ACKNOWLEDGMENTS

Much of the material in this section was supplied by members of the staff of Electronic Associates, Incorporated, and the author wishes especially to acknowledge the contributions of Dr. R. E. Finnigan and Mr. R. Hein (now with Finnigan Instruments Corporation), and of Dr. E. M. A. Willhoft (formerly with Basic Research Laboratories, Gas Council) for information on his free radical experiments.

## REFERENCES

1. M. Paul and H. Steinwedel, *Z. Naturforsch.* **8a**:448, 1953.
2. N. McLachlan, *Theory and Applications of Mathieu Functions*, Oxford Univ. Press, Oxford, England, 1947.
3. W. Paul, H. Reinhard, and V. Von Zahn, *Z. Physik* **152**(2):143, 1958.
4. P. Rice, *Quadrupole Mass Spectrometers*, Interim Rept. No. 2, Stanford Res. Inst., Stanford, California, 1962.
5. J. Beynon, *Mass Spectrometry and Its Applications to Organic Chemistry*, Elsevier Publishing Co., Amsterdam, 1960.
6. L. N. Thorpe, *LEED—The Answer to Surface Problems*, Appl. Bull., Electronic Associates, Inc., Palo Alto, California.
7. A. J. B. Robertson, *Proc. Roy. Soc. (London)* **A199**:394, 1949.
8. A. Pentenero and P. Le Goff, in: R. I. Reed (ed.), *Mass Spectrometry*, Academic Press, London, 1965.
9. R. Hein, private communication, Electronic Associates, Inc., Palo Alto, California.

# THE PRINCIPLE AND APPLICATION OF A VACUUM SPARK SOURCE MASS SPECTROMETER TO THE ANALYSIS OF SOLIDS

## P. Swift

*Consultant Laboratory*
*Scientific Apparatus Department*
*Associated Electrical Industries Limited*
*Manchester, England*

## INTRODUCTION

The preliminary work of Dempster [1] in 1946 indicated the potential value of vacuum spark source mass spectrometry as a technique for the analysis of inorganic solids. However, little further work was done until 1954 when Hannay [2] described an instrument for the analysis of impurities in semiconductors. Since then, commercial instruments have been available and spark source mass spectrometry has become a well established analytical technique.

The particular features of the technique are (1) the coverage of the majority of elements in any matrix in a single analysis, (2) the detection of those elements down to very low levels of concentration [3,4], (3) the approximate equality of sensitivity for all elements [5], and (4) the linearity over a very wide concentration range [3,6]. The simplicity of spectral interpretation and the ease of adaptation to new problems have led to the very wide field of application which the technique has found. This field of application is covered fully in a chapter, in this volume, entitled "A Survey of the Application of Spark Source Mass Spectrometry to the Analysis of Solids," by R. Brown.

The vacuum spark is the most suitable source for producing an ion beam which is closely representative of the sample composition. The ions produced in such a source have a very wide energy spread (approx. 2 kV), and, in order to obtain a sharp focus at the detector, it is necessary to employ a mass spectrometer of the double-focusing type. The ion current output

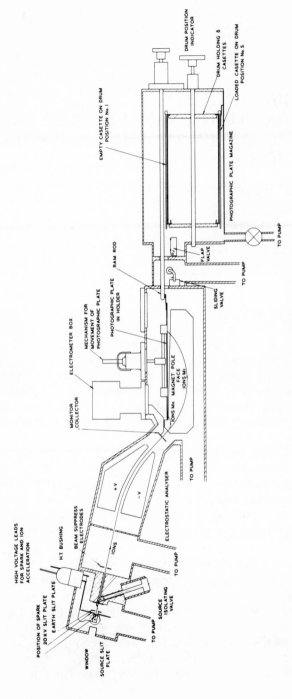

Fig. 1. MS702 mass spectrometer.

of the spark source is very erratic and so a method of integrating all the mass analyzed ion beams simultaneously is required. By using the Mattauch–Herzog [7] design of instrument the ion beams are brought to a focus along a plane and thus an ion-sensitive photoplate may be used as detector.

The principles of both single- and double-focusing mass spectrometers, which include the Mattauch–Herzog type, have been reviewed by Errock [8], while several spark source mass spectrometers have been described for the analysis of solids [2,9–12]. The purpose of this chapter is to illustrate the simplicity of both the operation of a spark source mass spectrometer and the interpretation of the spectrum it produces.

The chapter is divided into four parts: (1) the instrumentation and operation of a spark source mass spectrometer; (2) the photographic plate; (3) the interpretation of the mass spectrum; and (4) limits of detection.

## THE INSTRUMENTATION AND OPERATION OF A SPARK SOURCE MASS SPECTROMETER

The Associated Electrical Industries MS702 (see Fig. 1) will be described in order to illustrate the design and operation of a typical spark source mass spectrometer.

### The Ion Source

The electrodes of the sample material, preferably in the form of rods approximately 0.5 in. long by 0.05 in. square or round section, are prepared. These electrodes are mounted in tantalum clamps at the end of glass supports in the ion source such that their tips overlap by about 0.05 in. and are about 0.02 in. apart (see Fig. 2). The glass supports may be moved in three mutually perpendicular directions from outside the source by means of controls operating through bellows. This allows adjustment of the electrode position while the material is being sparked.

A tantalum boxlike shield, with a narrow hole in the front panel through which the electrodes may be seen, is then fitted in the source such that it surrounds the electrodes (see Fig. 3). A metal flange with an observation window, or a circular glass plate, is attached to the front of the ion source and this chamber is evacuated.

After the source has been evacuated, a pulsed radio-frequency voltage of up to 80-kV amplitude may be applied between the electrodes. The positive ions, representative of the sample composition, produced in this discharge are accelerated through a simple ion gun by a potential difference of 20 kV. This potential difference is established by raising the spark shield, the tantalum plate to which the shield is attached, and one sample clamp to

Fig. 2.   Electrodes mounted in the ion source of the MS702.

+20 kV, while the slit plates of the ion gun are held at ground potential (see Fig. 4).

One factor affecting the resolving power of the instrument [8] is the width of the third slit of the ion gun (labelled source slit in Figs. 1 and 4). For example, if a slit of 0.002-in. width is used, a resolution in excess of 3000 may be obtained routinely.

The source slit is also the only connection between the source and analyzer regions of the mass spectrometer. This, together with a further stage of pumping immediately preceding the electrostatic analyzer (see Fig. 1), enables a pressure differential of more than 10,000:1 to be maintained between the source and the analyzer. Large pressure rises in the source caused by outgassing during sparking therefore have no effect on the pressure in the analyzer region.

Fig. 3.   Ion source of the MS702.

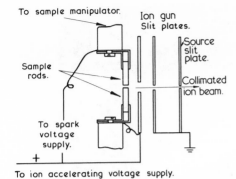

Fig. 4.   Diagram of ion gun.

## The Analyzer System

The source slit is placed at the principal focus of the electrostatic analyzer and, therefore, ions having the same energy (irrespective of their mass) leave the electric field along parallel paths. Ions of the same mass but having different energies leave the field along different paths such that on entering the magnetic field the dispersion in the magnetic sector caused by their different energies is compensated for by their different incoming trajectories. Overall energy focusing is therefore achieved [8].

The energy-focused ion beams leaving the magnetic field are now separated according to mass. Ions of different mass are brought to a focus in a plane, their distance along this focal plane being proportional to the square root of their mass-to-charge ($\sqrt{m/e}$) ratio [8]. An ion-sensitive photographic plate is placed in the focal plane and thus the mass spectrum of the sample being sparked is recorded.

## The Detector

The photographic plate normally used is 10 in. long and 2 in. wide, and this allows a mass range of approximately 45:1 to be covered in a single exposure. The magnetic field is usually adjusted so that the spectrum recorded covers the $m/e$ range 6–270. Ions falling outside this mass range can be recorded on separate exposures by setting the magnetic field or electric field, or both, at different values.

The photographic plate is supported in an aluminum holder which itself is held in a guide (see Fig. 1). The guide may be racked laterally across the magnet gap, while the plate is maintained in the focal plane, so that up to 32 exposures may be recorded on one photographic plate.

Up to eight photoplates, each in a lighttight cassette (see Fig. 5), may be stored under vacuum in the photoplate magazine (see Figs. 1, 6, and 7).

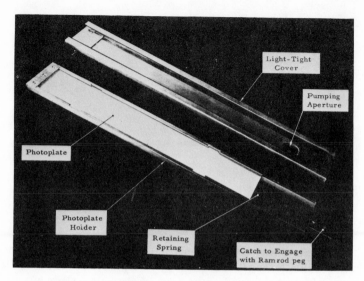

Fig. 5. Photoplate cassette.

By the use of a simple ramrod mechanism (see Figs. 1 and 6), a photoplate may be introduced or withdrawn from the guide which is situated above the magnetic analyzer pole pieces.

A sliding glass valve situated at the back of the analyzer (see Figs. 1 and 7) is closed after a plate has been introduced. This valve, together with

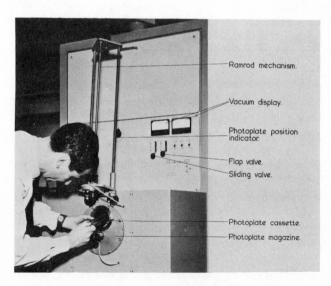

Fig. 6. Rear view of the MS702.

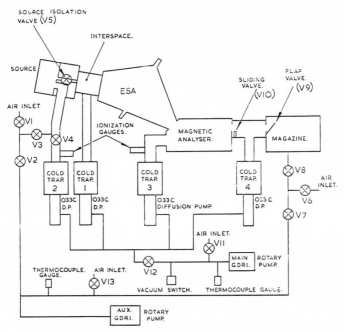

Fig. 7.    MS702 vacuum system schematic.

a further stage of pumping between the magazine and the analyzer, enables a pressure differential of about 500:1 to be maintained between the two.

## The Vacuum System

It is necessary to attain a pressure of the order to $10^{-8}$ torr in the analyzer region of the mass spectrometer if analyses covering limits of detection in the 0.01 to 0.001 ppm range are to be carried out. For the best limits of detection, it is preferable to have even lower pressures. In order to achieve such pressures, the vacuum system is constructed of stainless steel. Gold gaskets are used as seals where the various components of the tube assembly are joined together. This allows the whole system to be baked out at a temperature in excess of 200 °C in order to maintain clean vacuum conditions. In general, temperatures in excess of 120 °C are rarely required to achieve the pressures mentioned above.

The tube assembly is pumped by four 3-in. oil diffusion pumps fitted with liquid-nitrogen cold traps and backed by a rotary pump. Bayard–Alpert type insertion ionization gauges are used to measure source and analyzer pressures and the backing line pressure is measured by a thermocouple gauge (see Fig. 7). The meters associated with the ionization and thermocouple gauges are located on the front panel of the MS702 (see Fig. 8).

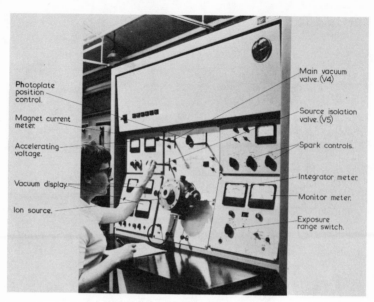

Fig. 8.   Front view of the MS702.

The vacuum system is designed to facilitate the rapid changing of both electrodes in the ion source and photographic plates in the analyzer and magazine, without loss of analyzer vacuum.

### Running an Analysis

When recording analytical exposures, it is not practical to measure the ion current output of the RF spark as a function of time because of its eratic nature. Therefore, it is necessary to determine the charge, and hence the number of ions, which are arriving at the photographic plate. The monitor collector is situated between the electric and magnetic fields (see Fig. 1), and its aperture size is such that approximately 50% of the ion beam is intercepted. The mean collected ion current, which may lie anywhere within the range $10^{-15}$ to $10^{-9}$ A, is displayed on a meter situated alongside the ion source at the front of the MS702 (this is the monitor meter shown in Fig. 8). Examination of this meter allows the spark conditions and the electrode position to be optimized while recording analytical exposures. The lengths of the exposures recorded may be read from a second meter alongside the ion source (see Fig. 8) which shows the integrated output of the monitor collector. The exposures are usually expressed in nanocoulomb units ($10^{-9}$ C = 1 nC).

When the required exposure is completed, a voltage is applied to the beam-suppress electrodes (see Fig. 1) and the ion beam is deflected so that it cannot pass through the analyzer system. At this point, the exposure length shown by the reading of the integrator meter may be noted and the photographic plate position changed. The beam-suppress electrodes are then returned to ground potential and the next exposure is recorded. In this way, a series of graduated exposures may be recorded which covers the concentration range required in the sample analysis.

Like the integrator and monitor collector meters, the beam-suppress voltage switch and the photographic plate position control are located at the front of the instrument. Thus, when an analysis is being carried out, the complete operation may be controlled by one operator situated at the front of the instrument (see Fig. 8).

## Changing Electrodes

The source can be vented to atmosphere after it has been isolated from the analyzer region by closing the valves V4 and V5 shown in Fig. 7. After the sample electrodes have been changed the source chamber is evacuated and the RF and accelerating voltages are applied to the electrodes ready for the next analysis.

All the vacuum valve controls concerned with venting the source to atmosphere are located at the front of the instrument (see Fig. 8), and the complete operation involved in changing sample electrodes between analyses takes about 10 min.

## Changing Photoplates

Photographic plates, in their cassettes, may be removed from the magazine after it is isolated from the pumping system by closing the flap valve (see Figs. 1 and 7). After the exposed plates have been developed, the cassettes are reloaded and replaced in the magazine and this chamber is evacuated. All vacuum controls concerned with venting the magazine to atmosphere are located at the back of the instrument alongside the magazine (see Fig. 6). The complete operation of removing, developing, and reloading photoplates in the magazine to the stage where they are ready for introduction into the analyzer takes about 1 hr.

The method of introducing photographic plates into the analyzer from the magazine has been described earlier; this operation takes less than 1 min.

## THE PHOTOGRAPHIC PLATE

Ion-sensitive photographic plates of the Schumann type are normally used to record mass spectra. The special feature of such a photoplate is that the silver halide grains are held at, or very close to, the surface of the emulsion upon which the ions are falling. The properties and characteristics of this type of emulsion have been described by Owens and Giardino [13], Franzen et al. [14], and Woolston et al. [15].

Figure 9 shows a typical ion response curve from an Ilford QII plate.

Table I summarizes the range of values obtained from the ion response curves of many Ilford QII photoplates.

**Table I.  Typical Range of Photoplate Characteristics of the Ilford QII Emulsion**

| | |
|---|---|
| Maximum density | From 1.0 to 1.5 |
| Linear range | |
| (a) Intensity | From 10:1 to 25:1 |
| (b) Density | From 0.14–0.9 to 0.18–1.3 |
| Emulsion background density (above clear glass) | Approximately 0.04 |

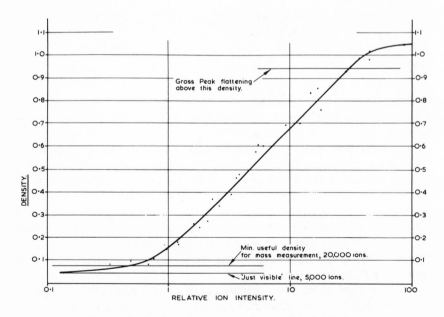

Fig. 9.   Typical ion response curve from an Ilford QII plate.

Commercially, Ilford QII and Kodak SWR are the most widely used ion-sensitive photoplates. Currently, investigations are being made into the use of gelatin-free ion-sensitive plates in an attempt to overcome some of the disadvantages inherent in the emulsions used at present [16,17].

## INTERPRETATION OF THE MASS SPECTRUM

### Nature of the Mass Spectrum

The mass spectrum of a solid, which has been ionized in an RF spark, is largely the sum of the mass spectra of the individual elements from which the sample material is composed. Furthermore, the relative intensity of the mass spectra of the individual elements is proportional to their concentration in the sample material. Thus, in short exposures (i.e., $10^{-13}$ C and less), only the spectra of the major components of the sample are observed. If the exposure length is increased, then the spectra of elements at lower concentration levels in the sample appear. Therefore, by running a series of increasing exposures across a photographic plate, a picture of the composition of the sample can be built up from the mass spectra obtained.

The mass spectrum of an element is relatively simple and can be predicted from a knowledge of its isotopic constitution. Portions of the mass spectra of two elements, lead and zirconium, are shown in Fig. 10, where it can be seen that the intensity of the spectral lines of each element corresponds with the abundance of its isotopes.

The highest proportion of ions produced in an RF spark carries only one positive charge, and the position at which ions are focused along the focal plane of the analyzer system is proportional to the square root of their mass-to-charge ratio ($\sqrt{m/e}$) [8]. Therefore, the most intense lines in the mass spectrum of an element will be those corresponding to the actual masses of its isotopes (i.e., if $e = 1$, then $m/e = m$).

Figure 11 shows the mass spectrum of copper, from which it can be seen that the most intense spectral lines are those at masses 63 and 65, which correspond to the two isotopes of the element.

ISOTOPIC ABUNDANCES.

| ZIRCONIUM. | | LEAD. | |
|---|---|---|---|
| 90 | 51·46 | 204 | 1·48 |
| 91 | 11·23 | 206 | 23·6 |
| 92 | 17·11 | 207 | 22·6 |
| 94 | 17·40 | 208 | 52·3 |
| 96 | 2·80 | | |

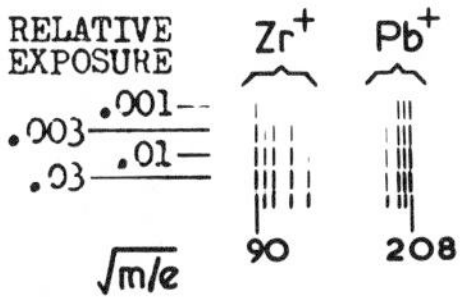

Fig. 10. Isotopic patterns of zirconium and lead.

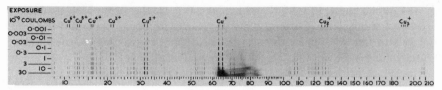

Fig. 11.   Mass spectrum of copper.

However, lines at fractions of the masses of the 63 and 65 isotopes can be seen in the spectrum and these arise from copper ions carrying more than one charge. For example, the lines at masses $31\frac{1}{2}$ and $32\frac{1}{2}$ are from doubly charged ions (i.e., if $e = 2$, then $m/e = m/2$) while those at masses 21 and $21\frac{2}{3}$ are from triply charged ions (i.e., if $e = 3$, then $m/e = m/3$).

The intensity of the multiply charged ions falls off with the multiplicity of the charge. The actual intensity ratio between the successively charged states is dependent upon both the element and the conditions under which the sample is sparked. In general, the decrease in intensity lies between the factors 3 and 50 for each degree of ionization.

Lines at masses 126, 128, and 130 can be seen in the spectrum shown in Fig. 11. These arise from diatomic copper ions carrying a single positive charge [i.e., $^{63}Cu_2^+$ at $m/e$ 126, $(^{63}Cu\,^{65}Cu)^+$ at $m/e$ 128, and $^{65}Cu_2^+$ at $m/e$ 130]. A further group of lines at masses 189, 191, 193, and 195 arising from singly charged triatomic copper ions also can be detected in the spectrum.

It can be seen that the intensity of the polyatomic ions is very low compared with the monatomic ions and, again, the relative intensity of these ions will depend on both the element and the conditions under which the sample is sparked. It is difficult to give a general rule for the intensity ratios of polyatomic ions, but samples whose matrices are composed of elements occurring in Group IV of the periodic table (i.e., C, Si, Ge, etc.) exhibit the most intense polyatomic spectra (see Fig. 12).

Molecular ions composed of atoms from more than one element also may be detected in some spectra. In the case of a fairly high-purity metal

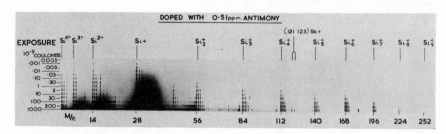

Fig. 12.   Mass spectrum of silicon.

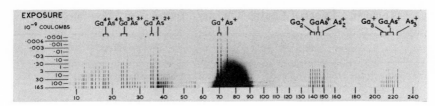

Fig. 13.   Mass spectrum of gallium arsenide.

matrix, the molecular ions most likely to occur are oxides and hydroxides (e.g., $MO^+$, $MOH^+$, $M_2O^+$, etc.). For example, in the spectrum shown in Fig. 11, the lines at masses 80 and 82 arise from copper hydroxide ions [i.e., $(^{63}Cu\,^{16}O^1H)^+$ at $m/e$ 80 and $(^{65}Cu^{16}O^1H)^+$ at $m/e$ 82].

However, in molecular matrices such as binary compounds (e.g., GaP, GaAs, InSb) and, to a lesser extent, alloys (e.g., Ni–Cr, Cu–Ni), ions representative of the molecular species in the matrix are observed in the spectra. Figure 13 shows the mass spectrum of gallium arsenide in which the molecular ions are easily detected. The occurrence of molecular species in Group III–V compounds has been reported by Ahearn and Thurmond [18].

The intensity ratio between singly and multiply charged polyatomic and molecular ions is usually so great that doubly charged species are seldom detected and triply charged ions are very rare indeed. In fact, one method of deciding whether a spectral line arises from a monatomic elemental ion or from a polyatomic or molecular ion is to examine the intensity ratio between the singly and doubly charged species.

Another feature of a mass spectrum is the presence of lines which arise from collisions between positive ions passing through the instrument and residual gas molecules. The result of such a collision is that one or more positive charges may be transferred from an ion to a gas molecule. This charge transfer process may be represented by the equation

$$X^{(N_0)^+} + Y = X^{(N)^+} + Y^{(N_0-N)^+}$$

where X is a positive ion, Y is a gas molecule, $N_0$ is the initial charge on X, and $N$ is the final charge on X ($N_0$ is always greater than $N$).

The effects of the collisions are summarized in Table II.

These results follow from a consideration of the effect that an alteration in charge has on the ion path after collision, with the assumption that the velocity and direction of the ion remain unchanged. Hannay has also discussed these effects [2]. In practice, the position of the lines in the spectrum is slightly lower than the calculated mass because of stray field effects.

The intensity of the lines and continuum in a mass spectrum, resulting from these charge transfer processes, is a function of the vacuum in the

### Table II.  Effect of Charge Transfer Processes on Mass Spectra*

| Location of collision | Effect |
|---|---|
| (a) Between the electrostatic and magnetic analyzers | Sharp lines at a mass of $(N_0/N^2)M_i$ |
| (b) In the electrostatic analyzer | Continuum extending downward from the line at mass $(N_0/N^2)M_i$ |
| (c) In the magnetic analyzer | Continuum extending upward from the line at mass $(1/N_0)M_i$ |

\* $M_i$ is the isotopic mass of X, the positive ion.

instrument, and the extent of the effects decreases linearly with decreasing pressure.

In the copper spectrum, shown in Fig. 11, weak lines may be detected at positions just lower than masses 125 and 129. These lines correspond to the charge transfer process labelled (a) in Table II, where $N_0 = 2$, $N = 1$, and $M_i$ is 63 and 65, respectively. Because of the very low intensity of the lines, it can be seen that the charge transfer process is only a minor feature of this spectrum.

However, the effect becomes more significant if the pressure in the instrument is relatively high (i.e., greater than $1 \times 10^{-7}$ torr) or the exposure is very long (e.g., $10^{-6}$ C). The bottom exposure in the silicon spectrum (see Fig. 12) is 30 times longer than that in the copper spectrum (see Fig. 11) and, therefore, the lines and continua arising from the charge transfer processes labelled (a) and (b) in the table are more pronounced (e.g., see the lines at the approximate masses 54, 82, and 109).

The remaining feature of a mass spectrum is the halation which occurs around the most intense lines. This halation is caused partly by the charging of the emulsion due to the high ion current of these intense lines and partly by secondary particles (especially ions) moving under the influence of the charged surface of the photographic plate.

The area of the emulsion affected by the halation will be dependent upon the length of the exposures and the rate at which they are recorded. For example, the blackening around the intense lines in the silicon spectrum (see Fig. 12) is worse than that seen in either the gallium arsenide spectrum (see Fig. 13) or the copper spectrum (see Fig. 11), where the longest exposures are smaller by factors of approximately 10 and 30, respectively.

The halation may be partially reduced by using relatively low ion currents (i.e., less than $3 \times 10^{-10}$ A) when recording the long exposures. Mai [19] and Addink [20] have described methods by which the halation or its effects on analysis may be further reduced.

## Qualitative Identification of Impurity Elements

The first step in identifying lines on the photographic plate is to calibrate the mass scale. Since the distance of a line along the photographic plate is proportional to the square root of its mass-to-charge ratio, it is possible to calculate the complete mass scale once two lines are identified. This is always possible since the major element and its doubly charged lines will be known. However, it is seldom necessary to calculate the position of a line in this way because, if fixed electric and magnetic fields are used, then the mass range covered in successive exposures will always be the same. Therefore, an unknown spectrum may be calibrated either by use of a previously exposed photoplate bearing the mass spectrum of an element having many identifiable lines (e.g., C, Si, Ge, etc.) or by use of a predetermined printed mass scale [21].

The presence of impurity elements is recognized by the occurrence of their characteristic isotope patterns. For example, some of the elements which can be identified in the copper spectrum (see Fig. 11) are listed in Table III.

One or more of the following criteria must be satisfied before an element can be reported as being present in a sample spectrum :

1. Line, or lines, is visible at a mass corresponding to the singly charged ions of the different isotopes of the element and is present in the correct abundance ratio.
2. Line, or lines, is visible at a fractional mass number corresponding to multiply charged ions of the element.

**Table III.  Some Impurity Elements Present in the Copper Spectrum Shown in Fig. 11**

| Element | Nominal mass of isotope | Abundance of isotope | Element | Nominal mass of isotope | Abundance of isotope |
|---------|------------------------|---------------------|---------|------------------------|---------------------|
| Bismuth | 209 | 100 | Tin | 124 | 5.98 |
| Lead | 208 | 52.3 | | 122 | 4.71 |
| | 207 | 22.6 | | 120 | 32.97 |
| | 206 | 23.6 | | 119 | 8.58 |
| | 204 | 1.5 | | 118 | 24.01 |
| Antimony | 123 | 42.75 | | 117 | 7.57 |
| | 121 | 57.25 | | 116 | 14.24 |
| Silver | 109 | 48.65 | | 115 | 0.34 |
| | 107 | 51.35 | | 114 | 0.65 |
| Gallium | 71 | 39.8 | | 112 | 0.95 |
| | 69 | 60.2 | | | |

3. The mass defect is found by accurate mass measurement corresponding to that of the element.

In the copper spectrum (see Fig. 11) criterion (1) is satisfied for lead, antimony, tin, silver, and gallium and, therefore, these elements may be reported as being present in the sample. For bismuth, which has only one isotope, criterion (2) is also applied in order to ascertain that the spectral line at mass 209 is from singly charged bismuth ions rather than from a molecular ion.

Sometimes two elements situated next to each other in the periodic table have isotopes of the same nominal mass and, therefore, spectral overlap will occur if both elements are present in the sample. However, all elements have at least one or two isotopes which are unaffected by this type of spectral interference, and it is from these isotopes that the presence of the element is detected in the spectrum. It is interesting to note that none of the monoisotopic elements suffer from this type of spectral overlap.

Table IV lists the isotopes of seven elements which are next to each other in the periodic table.

The copper spectrum (see Fig. 11) shows a group of spectral lines in the mass range 50 to 65 and Table IV lists the elements which have isotopes in this region of the spectrum.

The strong line at mass 52 could arise from chromium singly charged ions, so criterion (1) is applied. It can be seen that the intensity ratio of the

**Table IV.  Some Elements in Adjacent Groups in Period IV of the Periodic Chart**

| Element | Nominal mass of isotope | Abundance of isotope | Element | Nominal mass of isotope | Abundance of isotope |
|---------|------------------------|---------------------|---------|------------------------|---------------------|
| Vanadium  | 50 | 0.24  | Cobalt  | 59 | 100   |
|           | 51 | 99.76 | Nickel  | 58 | 67.76 |
| Chromium  | 50 | 4.31  |         | 60 | 26.16 |
|           | 52 | 83.76 |         | 61 | 1.25  |
|           | 53 | 9.55  |         | 62 | 3.66  |
|           | 54 | 2.38  |         | 64 | 1.16  |
| Manganese | 55 | 100   | Copper  | 63 | 69.1  |
| Iron      | 54 | 5.84  |         | 65 | 30.9  |
|           | 56 | 91.68 |         |    |       |
|           | 57 | 2.17  |         |    |       |
|           | 58 | 0.31  |         |    |       |

lines at masses 50, 52, and 53 correspond with the abundance of those isotopes and, therefore, chromium is present in the sample. However, the line at mass 54 is too intense to be solely from the chromium spectrum. The only other element hich has an isotope of nominal mass 54 is iron, and so criterion (1) is now applied to test for the presence of this element. The intensity ratio of the lines at masses 56 and 57 corresponds with the abundance of those isotopes and, thus, iron is identified in the spectrum. In this case, the line at mass 58 is too intense to fit into the isotope pattern for iron, and so nickel must be suspected and criterion (1) is applied for this element.

At this point it should be noted that the doubly charged ions of silver, tin, and antimony fall in this region of the mass spectrum and it is possible for further spectral overlap to occur. Silver and antimony present no such problem because their doubly charged ions occur at fractional mass numbers (e.g., $^{107}Ag^{2+}$ at $m/e$ $53\frac{1}{2}$ and $^{123}Sb^{2+}$ at $m/e$ $61\frac{1}{2}$). However, tin has several isotopes of even mass number and the doubly charged ions of these isotopes overlap the singly charged spectrum of nickel (i.e., $^{116}Sn^{2+}$ at $m/e$ 58, $^{120}Sn^{2+}$ at $m/e$ 60, $^{122}Sn^{2+}$ at $m/e$ 61, and $^{124}Sn^{2+}$ at $m/e$ 62). Nevertheless, the intensity ratio of the lines at masses 58 and 60 in the copper spectrum corresponds to the isotopic abundances of nickel rather than tin and, therefore, the contribution to the nickel spectrum from the doubly charged tin ions may be neglected in this example.

The singly charged isotope of manganese at mass 55 suffers no spectral interference and criteria (1) and (2) are applied to confirm the presence of this element in the sample. However, cobalt, which is also monoisotopic, is overlapped by a doubly charged tin isotope (i.e., $^{118}Sn^{2+}$ at $m/e$ 59) and it is necessary to apply criterion (2) and assess the tin contribution, before mass 59 can be positively identified as cobalt. A method for the quantitative determination of cobalt in stainless steel, where the mass 59 line suffered spectral interference, has been described by Brown [22].

## Appearance of Multiplets in the Mass Spectrum

In the description of the qualitative interpretation of a mass spectrum, only the nominal masses of isotopes have been mentioned and it should be noted that isotopes which are common to two or more elements have different actual masses (see Table V).

The divergence between the nominal and actual masses of an isotope is a function of the proton–neutron configuration in the nucleus of the atom and it is known as the mass defect. The mass defect may also be expressed as a function of the nominal mass and, in this form, is known as the packing fraction [23]. Duckworth has published a table listing the naturally occurring nuclides, their isotopic abundances, and masses in which $^{16}O$ is used as the standard isotopic mass (i.e., $^{16}O = 16.000000$) [23]. The graph in Fig. 14

shows the general trend in the relationship between the mass defects of isotopes and their nominal masses, in which $^{12}$C is used as the standard isotopic mass (i.e., $^{12}$C = 12.000000) [24].

**Table V.   The Actual Masses of Isotopes Common to Two Elements Listed in Table IV**

| Element | Nominal mass of isotope | Actual mass of isotope |
|---|---|---|
| Vanadium | 50 | 49.9472 |
| Chromium | 50 | 49.9461 |
|  | 54 | 53.9389 |
| Iron | 54 | 53.9396 |
|  | 58 | 57.9333 |
| Nickel | 58 | 57.9353 |

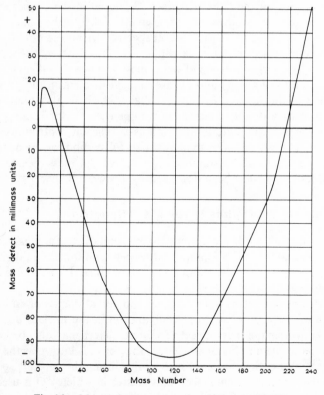

Fig. 14.    Mass defect curve based on $^{12}$C = 12.000000.

As mentioned previously, the position of a line in the spectrum is related to its mass-to-charge ratio. Therefore, two singly charged ions of the same nominal mass, but arising from isotopes of different elements, are focused at slightly different positions in the spectrum because of the difference between their mass defects. The theoretical resolving power required by an instrument, in order for it to separate two such ions into discrete spectral lines, may be calculated from the following expression:

$$\text{theoretical resolving power} = \frac{M}{\Delta M}$$

where $M$ is the nominal mass of the ions and $\Delta M$ is the difference between the actual masses of the two ions having the same nominal mass.

For example, consider the mass 54 isotopes of chromium and iron. The resolving power required in order to obtain a resolved doublet at mass 54 is

$$\frac{M}{\Delta M} = \frac{54}{53.9396 - 53.9389} = \frac{54}{0.0007} = 77,000$$

Resolving powers of this order of magnitude cannot be obtained with a spark source mass spectrometer because of the very wide energy spread of the ions produced by the spark. The factors affecting the resolution of a mass spectrometer have been discussed by Errock [8].

However, in many cases where spectral overlap arises through two or more ions having the same nominal mass, the resolution of the instrument is sufficiently high to separate the ions and multiplets are observed in the spectrum. Table VI gives some examples of pairs of ions of the same nominal mass which can be separated into well-resolved doublets because of the differences in their actual masses.

Figure 15 shows part of a gold spectrum in which a multiplet occurring at mass 29 can be seen.

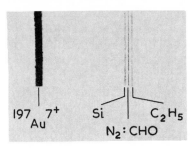

Fig. 15.   The multiplet at mass 29.

**Table VI.  Some Typical Doublets Which May Be Observed in a Mass Spectrum**

| Pairs of ions | Nominal mass of ions $M$ | Difference in actual masses of ion pairs $\Delta M$ | Resolution |
|---|---|---|---|
| $^{116}Sn^+$ and $^{232}Th^{2+}$ | 116 | 0.1170 | 990 |
| $^{93}Nb^+$ and $^{186}W^{2+}$ | 93 | 0.0711 | 1,310 |
| $^9Be^+$ and $^{27}Al^{3+}$ | 9 | 0.0184 | 490 |
| $^{48}Ti^+$ and $^{12}C_4^+$ | 48 | 0.0521 | 920 |
| $^{109}Ag^+$ and $(^{12}C_8{}^{13}C)^+$ | 109 | 0.0987 | 1,100 |
| $^{32}S^+$ and $^{16}O_2^+$ | 32 | 0.0177 | 1,810 |
| $^{29}Si^+$ and $(^{14}N^{15}N)^+$ | 29 | 0.0267 | 1,090 |
| $^{29}Si^+$ and $(^{12}C^1H^{16}O)^+$ | 29 | 0.0262 | 1,110 |
| $^{29}Si^+$ and $(^{12}C_2{}^1H_5)^+$ | 29 | 0.0625 | 465 |
| $(^{14}N^{15}N)^+$ and $(^{12}C_2{}^1H_5)^+$ | 29 | 0.0358 | 810 |
| $(^{12}C^1H^{16}O)^+$ and $(^{12}C_2{}^1H_5)^+$ | 29 | 0.0363 | 800 |
| $(^{14}N^{15}N)^+$ and $(^{12}C^1H^{16}O)^+$ | 29 | 0.0005 | 58,000* |

\* Unresolved doublet.

Frequently hydrocarbon ions are detected in the spectrum of an inorganic material. These may arise either from the sample electrodes themselves or from hydrocarbon molecules which are present in the residual gas in the ion source. However, because of the relatively high positive mass defect of hydrogen, element and hydrocarbon ions of the same nominal mass are easily resolved in the spectrum. A portion of an arsenic spectrum is shown in Fig. 16 where some element–hydrocarbon doublets can be observed.

## Quantitative Estimation of Impurity Concentrations

One of the major advantages of spark source mass spectrometric analysis is the linearity of the technique over a wide concentration range [3,6]. That is, the number of ions produced in the spark for a particular element will be directly proportional to the concentration of that element in the sample

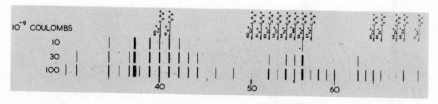

Fig. 16.  Partial mass spectrum of arsenic.

matrix. Therefore, if the concentration of any one element in the sample matrix is known, the photoplate sensitivity can be estimated and from this the concentration of the other impurities present in the spectrum may be determined.

The simplest and most rapid technique for estimating impurity concentrations is by the visual method [25]. This consists of visually estimating the exposures on which the standard and impurity isotope lines are of equal density. Because it is difficult to match line densities with the eye, the estimation is usually based on the exposures at which the "just detectable" (or first appearance) lines of the standard and impurity isotopes are observed.

The impurity concentrations are estimated in two steps and these are summarized as follows:

### Estimation of Plate Sensitivity

1. A suitable isotope line of an internal standard (often a weak isotope of a major constituent) is selected.

2. The exposure $E_s$ for which the selected isotope becomes just detectable is estimated.

3. The "plate sensitivity," $S_p$, is calculated from the relation

$$S_p = \frac{E_s}{E_{max}} \times \frac{C_s}{100} \times \frac{I_s}{100} \times 10^6 \text{ ppm (atomic)}$$

where $E_{max}$ is the maximum exposure on the plate, $C_s$ is the percent concentration (atomic) of the internal standard, and $I_s$ is the percent abundance of the selected isotope.

The value of $S_p$ so obtained, to a first approximation, represents the atomic concentration of any isotope line which is just detectable on the longest exposure.

### Estimation of Concentration of Individual Elements

1. A suitable isotope line of the impurity element is selected.

2. The exposure $E_i$ for which the selected isotope becomes just detectable is estimated.

3. The impurity concentration, $C_i$, is calculated from the relation

$$C_i = S_p \times \frac{E_{max}}{E_i} \times \frac{100}{I_i}$$

where $I_i$ is the percent abundance of the selected impurity isotope.

The spectrum shown in Fig. 17 is of a steel sample which contains 20 wt.% chromium, and this will be used to illustrate the quantitative determination of several elements in the sample.

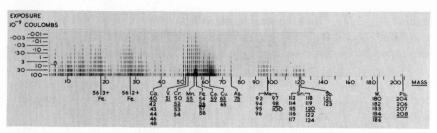

Fig. 17.    Mass spectrum of steel.


First, the plate sensitivity is estimated by using either iron or chromium as the internal standard. The most suitable isotope to choose if iron is used is that at mass 57, while, if chromium is the standard, the mass 53 isotope would be the most suitable. Because the atomic weights of chromium and iron are approximately the same, the percent atomic concentration of each element may be considered as equal to its percent weight concentration:
With $^{53}Cr^+$ as standard,

$$S_p = \frac{0.001}{100} \times \frac{20}{100} \times \frac{9.55}{100} \times 10^6 = 0.19 \text{ ppm}$$

With $^{57}Fe^+$ as standard,

$$S_p = \frac{0.001}{100} \times \frac{80}{100} \times \frac{2.17}{100} \times 10^6 = 0.17 \text{ ppm}$$


The agreement between these two values for the plate sensitivity is good and, as the visual estimation of impurity concentrations is not a highly accurate method, the $S_p$ may be corrected to 0.2 ppm.

Several elements which can be identified in the steel spectrum (see Fig. 17) are listed in Table VII. The table also gives the data from which the concentrations of the elements are calculated.

It is possible that the just detectable exposures quoted in the table will not correspond with those observed in the spectrum because of loss of sensitivity arising from the photographic reproduction of the spectrum. However, the just detectable exposures of both the standard and impurity elements will change by the same factor, and, therefore, by substituting the observed values for $E_s$ and $E_i$ into the appropriate equations, the reader should obtain the concentrations given in the column.

If more precise values than those obtained by the visual method are required, then the spectra of the standard and impurity elements may be scanned on a microdensitometer. The densities of the isotopic lines are then

**Table VII.   The Concentrations of Some Elements Detected in the Steel Spectrum**

| Element | Isotope used | $I_i$ | $E_i$ | $E_{max}$ | $S_p$ | Concentration (ppm atomic) |
|---|---|---|---|---|---|---|
| Lead | 208 | 52.3 | 10 | 100 | 0.2 | 4 |
| Tungsten | 184 | 30.6 | 10 | 100 | 0.2 | 7 |
| Antimony | 123 | 42.75 | 3 | 100 | 0.2 | 16 |
| Tin | 120 | 32.97 | 1 | 100 | 0.2 | 60 |
| Molybdenum | 98 | 23.75 | 0.3 | 100 | 0.2 | 280 |
| Arsenic | 75 | 100 | 0.1 | 100 | 0.2 | 200 |
| Copper | 65 | 30.9 | 0.1 | 100 | 0.2 | 650 |
| Cobalt | 59 | 100 | 0.1 | 100 | 0.2 | 200 |
| Manganese | 55 | 100 | 0.001 | 100 | 0.2 | 20,000 |
| Vanadium | 51 | 99.76 | 0.03 | 100 | 0.2 | 670 |
| Calcium | 40 | 96.97 | 0.1 | 100 | 0.2 | 210 |

plotted against the logarithms of their exposures in order to obtain the emulsion calibration curves for those elements. More sophisticated methods of obtaining calibration curves have been described by Churchill [26], Hull and Judsen [27], Kawano [28], and Desjardins et al. [5].

Figure 18 shows the linear portion of the curves obtained when four isotopes in the steel spectrum are scanned.

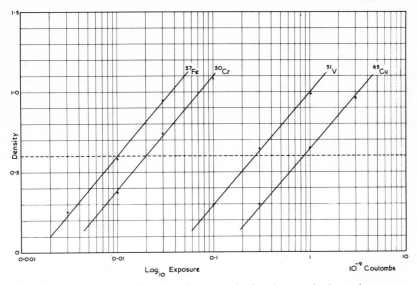

Fig. 18.   Line density as a function of exposure for four isotopes in the steel spectrum.

A density value approximately half way along the linear portion of the graphs is selected and the exposures of the standard $E_s$ and impurity $E_i$ isotopes which correspond with this density are substituted into the following equation in order to determine the impurity concentration, $C_i$:

$$C_i = \frac{E_s}{E_i} \times \frac{C_s}{100} \times \frac{I_s}{I_i} \times 10^6 \text{ ppm (atomic)}$$

where $C_s$ in the percent concentration (atomic) of the internal standard and $I_s$ and $I_i$ are the isotopic abundances of the standard and impurity isotopes, respectively.

For example, in Fig. 18 consider iron as the standard and chromium as the impurity element. Then $E_s = 0.01$, $I_s = 2.17$, $E_i = 0.02$, and $I_i = 4.31$. Hence,

$$C_i = \frac{0.01}{0.02} \times \frac{80}{100} \times \frac{2.17}{4.31} \times 10^6 = 201,000 \text{ ppm (atomic)}$$

Therefore, the concentration of chromium in the steel is 20 at.%. In the case of vanadium, $E_i = 0.27$, $I_i = 99.76$, and $C_i = 645$ ppm, while for copper $E_i = 0.86$, $I_i = 30.9$, and $C_i = 655$ ppm.

Whether the visual or the microdensitometric methods are used to evaluate impurity concentrations, the accuracy of the determinations will depend upon the sensitivities of the impurities relative to the standard element. In many analyses, the relative sensitivities are unknown and the assumption that all elements have equal sensitivity is made when estimating impurity concentrations. From experience, it has been shown that this assumption holds true to within an overall factor of approximately 3 for the majority of elements in nearly all types of sample matrix. Thus, if a completely unknown sample is analyzed on the spark source mass spectrometer, not only can the elements present be identified, but also a good semiquantitative estimate of their concentrations can be made from the spectra obtained.

When more accurate analyses are required, it is necessary to make corrections for the sensitivities of the elements. Many factors contribute to the relative sensitivity of an element, for example, the ionization conditions and ion accelerating voltage of the mass spectrometer [29,30], the line width and mass discrimination of the photographic emulsion [13], and the relative volatilities and diffusion rates of the impurity and matrix elements [31].

The relative sensitivity coefficient of an element is usually determined by analyzing a sample of known composition on the mass spectrometer. The coefficient is then determined as follows:

Relative sensitivity coefficient of $M$ = $\dfrac{\text{mass spectrometric value of } M}{\text{known concentration of } M}$

where $M$ is the element under consideration.

The accuracy of an analysis in which the relative sensitivities of the elements are taken into consideration is influenced by the following factors: (1) parameters of the mass spectrometer, (2) reproducibility of the photographic emulsion, (3) reproducibility of the spectral interpretation, and (4) homogeneity of the electrode material.

These factors have been investigated by Halliday et al. [30] and controlled analytical procedures have been described by Elliott and Swift [32], Jackson and Whitehead [33], and Nicholls et al. [34]. Currently, techniques for overcoming inhomogeneity by more representative sampling of the electrodes are being investigated by Aulinger [35], Brown et al. [36], Vossen et al. [37], and Bingham et al. [38].

## LIMITS OF DETECTION

Another major advantage of spark source mass spectrometry as a method of impurity analysis is its high sensitivity. Ultimate detection limits depend upon both the instrument design, including such factors as maximum intensity of total ion beam, analyzer vacuum and instrument resolving power, and the sensitivity of the photoplate.

For example, with the A.E.I. MS702, the basic limit of detection is approximately 0.001 ppm (atomic). This value is based on the just detectable line used in visual quantitative analysis, and this level of concentration is usually obtained on an exposure of 1000 nC ($10^{-6}$ C).

Such detection limits are of particular value in the fields of high-purity metals and reactor materials and Honig [39] has discussed the importance of mass spectrometry for the trace analysis of semiconductor materials. The limits of detection for a number of matrices have been tabulated [40] including graphite, aluminum, copper, silicon, gallium phosphide, and indium arsenide. As a typical example, Table VIII summarizes the detection limits of impurities in gallium arsenide.

Wolstenholme [3] has discussed the factors which can affect the detection limit of an element and these include its isotopic abundance, its relative sensitivity, the effects of spectral overlap, and photographic background.

The effect of halation, which arises from the most intense spectral lines, upon the just detectable line of the impurity element has been investigated by Elliott and Swift [4]. Mai [19] and Addink [20] have described techniques by which the halation may be reduced and, thus, the detection limits of the elements which suffer interference from the halation are improved.

Spectral overlap, where the resolving power of the mass spectrometer is not high enough to separate two ions of the same nominal mass, is only serious when an element suffering spectral overlap has no other isotopes free from interference. One of the worst examples of spectral interference causing

Table VIII.  Limits of Detection of Impurities in Gallium Arsenide

| Detection limit (ppm atomic) | Number of elements | Elements |
|---|---|---|
| 0.001–0.01 | 52 | U, Th, Bi, Pb, Tl, Hg, Au, Ir, Os, Re, W, Hf, Lu, Yb, Tm, Er, Ho, Dy, Tb, Eu, Sm, Pr, La, Cs, I, Te, Sb, Sn, In, Ag, Nb, Zr, Y, Zn, Cu, Ni, Co, Fe, Mn, Cr, V, Ti, Sc, Ca, K, Cl, P, Si, Al, F, B |
| 0.01–0.1 | 16 | Gd, Nd, Ce, Ba, Cd, Pd, Rh, Ru, Mo, Sr, Rb, Br, S, Mg, Be, Li |
| 0.1–1 | 4 | Ta, Se, Ge, Na |

Table IX.  Effect of Silicon Polyatomic Ions on Limits of Detection

| Ion | Elements affected | Approximate factor by which detection limit is raised |
|---|---|---|
| $Si_2^+$ | Fe, Ni, Co | 20 to 100 |
| $Si_3^+$ | Rb, Sr, Y | 3 to 100 |
| $Si_4^+$ | Cd, In | 2 to 5 |
| $Si_5^+$ | Ce, Pr, Nd | 2 to 30 |
| $Si_6^+$ | Tm, Yb, Lu | 2 to 5 |
| $Si_7^+$ | Au, Hg | 3 to 5 |

enhanced detection limits is that of the polyatomic spectra of silicon (see Fig. 12). Table IX lists the elements whose detection limits are enhanced because of overlap of their spectra by polyatomic silicon ions.

## ACKNOWLEDGMENT

This paper is published with the permission of Dr. J. D. Waldron, General Manager, A. E. I. Scientific Apparatus Department.

## REFERENCES

1. A. J. Dempster, MDDC 370, U.S. Department of Commerce, Washington, D.C., 1946.
2. N. B. Hannay, *Rev. Sci. Instr.* **25**:644, 1954.
3. W. A. Wolstenholme, *Limitations of Detection in Spectrochemical Analysis*, Hilger and Watts Limited, London, 1964, p. 119.
4. R. M. Elliott and P. Swift, *Proc. 13th Ann. ASTM E-14 Meeting Mass Spectrometry*, St. Louis, 1965, p. 74.
5. M. Desjardins, R. Stefani, R. Bourguillot, and A. Cornu, *Advances in Mass Spectrometry*, Vol. 3, Inst. Petroleum, London, 1965, p. 131.

6. N. B. Hannay and A. J. Ahearn, *Anal. Chem.* **26**:1056, 1954.
7. J. H. E. Mattauch and R. Herzog, *Z. Phys.* **89**:786, 1934.
8. G. A. Errock, *Mass Spectrometry*, Academic Press, New York, 1964, p. 1.
9. R. M. Elliott, R. D. Craig, and G. A. Errock, *Instruments and Measurements*, Vol. 1, Academic Press, New York, 1961, p. 271.
10. C. F. Robinson, G. D. Perkins, and N. W. Bell, *Instruments and Measurements*, Vol. 1, Academic Press, New York, 1961, p. 260.
11. K. E. Habfast, *Proc. 11th Ann. ASTM E-14 Meeting Mass Spectrometry*, 1963.
12. R. D. Craig and W. A. Wolstenholme, *Ind. Chim. Belge* **29**:3, 1964.
13. E. B. Owens and N. A. Giardino, *Anal. Chem.* **35**:1172, 1963.
14. J. Franzen, K. H. Maurer, and K. D. Schuy, *Z. Naturforsch.* **219**:37, 1966.
15. J. R. Woolston, R. E. Honig, and E. M. Botnick, *Proc. 14th Ann. ASTM E-14 Meeting Mass Spectrometry*, Dallas, 1966, p. 471.
16. M. H. Hunt, *Anal. Chem.* **38**:620, 1966.
17. J. R. Woolston, R. E. Honig, and D. A. Kramer, *Proc. 14th Ann. ASTM E-14 Meeting Mass Spectrometry*, Dallas, 1966, p. 481.
18. A. J. Ahearn and C. D. Thurmond, *J. Phys. Chem.* **66**:575, 1962.
19. A. Mai, *Advances in Mass Spectrometry*, Vol. 3, Inst. Petroleum, London, 1965, p. 163.
20. N. W. H. Addink, *Nature* **211** (5054): 1168, 1966.
21. R. Brown, *Assoc. Elec. Ind. Techn. Inform. Sheet* **A129**.
22. R. Brown, *Joyce-Loebl Spring Rev.*, 1963.
23. H. E. Duckworth, *Mass Spectroscopy*, Cambridge Univ. Press, Cambridge, England, 1960.
24. L. A. Konig, J. H. E. Mattauch, and A. H. Wapstra, 1961 Nuclilic Mass Tables, *Nucl. Phys.* (Netherlands) **31**:18, 1962.
25. R. D. Craig, G. A. Errock, and J. D. Waldron, *Advances in Mass Spectrometry*, Vol. 1, Pergamon Press, New York, 1959, p. 136.
26. J. R. Churchill, *Ind. Eng. Chem.* **16**:633, 1944.
27. C. W. Hull and C. M. Judsen, *Proc. 12th Ann. ASTM E-14 Meeting Mass Spectrometry*, Montreal, 1964, p. 470.
28. H. Kawano, *Bull. Chem. Soc. Japan* **37**:697, 1964.
29. R. E. Honig, *Trace Analysis of Solids by Mass Spectrometry*, U.S. Department of Commerce, Contract No. AF 19(638)-446, Project No. 4608, Task No. 460802, Washington, D.C.
30. J. S. Halliday, P. Swift, and W. A. Wolstenholme, *Advances in Mass Spectrometry*, Vol. 3, Inst. of Petroleum, London, 1965, p. 143.
31. N. W. H. Addink, *Z. Anal. Chem.* **206**:81, 1964.
32. R. M. Elliott and P. Swift, *12th Colleq. Spectroscop. Intern.*, Hilger and Watts Limited, London, 1965, p. 623.
33. P. F. S. Jackson and J. Whitehead, *Analyst* **91**:418, 1966.
34. G. D. Nicholls, A. L. Graham, E. Williams, and M. Wood, *Anal. Chem.* **39** (6):584, 1967.
35. F. Aulinger, *Z. Anal. Chem.* **221**:70, 1966.
36. R. Brown, P. Swift, and P. G. T. Vossen, *Proc. 15th ASTM E-14 Ann. Meeting Mass Spectrometry*, Denver, 1967, p. 185.
37. P. G. T. Vossen, P. F. S. Jackson, and J. Whitehead, *Anal. Chem.* **39** (14):1737, 1967.
38. R. Bingham, R. Brown, J. S. Halliday, P. Powers, P. G. T. Vossen, and P. F. S. Jackson, *Intern. Conf. Characterization Mater.*, Penn State University, November 1966.
39. R. E. Honig, *Trace Analysis of Semiconductor Materials*, Pergamon Press, New York, 1964.
40. *Assoc. Elec. Ind. Tech. Inform. Sheets* A2, A12, A13, A14, A16, A17 and A43, Manchester, England.

# METASTABLE IONS IN MASS SPECTRA

## J. H. Beynon and A. E. Fontaine

Imperial Chemical Industries Limited
Dyestuffs Division
Manchester, England

The mass spectra of most compounds contain weak diffuse peaks, usually occurring at nonintegral mass numbers. The shape of most of the peaks is roughly gaussian, but variations from "very diffuse and rounded" through "gaussian" to "narrow triangular" as well as peaks having "flat tops" or "dished tops" are observed, often in the same mass spectrum. All the types of diffuse peak have been shown to be due to the decomposition of metastable ions while in transit through the mass spectrometer. For magnetic sector instruments, Hipple and Condon [1] showed that the ion $m_2/e_2$ from the decomposition

$$\frac{m_1}{e_1} \to \frac{m_2}{e_2} + \frac{m_1 - m_2}{e_1 - e_2}$$

appears at a position on the mass scale $m^*$, where

$$m^* = \left(\frac{m_2}{e_2}\right)^2 \bigg/ \frac{m_1}{e_1}\left[1 + \frac{\mu(V - V^1)}{V}\right]$$

$$\mu = \frac{m_1 - m_2}{m_2}$$

and where $V$ is the accelerating voltage applied to the ion $m_1/e_1$ and $V^1$ is the potential difference through which the ion $m_1/e_1$ has fallen before decomposition occurs.

Due to the directional focusing properties of the magnet sector, the daughter ion $m_2/e_2$ has the greatest probability of reaching the collector,

**113**

if the decomposition takes place in the field free region very close to, or at, the magnet entrance slit. Thus for practical purposes

$$m^* \cong \left(\frac{m_2}{e_2}\right)^2 \Big/ \frac{m_1}{e_1}$$

For double-focusing geometry, discrimination occurs in the electrostatic analyzer against ions with less than the full accelerating voltage energy. Hence, only decomposition products produced in the interanalyzer space, or those produced from decompositions occurring in the electric sector with only a small percentage mass change [2], can enter the magnet and be recorded. In the case of double-focusing geometry, the relationship

$$m^* \cong \left(\frac{m_2}{e_2}\right)^2 \Big/ \frac{m_1}{e_1}$$

still obtains.

Since the introduction of commercial double-focusing mass spectrometers interest has increased tremendously in the fragmentation modes of molecular ions, correlation with structure, and rearrangement processes. A great part of this work centers on the observation of "metastable peaks" which serve to relate the precursor ion $m_1/e_1$, which may be a molecular ion or a fragment ion, to the daughter ion $m_2/e_2$. From observations of metastable peaks in mass spectra and their correlation with the structure of the molecule concerned, it is known that the fragments formed in most metastable decompositions are the combined result of bond fission and rearrangement, e.g.,

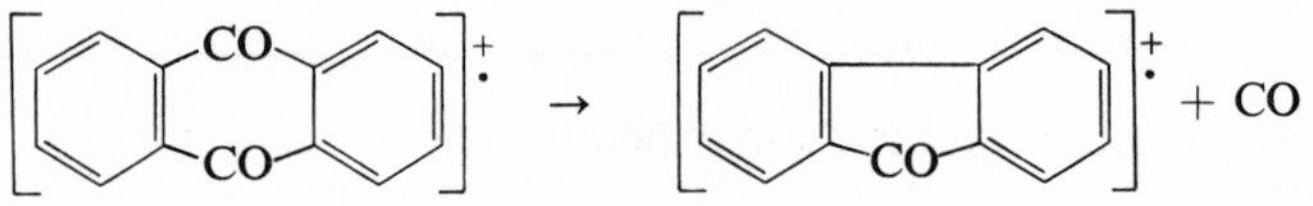

in anthraquinone

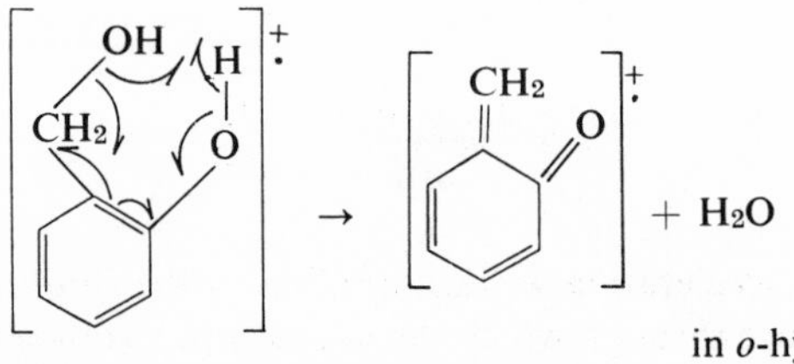

in o-hydroxybenzyl alcohol

Barber and Elliott [3] have discussed the relative sensitivities of single- and double-focusing geometries in the detection of daughter ions from

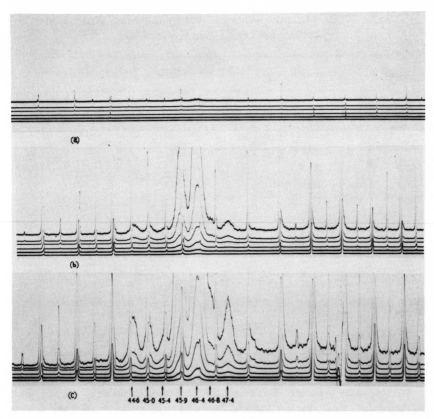

Fig. 1. Metastable peaks in *o*-nitrotoluene at resolutions of (a) 10,000, (b) 2500, and (c) 1000.

metastable decompositions. They conclude that the most favorable geometry is that of Nier–Johnson coupled with variable source and collector slits since even when working at fairly high resolution metastable sensitivity is still high. Chart spectra taken at resolutions between a few hundred and a few thousand contain many metastable peaks with minimum distortion due to adjacent normal peaks. Figure 1 shows metastable peaks in *o*-nitrotoluene at resolutions of 10,000, 2500, and 1000. Accurate measurements on shape and position of metastable peaks are therefore possible. The accuracy of mass measurement of a metastable peak, electrically or from a chart, is limited by noise. Measurements on a fairly intense peak have shown the standard deviation on a mass measurement from a chart to be ∼250 ppm. This is of the same order of accuracy as we have achieved with the electrical "peak matching" mass measurement technique using a known metastable peak as reference. Momigny [4] and Flowers [5] have also reported

### Table I. Metastable Decompositions in the Mass Spectra of Aniline and Long-Chain Hydrocarbons

| Transition | $m^*$ Calculated | $m^*$ Measured |
|---|---|---|
| *Aniline* | | |
| $93^+ \rightarrow 66^+ + 27$ | 46.8 | |
| $C_6H_7N^+ \rightarrow C_5H_6 + HCN$ | 46.876 | 46.883 |
| $C_6H_7N^+ \rightarrow C_4H_4N^+ + C_2H_3$ | 46.858 | |
| $92^+ \rightarrow 65^+ + 27$ | 45.9 | |
| $C_6H_6N \rightarrow C_5H_5^+ + HCN$ | 45.954 | 45.958 |
| $C_6H_6N \rightarrow C_4H_3N^+ + C_2H_3$ | 45.936 | |
| $94^+ \rightarrow 67^+ + 27$ | 47.8 | |
| $C_5{}^{13}CH_7N^+ \rightarrow C_4{}^{13}CH_6^+ + HCN$ | 47.796 | 47.799 |
| $C_5{}^{13}CH_7N^+ \rightarrow C_3{}^{13}CH_4N^+ + C_2H_3$ | 47.778 | |
| *Long-chain hydrocarbons* | | |
| $C_6H_{13}^+ \rightarrow C_4H_7^+ + C_2H_6$ | 35.616 | |
| $C_{10}H_{21}^+ \rightarrow C_5H_{11}^+ + C_5H_{10}$ | 35.797 | 35.789 |
| $C_6H_{13}^+ \rightarrow C_4H_{10}^+ + C_2H_3$ | 39.636 | |
| $C_9H_{19}^+ \rightarrow C_5H_{11}^+ + C_4H_8$ | 39.743 | 39.741 |

metastable mass measurements of similar accuracy. In order to use the peak matching technique for metastable peaks against normal reference peaks, the present scan widths of the MS9 mass spectrometer would require extensive modifications. It is possible that some improvement in accuracy would be obtained by this means. Examples of the accuracy which has been achieved are provided by the metastable peaks arising from three decompositions in the mass spectrum of aniline. Table I gives the alternative decompositions together with the calculated and measured values of $m^*$. Also included in the table are the two measurements on the metastable peaks observed in the spectra of long-chain hydrocarbons. The measured values leave no doubt as to which of the two alternative transitions to assign to the peak.

No explanation of the width, variation in width, profile, and variation in profile of a metastable peak has yet been offered. The position on the mass scale of a metastable peak is determined by the mass-to-charge ratio of the precursor and daughter ions. If it is assumed that no internal energy is released in a decomposition, then for Nier–Johnson geometry, each daughter ion formed in the interanalyzer region has the required direction to pass through the energy focus, enter the magnet sector, and be collected at $m^* = m_2{}^2/m_1$. The peak width and shape from such ions should therefore be the same as for a normal peak. Some broadening will, however, result from decompositions which occur in the fringe fields of the magnet or the electrostatic analyzer. If a small amount of energy is released in every metastable decomposition and the resulting velocity increments are spread in every possible direction, then the effective object point of the magnet sector is smeared out on each side of the energy slit and the peak appears wide. As metastable peaks of different widths and shapes can be observed in the same mass spectrometer from the same compound, other effects tending to modify peak shape also may be present.

Let us suppose that metastable decomposition occurs with a release of internal energy. Furthermore let the release of energy be parallel to the ion flight path and let every decomposition that takes place do so with release of $T$ eV. The metastable peak will then move from $m_2^2/m_1$ to a value $m_2^2/m_1 \pm x$, depending on whether the energy is released in the forward or backward direction, and where $x$ is a function of $T$. Thus, for a discrete energy release $T$ eV, the peak observed will have the shape shown in Fig. 2. It is easy to see that a continuous distribution of energies $0-T$ eV released from metastable decompositions may result in a peak shape as in Fig. 3. Beynon et al. [6] have considered the decomposition

$$m_1^+ \rightarrow m_2^+ + (m_1 - m_2) + T\,eV$$

occurring with longitudinal energy release. They show that the position on the mass scale $m^*$, of the metastable peak from this decomposition, is given by

$$m^* = \frac{m_2^2}{m_1}\left(1 \pm 2\sqrt{\frac{\mu T}{eV}} + \frac{\mu T}{eV}\right) \tag{1}$$

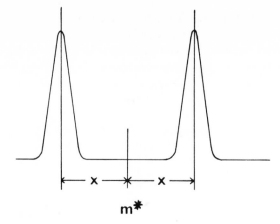

$$m^*$$

Fig. 2. Theoretical metastable shape for longitudinal energy release.

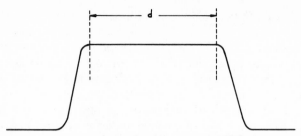

Fig. 3.  Flat-top wide metastable peak shape.

where $\mu = (m_1 - m_2)/m_2$, $V$ is the accelerating voltage, and $T$ is the energy release. Thus, the width of the peak $d$ will be

$$d = \frac{4 \, m_2^2}{m_1} \sqrt{\frac{\mu T}{eV}}$$

and the center of the peak will be shifted from the value $m_2^2/m_1$ by an amount $(m_2^2/m_1) \cdot (\mu T/eV)$; for most observed peaks, this shift corresponds to only about 100 ppm and is negligible. The metastable decomposition observed in the mass spectrum of $o$-nitrophenol as a wide, flat-topped peak was used to demonstrate the predicted dependence of peak width on accelerating voltage (see Fig. 4 and Table II). The width, in volts, of this peak was also obtained by using a retarding potential near the collector of a single-focusing mass spectrometer. The retarding potential at which the metastable peak began to disappear was between 780 and 785 V; it had vanished when the retarding potential had reached 825–830 V. The accelerating voltage used was 1020 V. The voltage difference, $45 \pm 5$ V, which corresponds to the width of the metastable peak, yields a value of $T = 0.74 \pm 0.16$ eV, in close agree-

**Table II.  Width $d$ of Flat-Top Metastable Peak due to Decomposition $p^+ \rightarrow (p\text{-NO})^+$ in $o$-Nitrophenol Against Accelerating Voltage**

| Accelerating voltage (kV) | $d$ (u) | $T = \left( \dfrac{d^2 m_1^2 eV}{4.4 \, m_2^4} \right)$ (eV) |
|---|---|---|
| 8.0 | 1.7 | 0.76 |
| 6.0 | 2.0 | 0.78 |
| 4.0 | 2.5 | 0.75 |
| 2.0 | 3.5 | 0.76 |

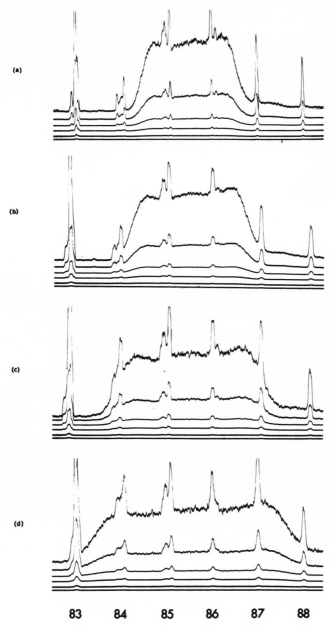

Fig. 4. Mass spectrometer scans of flat-top metastable peak in *o*-nitrophenol, due to decomposition $p^+ \rightarrow (p\text{-NO})^+$. Accelerating voltage: (a) 8 kV, (b) 6 kV, (c) 4 kV, and (d) 2 kV.

**Table III.  Decompositions that Give Wide Flat-Topped Metastable Peaks**

| Compound | Metastable ion | $m_1$ | $m_2$ | Neutral fragment | Energy released (eV) |
|---|---|---|---|---|---|
| o-Nitrophenol | $(p\text{-NO})^+$ | 109 | 81 | CO | 0.25 |
| p-Nitrophenol | $(p\text{-NO})^+$ | 109 | 81 | CO | 0.25 |
| m-Nitrophenol | $(p\text{-NO})^+$ | 109 | 81 | CO | 0.14 |
| o-Nitroaniline | $p^+$ | 138 | 108 | NO· | 0.81 |
| p-Nitroaniline | $p^+$ | 138 | 108 | NO· | 0.81 |
| 3-Nitro-p-toluidine | $p^+$ | 152 | 122 | NO· | 0.85 |
| 1-Nitronaphthalene | $p^+$ | 173 | 145 | CO | 0.18 |
| 2,6-Dinitrophenol | $p^+$ | 184 | 154 | NO· | 0.74 |
| Phenol | $p^+$ | 94 | 66 | CO | 1.20 |
| Furfuryl alcohol 5-carboxylic acid | $(p\text{-OH})^+$ | 125 | 97 | CO | 0.69 |
| Furfuryl alcohol 5-carboxylic acid | $(p\text{-1-H}_2\text{O})^+$ | 123 | 95 | CO | 0.20 |
| n-Heptadecane | $C_3H_7^+$ | 43 | 41 | $H_2$ | 0.24 |
| Cyclohexylamine | $C_3H_5^+$ | 41 | 39 | $H_2$ | 0.26 |
| Benzanthrone | $p^+$ | 230 | 202 | CO | 0.25 |
| N-methylphthalimide | $(p\text{-1})^+$ | 160 | 133 | HCN | 0.29 |
| N,N-dimethylguanidine | $p^+$ | 87 | 72 | $CH_3$· | 0.38 |
| 1-Hydroxy-2-nitronaphthalene | $p^+$ | 189 | 159 | NO· | 0.75 |
| 1-Hydroxy-2-nitro-4-phenyl benzene | $p^+$ | 215 | 185 | NO· | 0.75 |

ment with the values obtained by substituting values of peak width taken from charts in the relation

$$d = \frac{4 m_2^2}{m_1} \sqrt{\frac{\mu T}{eV}}$$

The value of $T$ obtained corresponds to the maximum amount of energy released.

Examples of other wide flat-topped metastable peaks which we have observed are listed in Table III. All these decompositions are suggested to occur as a consequence of the increased stability possible in the two fragments. All the neutral fragments in the table have well-known stable forms and in many cases stable structures can be proposed for the charged fragments. For example, the three isomeric nitrophenols all have metastable peaks in their mass spectra corresponding to the decomposition

$$p^+ \rightarrow (p\text{-NO})^+ + \text{NO·} \qquad m^* = 85.5$$

ortho and para compounds, the peaks are wide and
.tructures can be written for the $(p\text{-NO})^+$ ions. For the
however, the peak has a gaussian profile and no such
:an be written. Putting the decomposition in structural

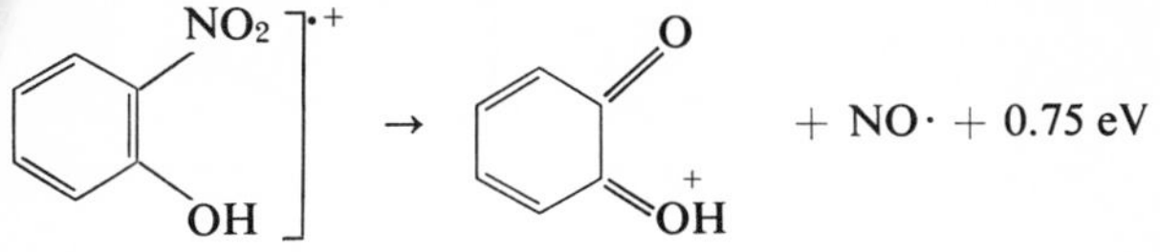

$$+ \; NO\cdot \; + \; 0.75 \text{ eV}$$

para

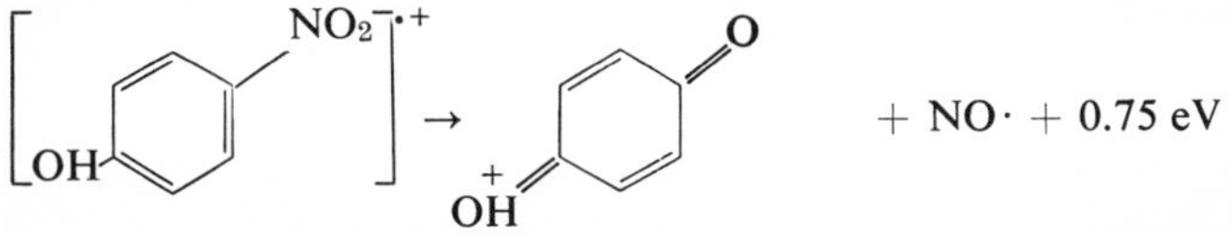

$$+ \; NO\cdot \; + \; 0.75 \text{ eV}$$

meta

$$+ \; NO\cdot$$

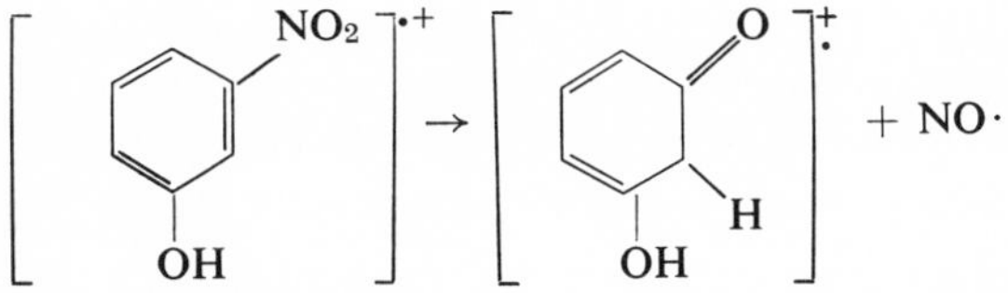

It appears that there may be some correlation between the stability of both
products of a decomposition and the production of a wide metastable
peak.

Jennings [7], in a study of the metastable decomposition

$$C_6H_6^{++} \;\rightarrow\; C_5H_3^+ + CH_3^+$$

in benzene, reports wide metastable peaks at $m/e$ 101.8 and $m/e$ 5.8 corresponding to the collection of the daughter ions $C_5H_3^+$ and $CH_3^+$, respectively. The widths of both peaks, when substituted in equation (1), are
consistent in giving the same $T$ value. Recent calculations by Elliott [8]
and Flowers [5] take into account the possibility of the energy release $T$
in a metastable decomposition producing a velocity component in the
daughter ion directed at an angle $\theta$ to the flight path of the precursor ion.
Both these workers have developed equations related to MS9 geometry [9],
which claim to give information on the width and profile of a metastable in
terms of $\theta$, the distance travelled in the field free region before decomposition $d$, and the energy released $T$. Both equations predict a peak shape
similar to that shown in Fig. 5. This is calculated for one value of $T$. Elliott,
having corrected his equation for beam and slit width, has shown that the
two wide metastable peaks observed by Jennings in benzene are very similar

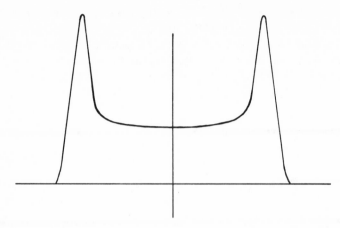

Fig. 5.   Metastable peak profile as calculated by Elliott [8] and Flowers [5].

in shape to a peak calculated from his equation on the assumption that each and every decomposition occurs with the same energy release.

Many other wide metastable peaks produced by decomposition of doubly charged ions to singly charged fragments are known. For example,

$$142^{++} \rightarrow 115^{+} + 27^{+} \qquad m^{*} = 186.2 \text{ and } 10.3 \quad T = 3.1 \text{ eV}$$

$$C_{11}H_{10}{}^{++} \rightarrow C_{9}H_{7}{}^{+} + C_{2}H_{3}{}^{+}$$

in diphenyl ether and methyl naphthalene, and

$$215^{++} \rightarrow 185^{+} + 30^{+} \qquad m^{*} = 318.3 \text{ and } 8.4 \quad T = 2.75 \text{ eV}$$

$$C_{12}H_{9}NO_{3}{}^{++} \rightarrow C_{12}H_{9}O_{2}{}^{+} + NO^{+}$$

in 1-nitro-2-hydroxy-4-phenyl benzene.

In the compositon of a doubly charged ion into two singly charged ions, some or all the energy released will arise from the separation of the two charges. Thus, every metastable decomposition of a doubly charged ion into two singly charged fragments will be accompanied by release of the repulsion energy and the metastable peak observed will be wide. The repulsion energy of the two charges at an equilibrium separation of $r_1$ cm is equal to the work necessary to bring the two charges to within that distance of each other from infinity. The work done is

$$\int_{\infty}^{r_1} \frac{ke^2}{r^2} dr = -\frac{ke^2}{r_1} \qquad k = 1$$

where $e$ is in esu and $r_1$ is in cm.

For the cases of peaks caused by decompositions of doubly charged ions listed above, the energies calculated by Beynon's equation are of the order 2.0–3.0 eV. Equating this order of energy with the integral, we get the order of magnitude of the equilibrium distance of the two charges in the ion. For $T = 2.8$ eV (benzene), $r_1 \simeq 5.2$ Å.

The release of energy in a direction parallel to the energy slit was neglected in the work of Elliott and Flowers. Any method for the derivation or calculation of metastable peak widths and profiles must take account of the possibility of energy release in all directions and the discriminations against daughter ions produced in decompositions involving large energy release, caused by slit dimensions and geometry. It seems likely that discrimination against ions which have gained velocity increments in the direction parallel to the energy slit and perpendicular to the main beam will have more effect on peak shape than discrimination in any other direction. In the case of a large amount of energy being released, the ions entering the magnet will be mostly those given velocity increments forward or backward in the direction of the main ion beam or very close to it. Thus, one would expect a peak shape approaching that of Fig. 2. For a wide range of energy releases, one would expect a filling in of the space between the peaks. The largest energies yet calculated are associated with the decomposition of doubly charged ion species. The shapes of many of the peaks resulting from these decompositions show well-defined "wings." This may indicate not only that discrimination occurs against ions given velocity increments parallel to the slit, but also that the energy released in the decompositions has only a small range of values. The variation of the two charges about their equilibrium distance is likely to be of the same order of distance as the amplitude of a normal molecular stretching mode; as these are small compared with the size of the molecule, the spread in repulsion energies expected will be slight. The distribution of energy values among the total number of ions decomposing in a given transition is an important factor affecting the profile of the peak. If one assumed various magnitudes and distributions of the energies released, then by using equations such as those described it may be possible to synthesize all metastable peak shapes observed in mass spectra and also to account for the differences observed in the same peak on different instruments.

The collection of daughter ions from metastable decompositions originating from the region before and inside the electrostatic analyzer has also been described [2,3].

The ratio of the accelerating voltage to electric sector voltage $V/E$, which controls the energy of the ions allowed through the electric sector, can be changed by a small amount on most double-focusing mass spectrometers.

On the MS9 mass spectrometer the effect of a change of $\pm 0.66\%$ in the ratio is to deflect the main ion beam completely, and allow only ions having an energy $1 \pm 0.0066$ times the energy of those in the main beam, to pass centrally through the electric sector. Hence, daughter ions ($m_2$) from metastable decompositions $m_1{}^+ \rightarrow m_2{}^+ + (m_1 - m_2)$ occurring before the electric sector can be transmitted through to the magnet and collecting system by increasing the accelerating voltage to $m_1/m_2$ of its normal value. By tuning the magnet to collect ions at $m_2$ on the mass scale, every decomposition producing $m_2$ as a daughter ion can be detected by variation of the accelerating voltage. It is a simple matter to introduce wiring modifications on the MS9 to allow a large precise and continuous variations in $V/E$. This technique has been used successfully by Jennings [10] with Nier–Johnson geometry and also by Futrell et al. [11] with a mass spectrometer of Mattauch–Herzog design.

The direction focusing properties of the electric sector partially correct for any divergence in the paths of the daughter ions ($m_2$) caused by energy release in the decompositions; the peak at the collector is therefore much narrower and the electrical signal produced correspondingly stronger than that produced by the collection of daughter ions from interanalyzer decompositions. Also under conditions of deflected main beam, detection sensitivity can be increased further by using the electron-multiplier detector near its maximum gain, and, hence, there is a considerable real gain in sensitivity in the detection of metastable decompositions. The facility with which the arrangement can be used is increased by use of a linear scan for the variation of $V/E$ together with a calibrated chart.

Figure 6 shows a scan for $m_2 = m/e$ 41 in $n$-hexane. By scanning every fragment ion in this compound with an abundance of greater than 5%, a total of 70 metastable decompositions were detected. This compares with

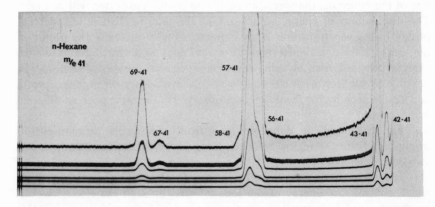

Fig. 6.   Linear scan of the $V/E$ ratio, with the mass spectrometer set to collect ions of $m/e$ 41, shows the presence of seven metastable decompositions producing ions at that mass number.

15 observed on a chart run under the same conditions (0.004-in. slits, RP≃1800).

Figure 6 also illustrates a limitation of the method. The peaks arising from the transitions $m/e$ 58 → $m/e$ 41, $m/e$ 57 → $m/e$ 41, and $m/e$ 56 → $m/e$ 41 are not "resolved." This is because the energy passband of the electrostatic analyzer and monitor slit is large enough to allow ions arising from these three decompositions to be transmitted through to the collector simultaneously. For the MS9 mass spectrometer, the width of the energy band is 1.3% of the energy of the accelerated ions; thus, for any decomposition $m_1^+ \rightarrow m_2^+ + \cdots$ ions $m_2$, produced from precursors within 0.013 $m_1$ mass units of $m_1$, can be transmitted simultaneously. This condition defines the "best resolution" that can be obtained if there is no kinetic energy release in the decompositions. Release of kinetic energy causes poorer "resolution." Thus, in the example, although the precursors $m/e$ 58, 57, and 56 have mass separations of about 1.8%, kinetic energy release in their decompositions broadens the beam, the mass separation is effectively less, and some $m/e$ 41 daughter ions from each precursor are transmitted simultaneously.

An arrangement closely resembling that described above has been used by O. Osberghaus and C. Ottinger of the University of Freiburg. They claim to have measured fragmentation energies in $n$-heptane and $n$-butane [12] and also in benzene [13]. They have used an electron-impact source with a 1-kV "draw-out" voltage followed by a 90° cylindrical condenser, a 60° magnet sector, and a multiplier detector. The magnet is tuned to detect the daughter ion $m_2^+$ at normal draw-out voltage. This voltage is increased from normal through $m_1/m_2$ times the normal value; the peak obtained has a profile which reflects the transmission properties of the 90° condenser and any energy release in the decomposition: $m_1^+ \rightarrow m_2^+ + (m_1 - m_2)$. The magnet is now tuned to $m_1^+$ and the profile of this peak is obtained by scanning the draw-out voltage through its normal value. By comparing the two profiles, Ottinger calculates fragmentation energy values.

The lifetimes of the metastable ions whose decompositions are detected in mass spectra are of the order of a few microseconds. The metastable ions so far considered have all been produced with a considerable amount of excess energy by electron impact, and it is well known that many metastable decompositions have well-defined appearance potentials. Beckey [14] has discussed metastable decompositions observed in field ionization mass spectra obtained using single-focusing mass spectrometers. The molecular ion from the field ionization process is formed with an excess energy of, at most, a fraction of an electron volt. Beckey differentiates between metastable decompositions occurring in the electric field only a few molecular vibration periods ($\sim 10^{-12}$ sec) after ionization and those occurring after a molecular ion lifetime of several microseconds in the field free region of the mass spectrometer. The peak profile of a fragment ion from the former process has a pronounced "tail" on the low mass side which Beckey has attributed to decompositions of short-lived molecular ions moving down the electric field after ionization. Unlike the decomposition of the longer-lived ($10^{-5}$ sec) ions in the field free region of the mass spectrometer, field dissociation is not governed by the rules of the statistical theory of mass spectra, as the field-induced decomposition occurs so soon after ionization that dissociation cannot be caused by energy transfer into a critical bond. The dissociation is also markedly dependent on the field, the intensity of the fragment peaks increasing with field strength.

Beckey [15] cites many examples of intense metastable peaks due to decompositions in the field free region, in paraffins and olefins, e.g., the two decompositons

$$p^+ \rightarrow (p\text{-}C_2\,H_5)^+$$

and

$$p^+ \rightarrow (p\text{-}C_2\,H_6)^+$$

in the paraffins from pentane to nonane. Many of those decompositions occur in the electron-impact mass spectra, although not always to the same extent. Robertson and Viney [16] and Beynon et al. [17] have reported the metastable decomposition

$$(CH_3COCH_3)\cdot{}^+ \rightarrow C_2H_3O^+ + CH_3\cdot$$

in the field ionization mass spectrum of acetone. This decomposition is of interest since it is not detected in the electron-impact mass spectrum of acetone, whereas the decomposition $(CH_3COCH_3)\cdot{}^+ \rightarrow (C_2H_2O)\cdot{}^+ + CH_4$ does occur. The loss of the methyl radical may be a consequence of the field ionization method, in which case the decomposition could still be said to be "field-dependent." It would be of some interest to prepare the acetone molecular ion with little excess energy, using photons perhaps, and determine if the transition involving loss of methane occurs or not.

Metastable peaks are valuable in basic studies of fragmentation mechanisms. By indicating that a particular fragment is lost as an entity, they suggest the steric configuration of the fragmenting ion and the origin of fragment ions of unexpected formulas. Thus, in the mass spectrum of dimethyl acetal $CH_3CH(OCH_3)_2$, peaks occur at mass 75 due to ions of formula $[CH(OCH_3)_2]^+$ presumably formed by single cleavage resulting in loss of a $CH_3\cdot$ group and at mass 47 of formula $[C_2H_7O]^+$.

Metastable peaks are observed at masses 63.1 and 29.4. They show that transitions

$$C_4H_9O_2{}^+ \rightarrow C_3H_7O_2{}^+ + CH_2$$

and

$$C_3H_7O_2{}^+ \rightarrow C_2H_7O^+ + CO$$

are occurring. The first of these transitions shows that at least some of the ions of mass 75 are not formed directly from the parent ion, but rather by loss of a methylene fragment from a parent ion which has already lost a hydrogen atom. The second transition shows that a 3- or 4-membered cyclic transition state must be formed by the ion of mass 75 from which it can eliminate the elements of neutral carbon monoxide.

Metastable peaks can also be used to distinguish fragmentation processes which can occur in a few microseconds even when they are accompanied by much more rapid fragmentations. Thus, in the mass spectrum of pure benzoic acid which has been 100% labeled with deuterium in the acid hydrogen position [18], a large peak is seen corresponding to loss of ·OD from the parent ion and this is accompanied by a much smaller peak corresponding to loss of ·OH. The corresponding metastable peaks for these two fragmentations are shown in Fig. 7, where it can be seen that, in the fragmentation of the metastable ion, loss of ·OH is twice as likely as loss of ·OD. In a few microseconds the carboxylic acid group can rotate many times, and it is visualized that randomization of the deuterium and the two ortho-hydrogens can occur via the intermediate species

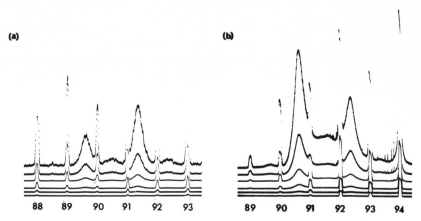

The probability of loss of ·OH is then twice that of ·OD.

Fig. 7.   (a) Metastable peak resulting from loss of ·OD and ·OH from the molecular ion in the mass spectrum of benzoic acid-$d_1$. (b) Metastable peaks resulting from loss of ·OD and ·OH from the ion of mass-to-charge ratio 124 in the mass spectrum of phthalic acid-$d_2$.

In a similar way the probabilities of loss of $\cdot OH$ and $\cdot OD$ from the parent ions of iso-phthalic and terephthalic acids both labeled 100% with deuterium in the carboxylic acid groups are in the ratios 3:2 and 2:1, respectively. In the corresponding deuterated phthalic acid, free rotation of the carboxylic acid groups is sterically hindered, but a fragment ion is formed by loss of $CO_2$ and this then loses $\cdot OH$ and $\cdot OD$ with relative probabilities in the ratio 1:2 [Fig. 7(b)]. The process can be visualized as

Thus metastable peaks are valuable in many ways in the understanding which they give of the mechanisms and energetics of ion fragmentations. Already, instruments are being modified to give these peaks with greater sensitivity and it is to be hoped that the time will not be long delayed before instruments, specifically designed to control the time of flight of ions within wide limits, are available to chemists to enable further and more quantitative studies to be carried out.

## REFERENCES

1. J. A. Hipple and E. U. Condon, *Phys. Rev.* **69**:347, 1946.
2. J. H. Beynon, R. A. Saunders, and A. E. Williams, *Nature* **204**:67, 1964.
3. M. Barber and R. M. Elliott, 12th Annual Conference on Mass Spectrometry and Allied Topics, Committee E.14 ASTM, Montreal, June 1964.
4. J. Momigny, private communication, 1964.
5. M. C. Flowers, *Chem. Commun.*, p. 235, 1965.
6. J. H. Beynon, R. A. Saunders, and A. E. Williams, *Z. Naturforsch.* **20a**:180, 1965.
7. K. R. Jennings, *Chem. Commun.*, p. 99, 1965.
8. R. M. Elliott, private communication, 1965.
9. R. D. Craig, B. N. Green, and J. D. Waldron, *Chimia (Aarau)* **17**:33, 1963.
10. K. R. Jennings, *J. Chem. Phys.* **43**:4176, 1965.
11. J. H. Futrell, K. R. Ryan, and L. W. Sieck, *J. Chem. Phys.* **43**:1842, 1965.
12. C. Ottinger, *Phys. Rev. Letters* **17**:269, 1965.
13. C. Ottinger, *Z. Naturforsch.* **20a**:1229, 1965.
14. H. D. Beckey, *Bull. Soc. Chim. Belges* **73**:326, 1964.

15. H. D. Beckey, in: R. I. Reed (ed.), *Mass Spectrometry* (NATO advanced study institute on theory, design, and applications, Glasgow, 1964), Academic Press, London, 1965.
16. A. J. B. Robertson and B. W. Viney, *Advances in Mass Spectrometry*, Vol. 3, Inst. Petroleum, London, 1966.
17. J. H. Beynon, A. E. Fontaine, and B. E. Job, *Z. Naturforsch.* **21a**:776, 1966.
18. J. H. Beynon, B. E. Job, and A. E. Williams, *Z. Naturforsch.* **20a**:883, 1965.

# THE MASS SPECTROMETRIC INVESTIGATION OF AMINO ACIDS AND PEPTIDES

## H. Budzikiewicz

*Institut für Organische Chemie*
*Technische Hochschule*
*Braunschweig, Germany*

The aim of this contribution is to demonstrate what information the natural products chemist may gain from mass spectrometric investigations, which difficulties he may encounter and how he may circumvent them, and where future developments seem to lead. Amino acids and peptides have been chosen for this purpose since this class of compounds, covering in mass the entire range so far accessible (going from glycine to oligopeptides with molecular weights well over 1000), poses many problems, both experimental and in the interpretation, which are typical for mass spectrometric work. In addition, owing to the great biological importance of these compounds, one can draw upon a large number of fundamental investigations which allow a well-founded picture to be presented.

Amino acids being zwitterions show a rather low volatility and much of the early work* has been devoted to the circumvention of this problem. Various esters (e.g., ethyl esters [2]) as well as N-acyl derivatives of the free acids and of their esters have been investigated [1] and so have phenylthio-hydantoins [3] (resulting from Edman degradation) and 2,4-dinitrophenyl derivatives [4] (introduced by Sanger). More recently the development of methods for the direct insertion of samples into the ion source allowed the investigation of free amino acids, too (see, e.g., [5]).

Thus, the first problem of any analysis by mass spectrometry has been solved, *viz.*, to vaporize the compound to be investigated undecomposed into the ionization region, and thus a mass spectrum can be obtained. The first feature of interest is that molecular ions can generally be observed though sometimes they may be of very low abundance. In this way an exact molecular

---

* Literature up to about 1964 has been covered in several summaries [1] and the reader may consult those for a detailed listing of references.

weight can be obtained, but a note of caution should be added here. As several other compounds containing either oxygen or nitrogen do, amino acid esters may abstract by a bimolecular reaction a hydrogen atom from a second molecule and give "$M+1$" peaks, as, e.g., structure I. Such species may, however, be recognized by repeating the measurement with a different sample pressure.

$$C_3H_7-CH-COOC_2H_5$$
$$|$$
$$NH_3^+$$

I

By use of a high-resolution instrument, the mass of the molecular ion may be determined with an accuracy of a few ppm which, in most cases, is sufficient to calculate the elemental composition of the ion. Yet, with the establishment of the gross formula of a compound, the information to be gained from the mass spectrum is by no means exhausted.

The next step is to analyze and interpret the fragmentation pattern. There are several ways to do so. The most gratifying one would be a purely theoretical approach. If one has a complete knowledge of the kinetics and energetic requirements of all fragmentation and rearrangement reactions, of the bond strengths, and of the spatial interactions of the various structural elements of the compound under investigation, one should be able to predict its mass spectrum at a given ionizing energy and, conversely, one should be able to extract structural information from the mass spectrum. This ideal situation is within the realm of reality at best for the simplest organic compounds. For more complicated molecules and, thus, especially for natural products, one has to look for a different approach.

What might be called a semiempirical approach to the interpretation of mass spectra is to try to find out how the various fragmentation reactions are triggered and which paths they follow. Obviously an ample background of information on the behavior of simple model compounds is necessary. Studies of the behavior of functional groups in specific surroundings will then allow an understanding of the mass spectrum of a more complex compound. In our case of amino acids and small peptides one has to draw upon data on aliphatic acids and their esters and amides, on aliphatic and alicyclic amines, and on ethers, sulfides, and aromatic compounds. (For surveys of the fragmentation behavior of these model compounds, see [6].)

Such an approach should be familiar to a chemist doing structural work by chemical means. He also relies generally on empirical information and its correlation, and a similar treatment of mass spectral data should be successful also, as long as one keeps in mind that all conclusions are based on analogies and that they are reliable only within the limits of the available comparison material and its correct interpretation.

It has proved useful to assume that the positive charge in a given molecular or fragment ion is localized at a specific center where it is especially well stabilized—at a heteroatom which has nonbonding electrons, in the $\pi$-cloud of a center of unsaturation, at a quaternary carbon, etc. —and that fragmentation is triggered by such centers. Certainly, if a molecule contains several such loci then—in the bulk of ionized molecules—the charge will reside to a greater or lesser degree on each of them and competing fragmentation will be observed.

From appearance potential data [5] it may be concluded that in aliphatic amino acids and their esters primary ionization occurs preferentially by removal of one of the nonbonding electrons of the nitrogen (II). The main fragmentation process of aliphatic amines is known to be $\alpha$-cleavage resulting in the loss of an alkyl radical and the formation of an immonium ion. The molecular ion II may do this in a twofold way, viz., by loss of the carb(alk)-oxyl group (a) or by elimination of an alkyl radical (b).

$$\overset{+}{H_2N}=CH-COOR \xleftarrow{\;-R'\cdot\;} R'-\underset{\overset{|}{\overset{+}{\cdot}NH_2}}{CH}-COOR \xrightarrow{\;-\cdot COOR\;} R'-CH=\overset{+}{NH_2}$$

$$b \hspace{4cm} II \hspace{4cm} a$$

Fragment a is generally very abundant and gives rise in many cases to the base peak of the mass spectrum. Since it retains the residue R', it is characteristic for the various amino acids, though it certainly does not distinguish between isomers such as norvaline (III) and valine (IV). Here secondary fragmentations will be of assistance. To some extent the positive charge in the molecular ion of valine (IV) will reside at the tertiary carbon of the isopropyl group and hence loss of a methyl group will be more pronounced from IV than from III.

$$CH_3-CH_2-CH_2-\underset{\overset{|}{NH_2}}{CH}\overset{72}{\vert}COOR \hspace{2cm} \underset{CH_3}{\overset{CH_3}{\diagdown}}CH-\underset{\overset{|}{NH_2}}{CH}\overset{72}{\vert}COOR$$

$$\hspace{9cm} M-15$$

$$III \hspace{5cm} IV$$

In the mass spectra of leucine and its esters (V, cf. Fig. 1) we encounter two more abundant peaks whose presence is unexpected at the first glance. Furthermore, they are isobaric with what would be the characteristic $\alpha$-cleavage products of glycine (VI, $m/e$ 30) and alanine (VII, $m/e$ 44) and might be taken as an indication of an admixture of these compounds.

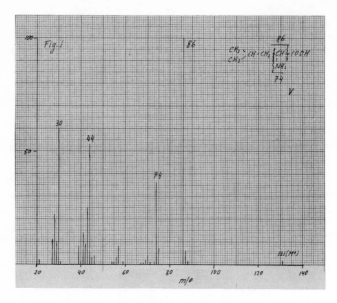

Fig. 1.   Mass spectrum of leucine (redrawn from [5]).

However, knowledge [6] about the fragmentation behavior of simple aliphatic amines accounts for their presence.

$$
\begin{array}{cccc}
CH_3 & 86 & 30 & 44 \\
\diagdown & \overline{\qquad} & \overline{\qquad} & \overline{\qquad} \\
CH-CH_2-CH\!\!\mid\!\!COOR & CH_2\!\!\mid\!\!COOR & CH_3-CH\!\!\mid\!\!COOR \\
\diagup & | & | & | \\
CH_3 & NH_2 & NH_2 & NH_2 \\
\\
V & & VI & VII
\end{array}
$$

Ions of the type *a* may decompose in two ways provided that the alkyl chain is long enough, both consisting in the loss of the elements of an olefin with concomitant hydrogen rearrangement. The fragment of mass 44 is probably formed by collapse of *a* in a six-membered transition state with specific transfer of a $\delta$-hydrogen atom [7, 8], while during the genesis of the *m/e* 30 species a hydrogen atom may be abstracted randomly from any position of the alkyl chain [7].

If a second functional group is present in the molecule, its competing influence will be noticeable. Primary ionization may also occur at those centers exemplified by the formation of the base peaks *m/e* 107 (*c*) from tyrosine (VIII) and *m/e* 61 (*d*) from methionine (IX) (*cf*. Fig. 2). Advantage may be taken of these fragments for the further characterization of certain amino acids.

$$CH_2=CH-\overset{+}{N}H_2 \longrightarrow CH_2=\overset{+}{N}H_2+C_4H_8$$

a          m/e 30

$$CH_2=CH-\overset{+}{N}H_3 + C_3H_6$$

a          m/e 44

From the preceding it is obvious that amino acids as well as their derivatives may be readily identified from their mass spectra. This method is of no great importance as long as one is dealing with the common representatives, paper chromatography being generally the method of choice. However, mass spectrometry immediately gains importance if one encounters unusual amino acids which cannot be identified by chromatographic methods. Such compounds are frequently isolated in amounts which prevent a structure elucidation by conventional methods, while amounts far less than one milligram are sufficient for a mass spectrum.

The following example may serve as an illustration [9]. An amino acid had been isolated from apples; two alternative structures (X and XI) had

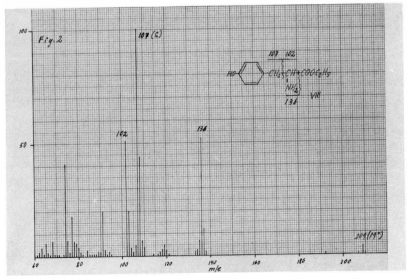

Fig. 2.   Mass spectrum of threonine ethyl ester (redrawn from [2]).

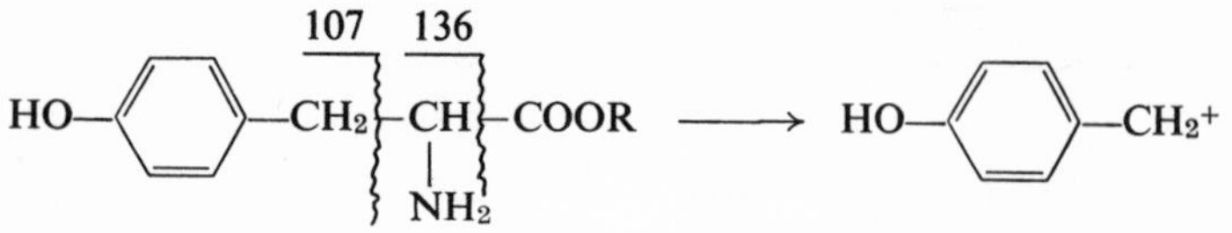

VIII        $c$, $m/e$ 107

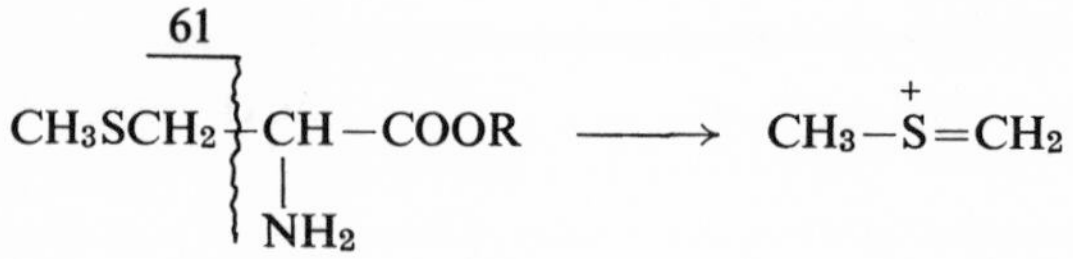

IX        $d$, $m/e$ 61

been proposed for its ethyl ester. The molecular ion ($m/e$ 173) and the main fragment (loss of the carbethoxyl group yielding $e$ or $e'$) were in agreement with either formulation. However, as in the case of valine (IV), a minor fragmentation process should allow a decision. If structure X were correct, one would expect an $M-15$ peak due to the loss of the methyl group from the quaternary center. From structure XI fragments at $m/e$ 142 ($M-CH_2OH$) and 31 ($CH_2 \overset{+}{=} OH$) should be formed. The latter being actually the case, structure XI is correct for this new amino acid.

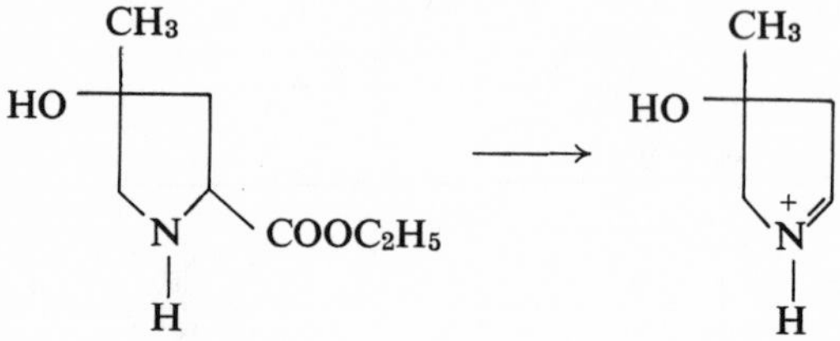

X        $e$, $m/e$ 100

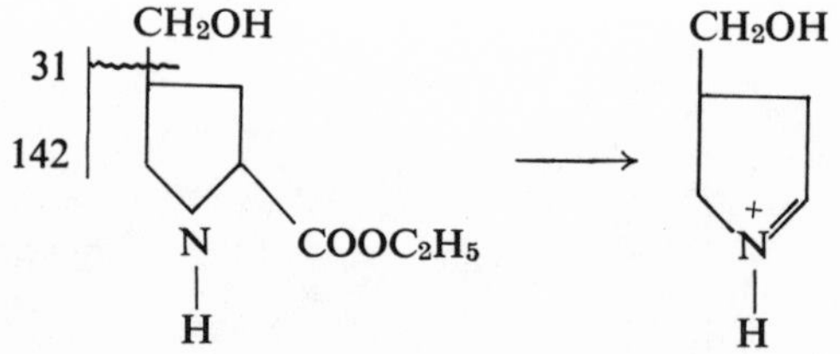

XI        $e'$, $m/e$ 100

The characteristic mass spectra of the various amino acids allow also a qualitative and quantitative analysis of a mixture. Quantitative work poses certain difficulties because of the great differences in volatility of the various free amino acids [10]. One can circumvent this by preparing suitable derivatives (e.g., esters [11]), but then one has to make sure that the reaction is quantitative for all compounds present in order to avoid a new source of error. Again, the mass spectrometric technique will be of advantage only if analyses by conventional methods fail to give results.

Another field where the mass spectrometric investigation of animo acids will give invaluable results is the exploration of biogenetic pathways. The fragmentation pattern and its interpretation being known, incorporated nonradioactive isotopes ($^2$H, $^{13}$C, $^{15}$N, $^{17}$O) can be recognized and to some extent even localized, and this, again, with amounts that would forbid any chemical degradation. Incidentally, the same pertains to the elucidation of reaction mechanisms by the use of heavy isotopes [12].

Another and perhaps the most important application of mass spectrometry in this field consists in the sequential analysis of oligopeptides, which is still somewhat unsatisfactory by conventional means.

Various methods have been proposed. One of the earliest stems from Biemann [13] who reduced oligopeptides with lithium aluminum deuteride to the corresponding $\beta$-polyamines. Their main fragmentations are the well-known $\alpha$-cleavages triggered by the amino groups, and the sequence may be deduced from the fragment masses (*cf.* Fig. 3).

$$CH_3CO-NH-CH-CO-NH-CH-CO-NH-CH_2-CO-NH-CH-COOC_2H_5$$
$$\qquad\qquad\quad | \qquad\qquad\qquad\quad | \qquad\qquad\qquad\qquad\qquad\qquad\qquad\quad |$$
$$\qquad\qquad\quad CH_2 \qquad\qquad\qquad CH_3 \qquad\qquad\qquad\qquad\qquad\qquad\quad CH_2$$
$$\qquad\qquad\quad |$$
$$\qquad\qquad\quad CH(CH_3)_2 \qquad\qquad\qquad\qquad\qquad\qquad\qquad\qquad\qquad CH(CH_3)_2$$

$$(1)\ \text{LiAlD}_4$$
$$(2)\ \text{SOCl}_2$$
$$(3)\ \text{LiAlD}_4$$

$$CH_3-CD_2-NH-CH-CD_2-NH-CH-CD_2-NH-CH_2-CD_2-NH-CH-CD_3$$
$$\qquad\qquad\qquad\quad | \qquad\qquad\qquad\quad | \qquad\qquad\qquad\qquad\qquad\qquad\qquad\quad |$$
$$\qquad\qquad\qquad\quad CH_2 \qquad\qquad\qquad CH_3 \qquad\qquad\qquad\qquad\qquad\qquad\quad CH_2$$
$$\qquad\qquad\qquad\quad |$$
$$\qquad\qquad\qquad\quad CH(CH_3)_2 \qquad\qquad\qquad\qquad\qquad\qquad\qquad\qquad CH(CH_3)_2$$

This method has its disadvantages. First, it requires three steps since the first reduction leads only to amino alcohols. Second, side reactions may occur, as the cleavage of amide bonds, making a chromatographic purification of the material necessary. Finally, one has to use lithium aluminum deuteride instead of hydride, since oxygen-containing functional groups are reduced to

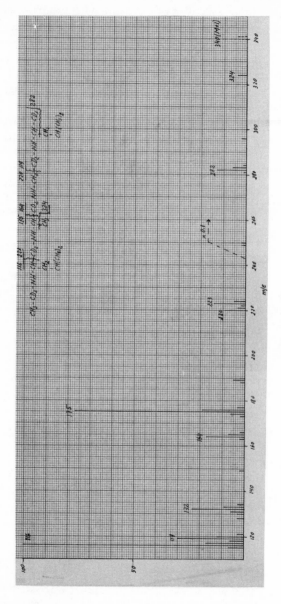

Fig. 3. Mass spectrum of the reduction product of Ac-Leu-Ala-Gly-Leu (redrawn from [13]).

alkyl chains. Thus, $\alpha$-aminobutyric acid (XII), threonine (XIII), and aspartic acid (XIV) would yield the same reduction product, an ethyl group. However, the different amount of deuterium atoms introduced during the deuteride reduction allows their differentiation.

$$CH_3-CH_2-\underset{\underset{NH_2}{|}}{CH}-COOH \qquad CH_3-\underset{\underset{OH}{|}}{CH}-\underset{\underset{NH_2}{|}}{CH}-COOH \qquad HOOC-CH_2-\underset{\underset{NH_2}{|}}{CH}-COOH$$

XII           XIII           XIV

Another approach that has been suggested by several groups [1] is to investigate directly terminal N-acyl derivatives of free amino acids or of their esters. Preferential cleavages of the peptide bonds should allow determination of the sequence of the amino acids. Good results are obtained for di- and tripeptides, but for larger compounds the mass spectra become rather complex. Bond ruptures other than those of the peptide bonds result in additional fragments (see $m/e$ 299, 353, 392, and 452 in Fig. 4) and ions formed by primary fragmentation may decompose further (see $m/e$ 30 and 70 in Fig. 4). The mass spectrum of Ac-Pro-Leu-Gly-Val-Hypro-OH (XV) may serve as an example (Fig. 4) [14].

XV

The picture becomes somewhat clearer if one employs a method suggested by Lederer [15]. He used oligopeptides which were terminally N-acylated with $C_{15}$ to $C_{20}$ aliphatic carboxylic acids. Thus, the characteristic fragmentation is shifted from the low mass range to above $m/e$ 250, because only fragments formed by cleavages of the amide bonds and containing the intact acid chain are of interest for the sequential analysis. If one goes a step further and uses an equimolecular mixture of homologous acids or of an acid and its deuterium analog, then the characteristic fragments will always occur as doublets of peaks with equal intensity. Fragmentations involving partial or total loss of the acid chain result, accordingly, in a single peak and can be disregarded. A typical example is the nonapeptide fortuitine (XVI), which contains unusual amino acids which gave some difficulties during conventional investigations.

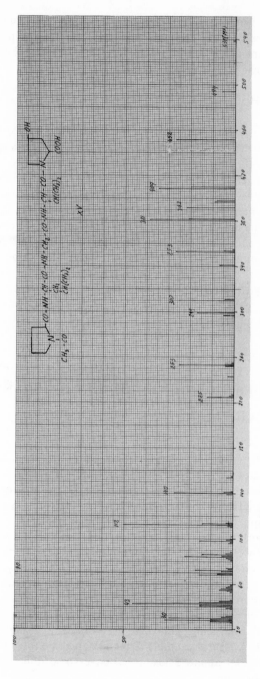

Fig. 4.   Mass spectrum of Ac-Pro-Leu-Gly-Val-Hypro-OH (redrawn from [14]).

$$CH_3(CH_2)_{18 \text{ and } 20} CO-Val-MeLeu-Val-4Val-MeLeu-Thr-Thr-Ala-Pro-OMe$$
$$\underset{Ac}{|} \quad \underset{Ac}{|}$$

XVI $m/e$ 1331 and 1359

Generally, a differentiation of isomeric amino acids like the leucines will be difficult. An independent analysis of the total hydrolysate by paper chromatography or by mass spectrometry in order to determine which amino acids are actually present in the peptide will eliminate this difficulty in many cases.

A similar approach, but using high-resolution data and their analysis by a computer, has been proposed by Biemann [16]. The computer is given the mass of the N-terminal group X and of all expected amino acid residues R. By scanning the observed fragments, the moieties $A_1$, $B_1$, $A_2$, $B_2$, ..., are identified and the sequence is thus determined. There are other computer-aided procedures for the analysis of oligopeptides [17] and one of them will be the subject of another contribution in this volume.

$$X-NH-CH+CO+NH-CH+CO+NH-CH\{\cdots\cdots\}CO|OH$$

The results available today indicate that the limit for undecomposed vaporization into an ion source is about a decapeptide. A possibility for larger molecules would be to obtain major fragments by enzymatic partial hydrolysis which then may be examined conveniently. This automatized sequential analysis by mass spectrometry is still rather young and has to be tested further and possibly modified. But the results available so far promise a real breakthrough in peptide chemistry. A considerable instrumental armamentarium is needed, but once set up it might well become a routine method.

## REFERENCES

1. K. Biemann, *Chimia (Aarau)* **14**:393, 1960; K. Biemann, *Mass Spectrometry*, McGraw-Hill, New York, 1962, Chapter 7; H. Budzikiewicz, C. Djerassi, and D. H. Williams, *Structure Elucidation of Natural Products by Mass Spectrometry*, Vol. 2, Holden-Day, San Francisco, 1964, Chapter 26.
2. K. Biemann, J. Seibl, and F. Gapp, *J. Am. Chem. Soc.* **83**:3795, 1961.
3. N. S. Wulfson, V. M. Stepanov, V. A. Puchkov, and A. M. Zyakoon, *Izv. Akad. Nauk SSSR Otd. Khim. Nauk*, p. 1524, 1963.

4. T. J. Penders, H. Copier, W. Heerma, G. Dijkstra, and J. F. Arens, *Rec. Trav. Chim.* **85**:216, 1966.
5. G. Junk and H. Svec, *J. Am. Chem. Soc.* **85**:839, 1963.
6. H. Budzikiewicz, C. Djerassi, and D. H. Williams, *Mass Spectrometry of Organic Compounds*, Holden-Day, San Francisco, 1967.
7. C. Djerassi and C. Feneslau, *J. Am. Chem. Soc.* **87**:5752, 1965.
8. C. Djerassi, M. Fischer, and J. B. Thomson, *Chem. Commun.*, p. 12, 1966.
9. K. Biemann, G. G. J. Deffner, and F. C. Steward, *Nature* **191**:380, 1961.
10. G. A. Junk and H. J. Svec, *Anal. Chim. Acta* **28**:164, 1963.
11. K. Biemann and W. Vetter, *Biochem. Biophys. Res. Commun.* **9**:93, 1960.
12. G. A. Junk and H. J. Svec, *J. Org. Chem.* **29**:944, 1964.
13. K. Biemann and W. Vetter, *Biochem. Biophys. Res. Commun.* **3**:587, 1960.
14. K. Heyns and H.-F. Grützmacher, *Liebigs Ann. Chem.* **669**:189, 1963.
15. M. Barber, P. Jolles, E. Vilkas, and E. Lederer, *Biochem. Biophys. Res. Commun.* **18**:469, 1965.
16. K. Biemann, C. Cone, and B. R. Webster, *J. Am. Chem. Soc.* **88**:2597, 1966.
17. M. Senn, R. Venkataraghavan, and F. W. McLafferty, *J. Am. Chem. Soc.* **88**: 5593, 1966.

# PYROLYSIS, PHOTOLYSIS, AND ELECTRONOLYSIS*

## Allan Maccoll

*William Ramsay and Ralph Forster Laboratories*
*University College*
*London, England*

There is currently an increasing interest in the analogy between electron impact fragmentations and similar reactions occurring under the influence of heat or light. Such interest goes back to the early days of mass spectroscopic studies of organic molecules [1]. The specific reactions to be considered here are isomerization, dissociation, elimination, and ionization. These are best illustrated first in the thermal field, since this is the area which is most widely explored at the present time. Thus, on being heated, cyclopropane [2], cyclobutane [3], and vinyl allyl ether [4] all undergo isomerization in the gas phase to propene, butadiene, and allyl acetaldehyde, respectively:

$$
\begin{array}{ccc}
\begin{array}{c} CH_2 \\ \diagup \diagdown \\ CH_2\!-\!CH_2 \end{array}
&
\begin{array}{c} \varDelta \\ \rightarrow \end{array}
&
\begin{array}{c} CH_3 \\ \diagdown \\ \phantom{xx}CH\!=\!CH_2 \end{array}
\end{array}
$$

$$
\begin{array}{ccc}
\begin{array}{c} CH_2\!-\!CH_2 \\ |\phantom{xx}| \\ CH\!=\!CH \end{array}
&
\begin{array}{c} \varDelta \\ \rightarrow \end{array}
&
\begin{array}{c} CH_2 \phantom{xxxx} CH_2 \\ \diagdown \phantom{xx} \diagup \\ CH\!-\!CH \end{array}
\end{array}
$$

$$
\begin{array}{ccc}
\begin{array}{c} CH_2\!=\!CH \\ \diagdown \\ CH_2 \phantom{xxxx} O \\ \diagdown \phantom{xx} \diagup \\ CH\!-\!CH_2 \end{array}
&
\begin{array}{c} \varDelta \\ \rightarrow \end{array}
&
\begin{array}{c} CH_2\!-\!CH \\ \diagup \phantom{xxx} \diagdown \\ CH_2 \phantom{xxxx} O \\ \diagdown \phantom{xx} \diagup \\ CH\!=\!CH_2 \end{array}
\end{array}
$$

---

* Based in part on the Esso Lecture to the University of Sydney Chemical Society, April 1966.

All these reactions have been shown to be well-behaved, homogeneous unimolecular reactions. The study of dissociation, on the other hand, is by no means so clear-cut, since secondary reactions consequent upon the initial step are responsible for the observed products. Thus, ethyl bromide can dissociate thermally into an ethyl radical and a bromine atom, both of which can abstract hydrogen from the substrate:

$$C_2H_5Br \xrightarrow{\varDelta} C_2H_5\cdot + Br\cdot \tag{1}$$

$$Br\cdot + C_2H_5Br \rightarrow C_2H_4Br\cdot + HBr \tag{2}$$

$$C_2H_5\cdot + C_2H_5Br \rightarrow C_2H_4Br\cdot + C_2H_6 \tag{3}$$

Chains are sustained by the bromine atoms formed by the dissociation of the bromoethyl radicals [reaction (4)],

$$C_2H_4Br\cdot \rightarrow C_2H_4 + Br\cdot \tag{4}$$

and chain-ending may come about by the recombination of the radical or atom species. However, Sehon and Szwarc [5] have shown that for bromides *not* containing a $\beta$-carbon–hydrogen bond, the chain mechanism may be inhibited by carrying out the reaction in a flow system, using toluene as the carrier gas. In this case, reaction (5)

$$CH_3\cdot(Br\cdot) + CH_3\!-\!\langle\bigcirc\rangle \rightarrow CH_4(HBr) + \dot{C}H_2\!-\!\langle\bigcirc\rangle \tag{5}$$

effectively competes with reaction (2) in suppressing the chains. The benzyl radicals dimerize to form dibenzyl [reaction (6)]

$$2\dot{C}H_2\!-\!\langle\bigcirc\rangle \rightarrow \langle\bigcirc\rangle\!-\!CH_2\!-\!CH_2\!-\!\langle\bigcirc\rangle \tag{6}$$

and so the rate of the reaction (7)

$$CH_3Br \xrightarrow{\varDelta} CH_3\cdot + Br\cdot \tag{7}$$

may be determined, and the activation energy is the homolytic bond dissociation energy $D(R\!-\!Br)$. Some values are shown in Table I.

**Table I.  $D(R-Br)$ for the Bromomethanes [5]**

| Molecule | $CH_3Br$ | $CH_2Br_2$ | $CHBr_3$ | $CBr_4$ |
|---|---|---|---|---|
| $D(R-Br)$ (kcal/mole) | (67.5) | 62.5 | 55.5 | 49.0 |

Many chain reactions are believed to be initiated by steps of this type, e.g.,

$$RX \xrightarrow{\Delta} R\cdot + X\cdot$$

$$CH_3-CH_3 \xrightarrow{\Delta} 2CH_3\cdot$$

$$CH_3-CHO \xrightarrow{\Delta} CH_3\cdot + \dot{C}HO$$

Large radicals, when formed, may undergo isomerization [6]. Thus, hydrogen migration

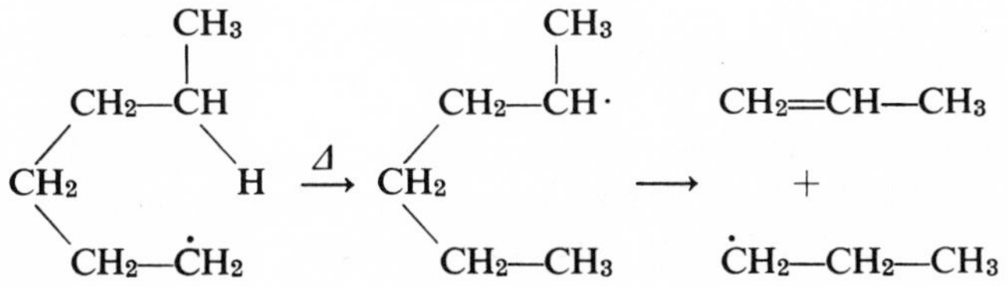

has been observed in studies of the addition of radicals to olefines. Again alkyl or aryl transfer has been observed [6]:

$$(CH_3)_3C-\dot{C}=CH_2 \xrightarrow{\Delta} (CH_3)_2\dot{C}-C(CH_3)=CH_2$$

$$(CH_3)_2PhC-\dot{C}HMe \xrightarrow{\Delta} (CH_3)_2\dot{C}-CHPhMe$$

In the former case, the driving force is presumably the formation of a stable allylic system. Such processes as these are common in reactions involving radicals.

There are also many elimination reactions known which have been extensively studied and shown to be molecular in nature. These all involve the breaking of at least two bonds and the forming of two or more. Where no atom or group is transferred from one atom to another, it is convenient to talk of simple elimination. Thus, the pyrolysis of cyclobutane [7] and the retro-Diels–Alder reactions [8] would fall in this class:

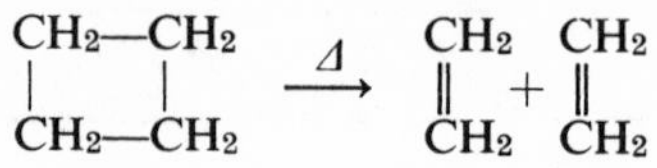

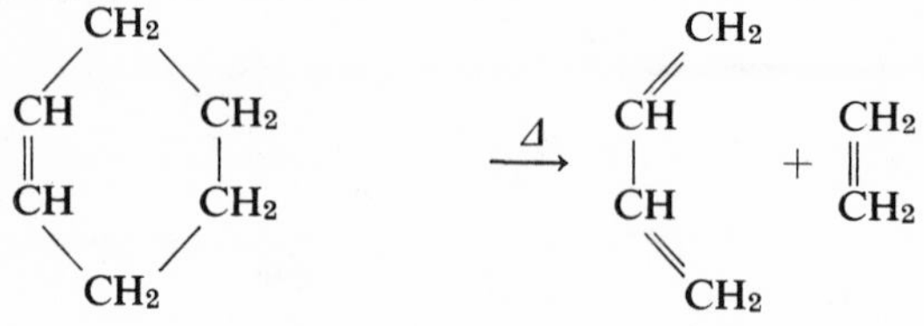

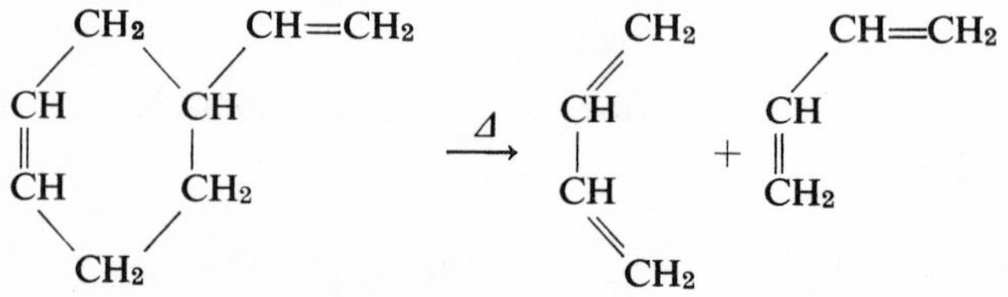

$$
\begin{array}{c}
CH_2\!-\!CH_2 \\
|\qquad\quad| \\
CH_2\!-\!CH_2
\end{array}
\ \xrightarrow{\ \Delta\ }\ 
\begin{array}{c}
CH_2 \\
\| \\
CH_2
\end{array}
\ +\ 
\begin{array}{c}
CH_2 \\
\| \\
CH_2
\end{array}
$$

On the other hand, rearrangement elimination is also known. The simplest examples are provided by formal 1-3 or 1-5 hydrogen shifts, as observed in the pyrolysis of halides and esters, respectively:

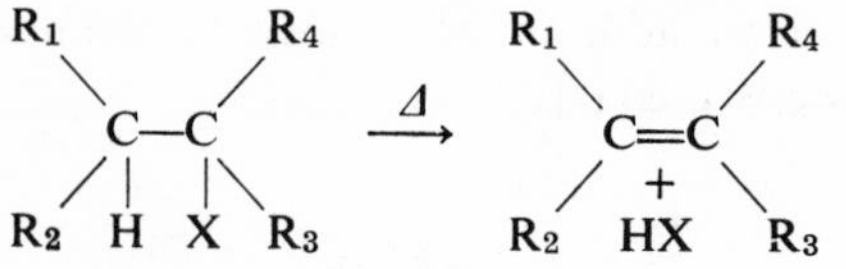

$X = Cl, Br, I$

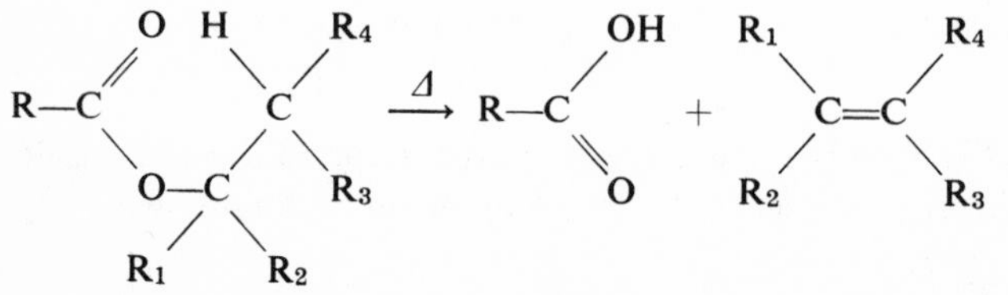

$R = H, Cl, CH_3$

The migration of alkyl groups has also been reported. Thus, Maccoll and Swinbourne [10] and Lewis and Herndon [11] have demonstrated the formations of methylbutenes from neopentyl chloride and neopentyl chloroformate, respectively. These molecules contain no $\beta$-hydrogen atom and so, if elimination is to occur, a methyl group must migrate:

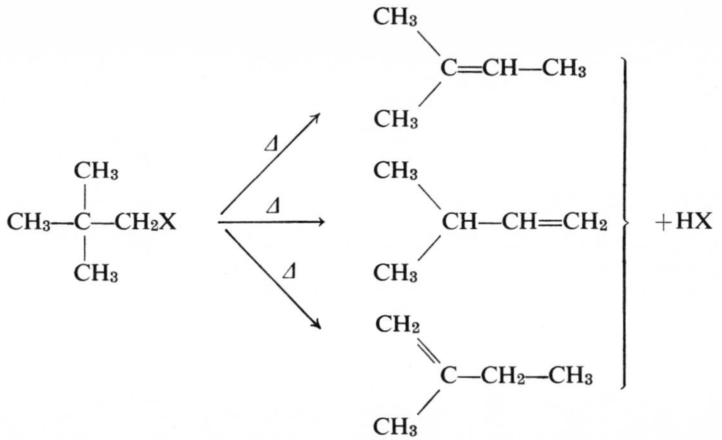

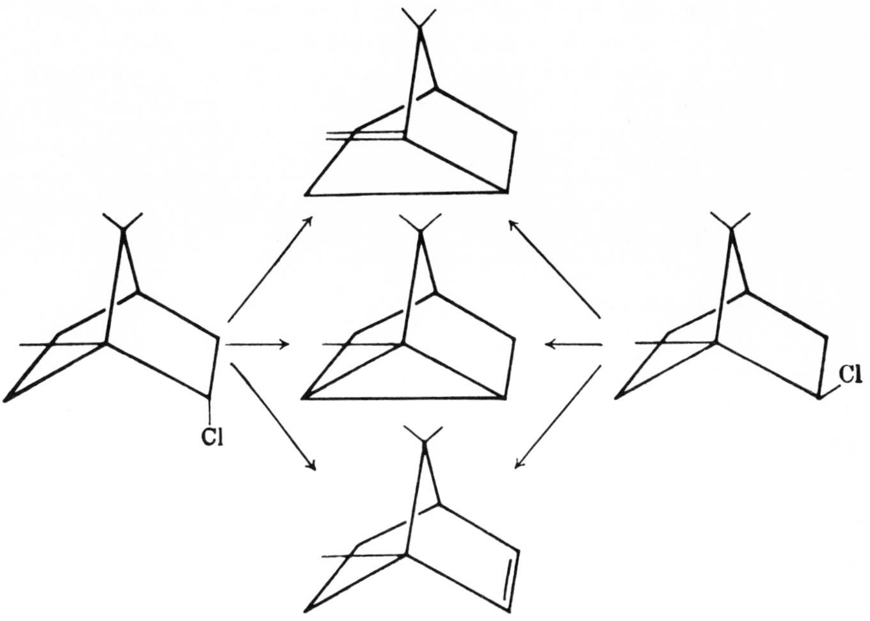

Later Bicknell showed that similar rearrangements occur in the pyrolysis of bornyl and isobornyl chlorides leading to tricyclene and camphene as well as to the expected bornylene [12]. A case of phenyl migration has also been reported [13] in the pyrolysis of diphenyl carbonate, although this is just one of the routes of decomposition:

$$
\begin{array}{ccc}
\text{Ph—O} & & \text{Ph—O—Ph} \\
\quad \diagdown & & \\
\quad \quad \text{C=O} & \xrightarrow{\Delta} & + \\
\quad \diagup & & \\
\text{Ph—O} & & \text{CO}_2
\end{array}
$$

Two other processes are possible which are worthy of mention, namely, thermal excitation and thermal ionization. The first of these refers to the reverse process of internal conversion where a molecule in the optically excited state passes to the ground state by a radiationless transfer, the energy being converted to heat. It

$$ M^* \rightarrow M + \Delta $$

is repesented by

$$ M + \Delta \rightarrow M^* $$

Such a molecule could then react from the excited state. Again, at high temperatures the process

$$ M \xrightarrow{\Delta} M^{+\cdot} + e $$

is possible, although there would be many other routes of lower energy available to the system. Such processes have been observed in the shock tube in the case of the rare gases. Since molecular ionization potentials are of the order of 10 eV, $\sim$ 230 kcal/mole, it would be only at very high temperatures that an appreciable concentration of ions would be set up.

Thus the following processes occurring thermally have been identified:

1. molecular isomerization $\qquad$ $M \xrightarrow{\Delta} M'$

2. radical dissociation $\qquad$ $R_1—R_2 \xrightarrow{\Delta} R_1\cdot + R_2$

3. radical rearrangement $\qquad$ $R\cdot \xrightarrow{\Delta} R'\cdot$

4. molecular elimination $\qquad$ $M_1M_2 \xrightarrow{\Delta} M_1 + M_2$

5. rearrangement elimination $\qquad$ $M_1M_2 \xrightarrow{\Delta} M_3 + M_4$

It will now be seen what evidence exists for such processes under conditions of photon and electron impact.

When a molecule M absorbs radiation in the visible or ultraviolet region of the spectrum, it is raised to an excited state, M*:

$$M \xrightarrow{h\nu} M*$$

It should be borne in mind that the geometry of the excited state may differ from that of the ground state. Thus, Ingold and King [14] showed that the first excited state of acetylene is nonlinear:

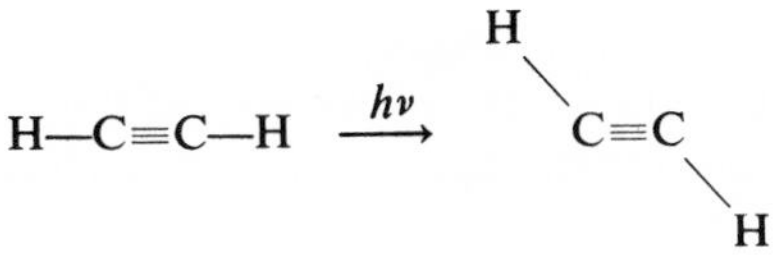

Similarly, Brand [15] showed that, in the case of formaldehyde, the first excited state is pyramidal:

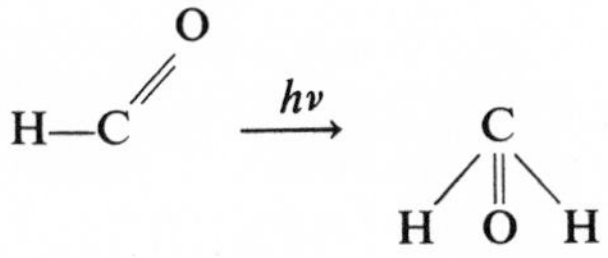

These can be regarded as cases of photoisomerism. However, even more striking cases have been reported. Bryce-Smith and co-workers [16] demonstrated that benzene, upon illumination with ultraviolet light, was converted in part to fulvene:

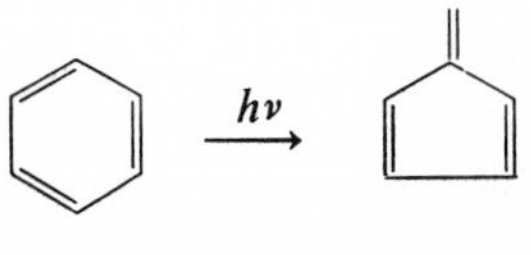

and Srinivasan and Cremer [17] have isolated the following reaction in cyclic ketones:

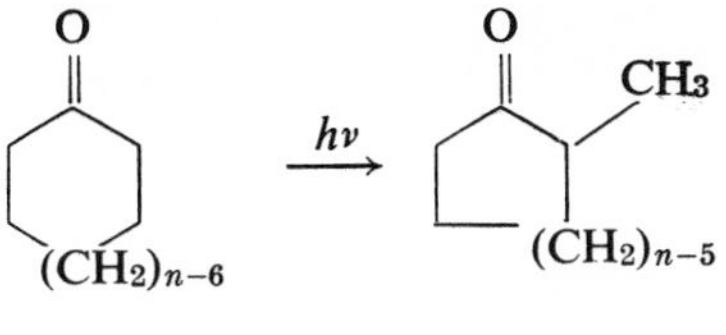

So much for photoisomerism. Photodissociation is a common phenomenon. Thus, when halogens are illuminated, halogen atoms are produced:

$$X_2 \xrightarrow{h\nu} X\cdot + X:$$

Similarly, when acetone is irradiated, methyl radicals are produced:

$$CH_3COCH_3 \xrightarrow{h\nu} CH_3\dot{C}O + CH_3\cdot$$

This reaction has often been employed in investigating the reactivity of these radicals. This process also affords an example of radical dissociation

$$CH_3\dot{C}O \xrightarrow{\Delta} CH_3\cdot + CO$$

which, of course, is thermal in origin. Molecular elimination also occurs in photochemistry. Thus, one of the processes used for producing methylene is the photolysis of diazomethane:

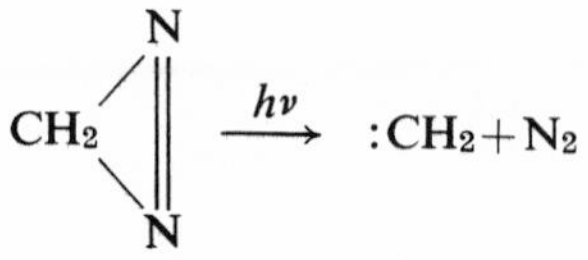

$$CH_2 \overset{N}{\underset{N}{\diagup\!\!\parallel\!\!\diagdown}} \xrightarrow{h\nu} \ :CH_2 + N_2$$

The process is facilitated by the very stable nitrogen molecule produced. Rearrangement elimination also is known in photolysis, for example, ethyl iodide [18, 19] and methyl propyl ketone [20]:

$$C_2H_5I \quad \overset{h\nu}{\nearrow} \quad C_2H_5\cdot + I\cdot$$
$$\underset{h\nu'}{\searrow} \quad C_2H_4 + HI$$

$$CH_3COCH_2CH_2CH_3 \quad \overset{h\nu}{\nearrow} \quad CH_3CO\cdot + CH_3CH_2CH_2\cdot$$
$$\underset{h\nu'}{\searrow} \quad CH_3CHO + CH_3CH\!=\!CH_2$$

It often occurs along with dissociation, as in the above examples. Finally there is the phenomenon of photoionization,

$$M \xrightarrow{h\nu} M^{\ddagger} + e$$

which may occur as a two-stage process,

$$M \xrightarrow{h\nu} M^*$$

$$M^* \longrightarrow M^{\overset{+}{\cdot}} + e$$

in which case it is known as autoionization. Thus, many of the reaction paths well known in pyrolysis are also found to occur in photolysis.

Similar phenomena are also found in electron impact experiments. The simplest process, occurring at low energies, is ionization,

$$M \xrightarrow{e} M^{\overset{+}{\cdot}} + 2e$$

and the minimum energy corresponding to the process is the ionization potential. However, it must not always be assumed that the ion produced has the same geometry as the original substance. Momigny *et al.* [21] have shown that benzene and butadienyl acetylene

$$CH_2{=}CH{-}C{=}CH{-}C{\equiv}CH$$

have identical mass spectra (Fig. 1), which suggests that either one isomerizes to the other under electron impact. Thus, the phenomenon of ionization isomerization can be of the greatest importance in understanding fragmentation mechanisms.

When the electron beam energy is increased above the ionization potential, fragmentation may occur. Such processes are of the utmost importance in structure determination. Examples are

$$e + CH_3{-}\overset{\overset{\textstyle CH_3}{|}}{CH}{-}CH_2CH_3 \Big\langle \begin{array}{l} CH_3{-}\overset{+}{CH}{-}CH_2{-}CH_3 + CH_3 \cdot \\[2ex] CH_3{-}\overset{\cdot}{CH}{-}CH_2CH_3 + CH_3{}^+ \end{array} \Big\rbrace + 2e$$

$$e + CH_2{=}CH{-}CH_2{-}CH_3 \longrightarrow \overset{+}{\overset{\frown}{CH_2{-}CH{-}CH_2}} + CH_3 \cdot + 2e$$

$$e + CH_3{-}\overset{\overset{\textstyle O}{\|}}{C}{-}CH_2 \longrightarrow CH_3{-}C{\equiv}O^+ + CH_3 \cdot + 2e$$

indicating the tendency for C–C bonds to break (1) at a branch point,

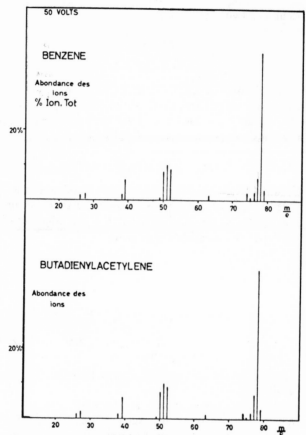

Fig. 1. Mass spectra of benzene and butadienyl acetylene (Momigny *et al.* [21]), reproduced by permission of the authors and of the editor of the *Bull. Classe Sci. Acad. Roy. Belg.*

(2) $\beta$ to a double bond, and (3) adjacent to a heteroatom. Fragmentation to give a radical ion and a radical may also occur with rearrangement. Thus, peaks occur in the mass spectra of isobutane, methyl thiourea, and benzene corresponding to the processes

$$e + CH_3\!-\!\overset{\displaystyle CH_3}{\underset{\displaystyle |}{CH}}\!-\!CH_3 \longrightarrow C_2H_5^+ + C_2H_5\cdot + 2e$$

$$e + CH_3\!-\!\underset{\displaystyle NH_2}{\overset{\displaystyle CH_3-NH}{\diagdown\!\diagup}}C\!=\!S \longrightarrow CH_3\!-\!N\!=\!C\!=\!\overset{+}{N}H_2 + HS\cdot + 2e$$

$$e + \text{[benzene]} \longrightarrow [C_5H_3]^+ + CH_3 \cdot + 2e$$

Such rearrangement ions can confuse the structural problem, unless recognized.

Elimination reactions are also observed under electron impact, the products being a molecule ion and a molecule. Thus, compounds of the type $M_1M_2$ can undergo fragmentation of the type

$$e + M_1M_2 \longrightarrow \overset{+}{M_1} + M_2 + 2e$$

as in the following examples:

$$e + \text{[benzene]} \longrightarrow [C_4H_4]^{+\cdot} + C_2H_2 + 2e$$

$$e + \text{[cyclohexanone]} \longrightarrow [\text{cyclopentane}]^{+\cdot} + CO + 2e$$

$$e + \text{[tetralin]} \longrightarrow [\text{benzocyclobutene}]^{+\cdot} + C_2H_4 + 2e$$

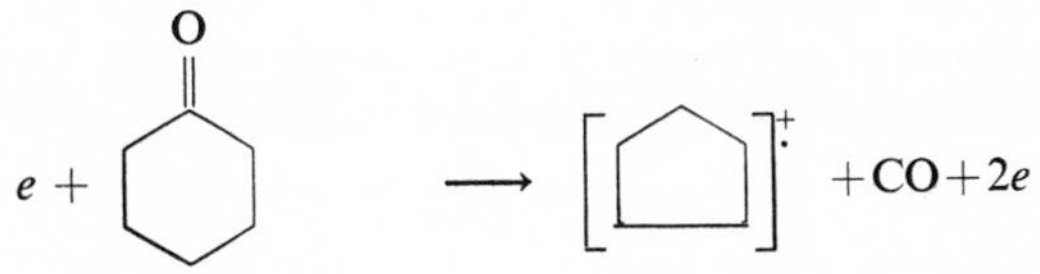

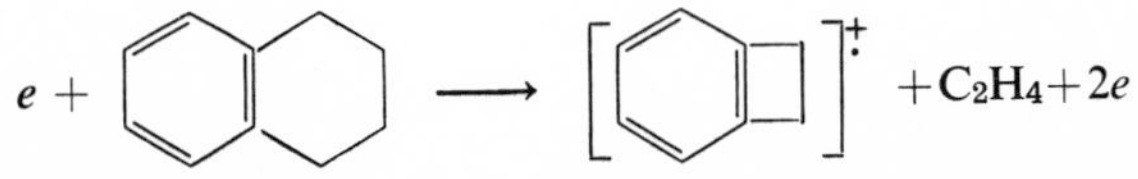

It is interesting that for the first process, as Macdonald and Shannon [22] have shown by a study of $C_6H_3D_3$, the hydrogen atoms eliminated in $C_2H_2$ come randomly from the molecule. On the other hand, rearrangement elimination is also well known:

$$e + R_1R_2CH{-}CR_3R_4X \longrightarrow [R_1R_2C{=}CR_3R_4]^{+\cdot} + HX + 2e$$

$$e + \begin{matrix} R_1NH \\ \diagdown \\ C{=}S \\ \diagup \\ R_2NH \end{matrix} \longrightarrow [R_1N{=}C{=}NR_2]^{+\cdot} + H_2S + 2e$$

$$e + \begin{matrix} R_1NH \\ \diagdown \\ C{=}S \\ \diagup \\ R_2R_3N \end{matrix} \longrightarrow [R_1N{=}C{=}S]^{+\cdot} + R_2R_3NH + 2e$$

One can note in passing that this last reaction is the reverse of the process used in the synthesis of thiourea. For the compounds $C_2H_5X$, the rearrangement elimination occurs alongside simple dissociation:

$$C_2H_5^+ + X + 2e$$

$$C_2H_5X + e \nearrow$$
$$\searrow$$

$$C_2H_4 + HX + 2e$$

The abundance of these two types of fragmentation is shown in Table II. Values for ethane are taken from the A.P.I. [23] compilation; those for the remaining spectra from Collin [24], and the metastable values from unpublished work by Flowers. There is no very obvious trend in these results. When higher homologs are examined using the technique of deuterium labeling, it is found that elimination other than 1-2 can occur. Thus, in the case of 2-bromobutane it has been established that while more than 86% of the hydrogen came from C-2 or C-4, more than 73% of this came in fact from C-4. Thus, 1-3 elimination predominated [25].

Verification that a given fragment is produced in part by a one-step reaction comes from a study of the metastable peaks in the mass spectrum. Such a metastable peak in the mass spectrum of anisole is shown in Fig. 2 and corresponds to the process

*m/e* 108                     *m/e* 78

**Table II.  Simple Fragmentation and Rearrangement Elimination in Some Ethyl Compounds**

| Compound | Fragment $[C_2H_4]^+$, % base | Metastable Obs. | Metastable Calc. | Fragment $[C_2H_5]^+$, % base | Metastable Obs. | Metastable Calc. |
|---|---|---|---|---|---|---|
| $C_2H_6$ | 100 | 26.1 | 26.14 | 21.5 | — | — |
| $C_2H_5Cl$ | 100 | 12.281 | 12.276 | 93.3 | 13.16 | 13.17 |
| $C_2H_5Br$ | 13.4 | 7.28 | 7.281 | 68.0 | 7.68 | 7.672 |
| $C_2H_5I$ | 5.8 | 5.0 | 5.040 | 59.0 | 5.411 | 5.409 |
| $C_2H_5NH_2$ | 30.4* | — | — | 7.7† | — | — |
| $C_2H_5OH$ | 8.2 | — | — | 27.7‡ | — | — |
| $C_2H_5SH$ | 28.1 | — | — | 45.9 | — | — |

\* This peak also contains $CH_2N$.
† This peak also contains $CH_3N$.
‡ This peak also contains $CHO$.

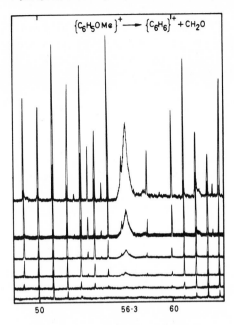

$$\{C_6H_5OMe\}^+ \longrightarrow \{C_6H_6\}^{+} + CH_2O$$

50          56·3     60

Fig. 2. A metastable peak in the mass spectrum of anisole [A. Maccoll, *Chem. Ind.* (*London*), p. 908, 1964, reproduced by permission of the editor of *Chem. Ind.*].

Such peaks are diffuse, compared with the normal peaks. Their origin is as follows. If an ion has a lifetime of order of magnitude less than $10^{-6}$ sec, it will not be observed as such, but only as its dissociation products. Thus, in the case tertiary butyl chloride, the abundance of the molecular peak is about 0.01% of the base peak ($m/e = 57$, $C_4H_9^+$) and this can be ascribed to the tendency of the molecular ion to dissociation with a very short half-life:

$$e + \text{t-}C_4H_9Cl \longrightarrow [\text{t-}C_4H_9Cl]^{\cdot+} + 2e \longrightarrow \text{t-}C_4H_9^+ + Cl\cdot + 2e$$

If, however, the lifetime is of the order of a microsecond, then the ion may be electrostatically accelerated at $m_1/e$, decompose before entering the magnetic analyzer, and be magnetically analyzed at $m_2/e$. Under such circumstances, the decomposition

$$m_1^+ \longrightarrow m_2^+ + (m - m_2)$$

will result in a diffuse peak produced at a mass number ($m^*$) usually non-integral and given by

$$m^* = m_2^2/m_1$$

The observation of such a metastable peak confirms that the fragment of mass $m_2$ must in part at least have been produced from $m_1$. In this way, fragmentation routes can be traced. Two such examples are benzene [26] and ethyl chloride [27] (Figs. 3 and 4).

What can be said about the mechanism of the processes that have been discussed? Organic chemists interested in carbonium ion chemistry have long thought in terms of two electron shifts. Thus, heterolytic dissociation, for example, the ionization of an alkyl halide, can be represented by

$$CH_3 \frown I \longrightarrow CH_3^+ + I^- \qquad \text{(simple ionization)}$$

$$
\begin{array}{ccc}
CH_3 & & CH_3 \\
\diagdown & & \diagdown \\
CH_3\!-\!C\!-\!CH_2 \frown X & & \overset{+}{C}\!-\!CH_2CH_3 + X^- \quad \text{(rearrangement ionization)} \\
\diagup & & \diagup \\
CH_3 & & CH_3
\end{array}
$$

In these cases, it is a pair of electrons that is pictured as moving. On the other hand, for homolytic dissociation, the process is best represented by single electron shifts,

$$CH_3\!-\!I \longrightarrow CH_3 \cdot + I \cdot$$

this fact being emphasized by the use of a single-headed arrow or fish hook arising from a suggestion of Shannon [28].

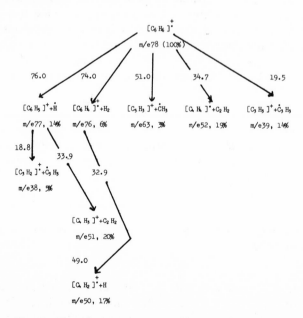

Fig. 3. Electron impact fragmentation of benzene (after Jennings [26]).

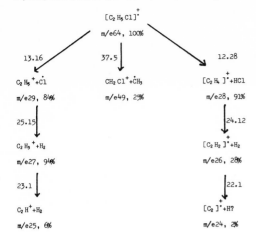

Fig. 4. Electron impact fragmentation of ethyl chloride (after Flowers [27]).

When one comes to consider some of the reactions discussed earlier, they may be represented in the above terms. Thus, the isomerization of cyclopropane may be pictured in either of two ways, biradical intermediate or synchronous, that is,

or

It is not possible at the present time to decide between these two representations. The assessment of the situation is complicated by the fact that cis-1,2-dideuteropropylene undergoes geometrical isomerization more rapidly than structural isomerization into dideuteropropylene. Similar ambiguity also exists in the case of cyclobutene:

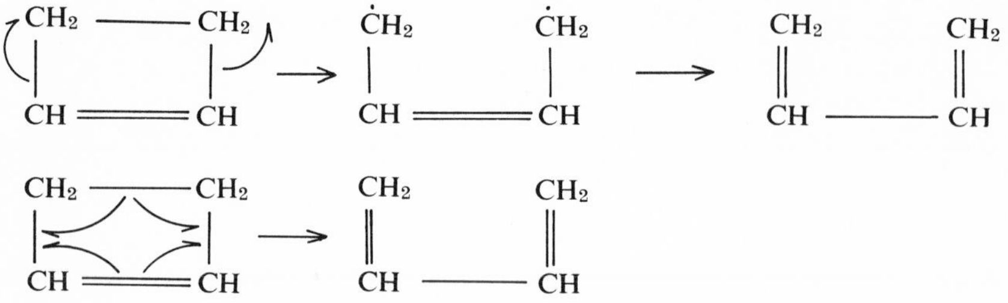

Again two mechanisms have been suggested in the case of the elimination reactions of alkyl halides, the first homolytic [29] and the second heterolytic [30]. On the latter representation, the transition state is regarded as an intimate ion pair:

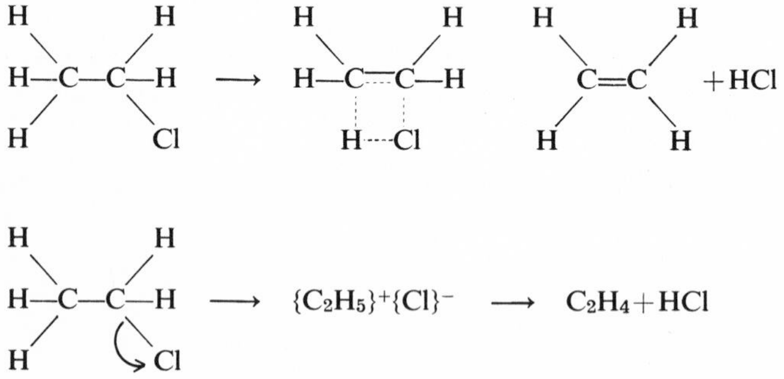

Evidence that this is essentially correct comes from the very simple relation that has been shown to exist between the activation energy for elimination and the heterolytic bond dissociation energy (Fig. 5) for $R = C_2H_5$, i-$C_3H_7$, t-$C_4H_9$, and $X = Cl$, Br, I, namely,

$$E(HX) = 0.29 \, D(R^+X^-)$$

The heterolytic bond dissociation energy is defined by

$$A:B \rightarrow A^+ + B:, \quad D(R^+X^-) = -\Delta H$$

and can be obtained from the appearance potential of $A^+$ from AB.

When one comes to consider either electronically excited states of molecules or, alternatively, ions, the question arises as to the delocalization or otherwise of the electron that is excited or removed. One can take the extreme view that such processes make themselves felt throughout the whole molecule by delocalization. On the other hand, spectroscopists have gone quite a long way in classifying excited states in terms of $n \rightarrow n^*$, $n \rightarrow \pi^*$, or $\pi \rightarrow \pi^*$, with $\pi^*$ and $n$ representing antibonding and nonbonding orbitals, respectively. So it would not seem unreasonable to think, in the case of ionization, of the positive charge residing on different atoms in different states of the ion. Thus, if we consider three modes of rearrangement fragmentation of the thioureas [31] leading to loss of HS, $H_2S$, and $R_1R_2NH$, these can be represented as

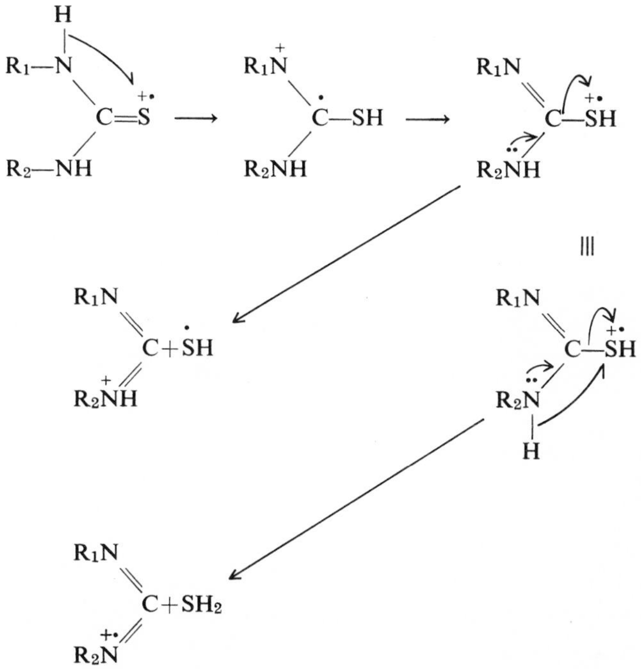

$$
\begin{array}{ccc}
\underset{\substack{\text{H}\\|\\R_1\text{—N}}}{\overset{}{\underset{R_2\text{—NH}}{\text{C}\overset{+\cdot}{=}\text{S}}}} & \longrightarrow & \underset{\substack{R_1\overset{+}{N}\\R_2\text{NH}}}{\overset{}{\text{C}\text{—SH}}} & \longrightarrow & \underset{\substack{R_1\text{N}\\R_2\text{NH}}}{\overset{}{\text{C}\overset{+\cdot}{\text{—SH}}}}
\end{array}
$$

$$\text{III}$$

$$
\underset{\substack{R_1\text{N}\\\overset{+}{R_2\text{NH}}}}{\text{C}+\text{SH}} \qquad\qquad \underset{\substack{R_1\text{N}\\R_2\text{N}\\|\\\text{H}}}{\text{C}\overset{+\cdot}{\text{—SH}}}
$$

$$
\underset{\substack{R_1\text{N}\\\overset{+\cdot}{R_2\text{N}}}}{\text{C}+\text{SH}_2}
$$

and

$$
\underset{\substack{\overset{+\cdot}{R_1R_2N}\\\\H\text{—NR}_3}}{\text{C}=\text{S}} \longrightarrow [R_1R_2N=C=S]^{+\cdot} + R_1R_2NH
$$

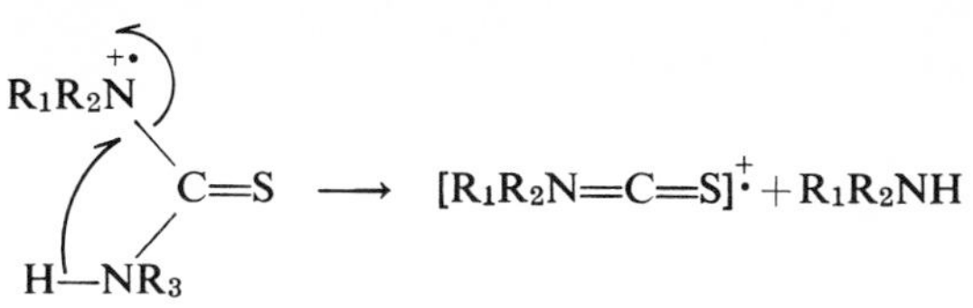

This implies that, in the former case, ionization results in the loss of a non-bonding sulfur electron and, in the latter, a nonbonding nitrogen electron. It is interesting to note that there is no appreciable loss of OH or $H_2O$ from the corresponding ureas [28].

These ideas have been supported by measurements of the ionization potentials of the methyl ureas and thioureas [32] (Table III).

Table III.  Ionization Potentials of Methyl Ureas and Thioureas

| Compound | Ionization potential (eV) | | | | |
|---|---|---|---|---|---|
| | Urea | Thiourea | $R_1R_2R_3N$ [33] | $R_1R_2O$ [33] | $R_1R_2S$ [33] |
| Unsubstituted | 10.27 | 8.50 | 10.41 | 12.75 | 10.48 |
| Methyl | 9.73 | 8.29 | 9.47 | 10.91 | 9.44 |
| N,N-dimethyl | 9.10 | 8.34 | 9.21 | 10.1 | 8.73 |
| N,N′-dimethyl | 9.42 | 8.17 | — | — | — |
| Trimethyl | 8.94 | 7.93 | 8.60 | — | — |
| Tetramethyl | 8.74 | 7.95 | — | — | — |

A typical ionization efficiency curve [31] is shown in Fig. 6. It will be seen that while the spread of values in the ureas approximates that of the amines, in the case of the thioureas it is very much less than that of the amines or the sulfides. This leads to the conclusion that, in the case of the ureas, methylation exerts a first-order effect on the nitrogen atom, whereas in the thioureas the effect is second-order on the sulfur atom. This in turn suggests that

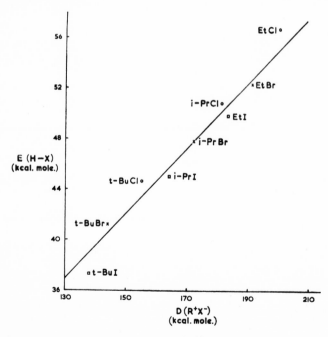

Fig. 5.  The linear relationship between activation energy for elimination and heterolytic bond dissociation energy.

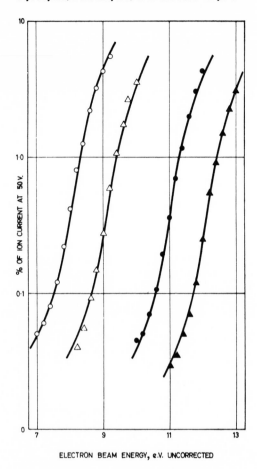

% OF ION CURRENT AT 50 V.

ELECTRON BEAM ENERGY, e.V. UNCORRECTED

Fig. 6. The ionization efficiency and electron beam energy plots for thiourea. O, ●-Thioruea runs 1 and 2. Δ, ▲-Methyl iodide runs 1 and 2. For the pair of duplicate runs at the right-hand side of the diagram, the scale has been shifted by +3 eV.

the ground states of the ions in the ureas and thioureas are best represented by I and II, respectively,

$$
\begin{array}{cc}
\overset{+\cdot}{R_1R_2N} & R_1R_2N \\
\diagdown & \diagdown \\
C=O & C=\overset{+\cdot}{S} \\
\diagup & \diagup \\
R_3R_4N & R_3R_4N \\
\text{I} & \text{II}
\end{array}
$$

with the positive charge localized on the nitrogen and sulfur atoms, respectively. This would account for the inversion of the values of the N, N- and N, N′-dimethyl compounds in the two series.

McLafferty [34] has used these concepts to rationalize the appearance of M—R' and M—R'CH$_2$O peaks in ethers:

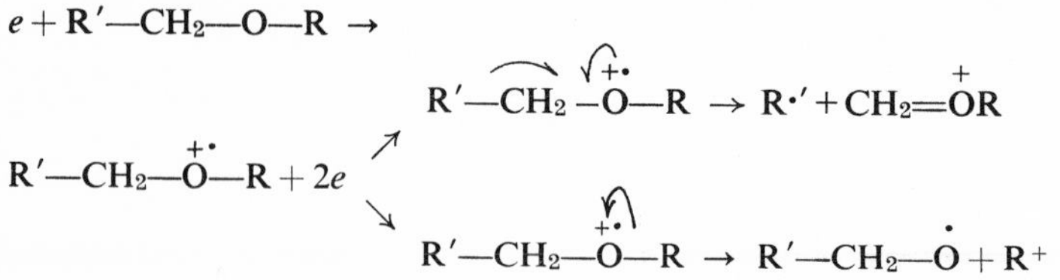

$$e + R'-CH_2-O-R \rightarrow$$

$$R'-CH_2-O-R \rightarrow R\cdot' + CH_2\text{=}\overset{+}{O}R$$

$$R'-CH_2-\overset{+\cdot}{O}-R + 2e$$

$$R'-CH_2-O-R \rightarrow R'-CH_2-\overset{\cdot}{O} + R^+$$

In the second type of fragmentation, an electron pair, as implied by the arrow, is regarded as moving.

We have already seen that, in the elimination of C$_2$H$_2$ from benzene, the hydrogen atoms come randomly from the whole molecule. There are many other nonspecific rearrangement processes known in mass spectrometry. One that has been reported by Djerassi and Feneslau [35] is the decomposition of even electron ions observed in the mass spectra of amines, leading to H$_2\overset{+}{N}$=CH$_2$, $m/e$ = 30:

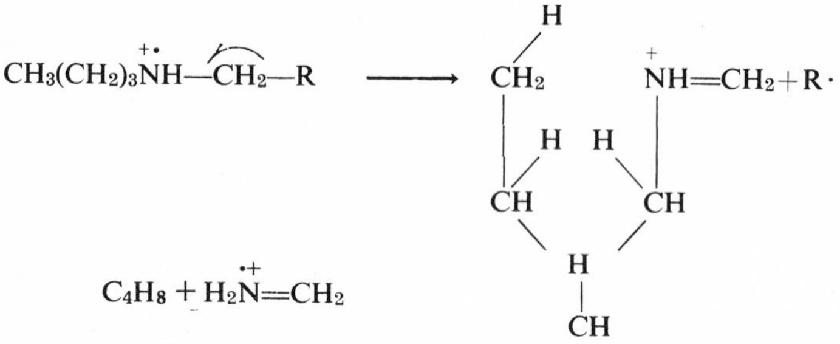

$$CH_3(CH_2)_3\overset{+\cdot}{N}H-CH_2-R \longrightarrow$$

$$C_4H_8 + H_2\overset{\cdot+}{N}\text{=}CH_2$$

On the other hand, the well-known McLafferty rearrangement observed in ketones, esters, etc., is completely specific in that deuterium labeling has shown that it is the γ-hydrogen that is removed [36]. The process is represented by

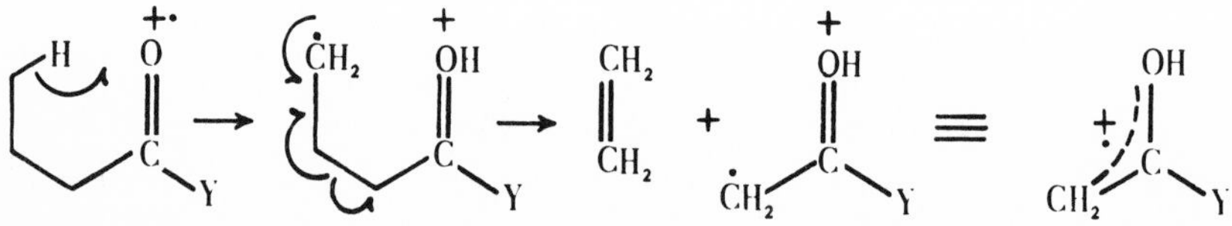

This type of six-centered transition state is well-known in the pyrolysis of esters [37], as discussed earlier:

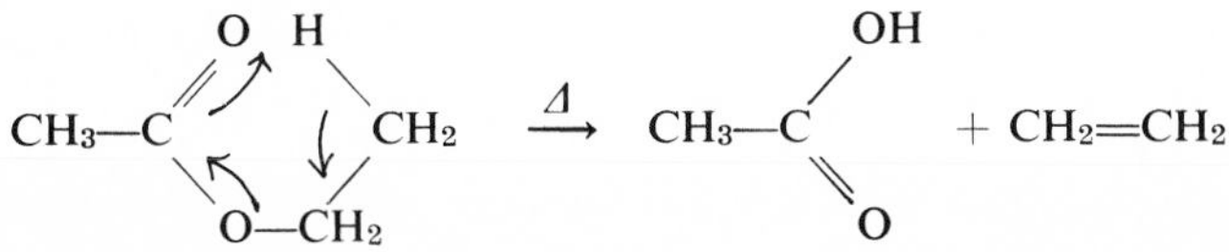

$$CH_3-C \overset{O}{\underset{O-CH_2}{\diagup}} \overset{H}{\underset{CH_2}{\diagdown}} \xrightarrow{\Delta} CH_3-C \overset{OH}{\underset{O}{\diagdown}} + CH_2{=}CH_2$$

Another reaction well-known both in pyrolysis and electronolysis is the retro-Diels–Alder reaction, which for the case of cyclohexene is

giving rise to $m/e$ 54, 80%. Two series of retro-Diels–Alder reactions have been studied at University College and are based on tetralin III [38] and IV (X = CH$_2$) and crotonosine (R$_1$ = R$_2$ = H) [39] V. The abundance of the retro-Diels–Alder fragments is shown in Tables IV and V.

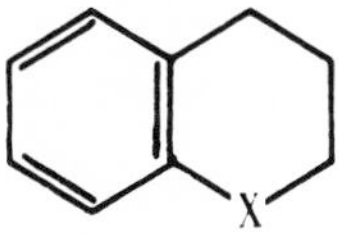

III 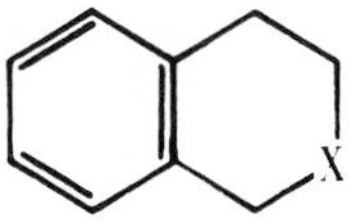            IV 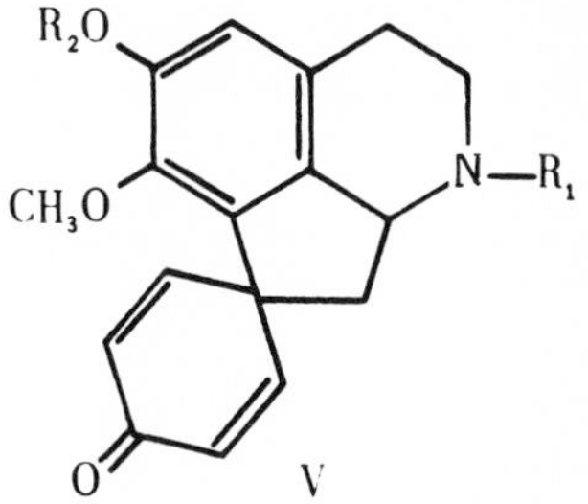            V

#### Table IV. The Retro-Diels–Alder Reaction in the Series $C_9H_{10}X$

| Molecule | III (X = H) | III (X = NH) | IV (X = NH) | III (X = O) | IV (X = O) | III (X = S) | IV (X = S) |
|---|---|---|---|---|---|---|---|
| $m/e$ | 104 | 105 | 104 | 106 | 104 | 122 | 104 |
| % Base | 100 | 6 | 100 | 19 | 100 | 32 | 100 |

#### Table V. The Retro-Diels–Alder Reaction in the Crotonosine Series

| Molecule (R$_1$R$_2$) | H, H | CH$_3$, H | H, CH$_3$ | CH$_3$, CH$_3$ |
|---|---|---|---|---|
| $m/e$ | 254 | 254 | 268 | 268 |
| % Base | 34 | 34 | 45 | 30 |

In each case, it is seen that this type of fragmentation is of considerable importance. A full discussion of retro-Diels–Alder fragmentation has been given by Budzikiewicz *et al.* [40].

Three specific examples will now be given to illustrate the importance of analogies between pyrolysis, photolysis, and electronolysis. The first is a very interesting reaction reported by Fields and Meyerson [41], namely, the production of benzyne from the pyrolysis of phthallic anhydride. The problem was suggested by the occurrence of a peak at $m/e = 76$ in the mass spectrum of this compound. The reaction scheme observed was

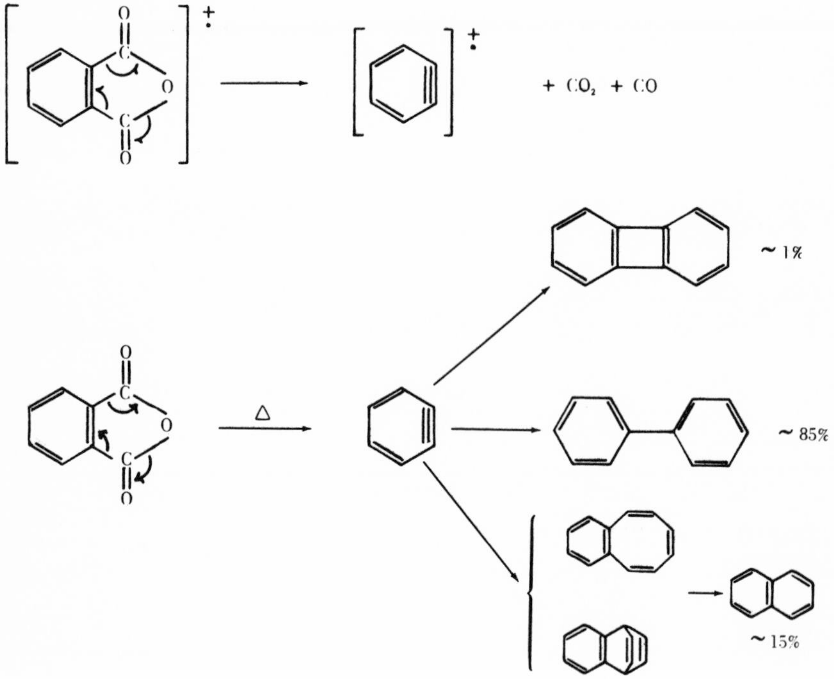

The presence of a trace of fluorenone in the products suggested that the loss of $CO_2$ and CO was in fact stepwise:

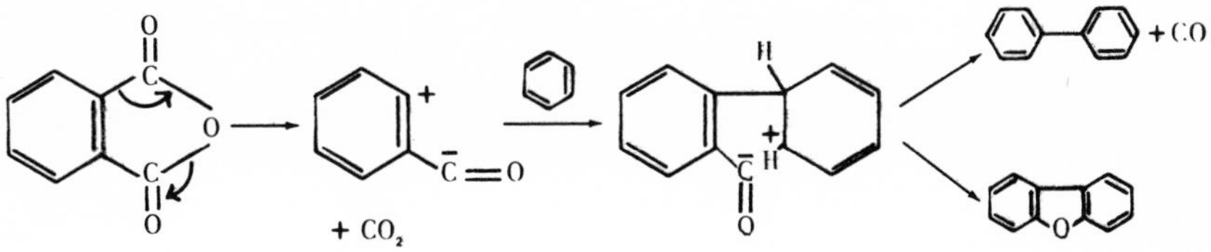

Chapman *et al.* [42] have reported some interesting photochemical studies of nitrocompounds which behave under the influence of ultraviolet light in a manner analogous to their behavior under electron impact. Beynon *et al.* [43] have shown that at peak at $M$-30 in certain aromatic nitrocompounds corresponds to a loss of NO. This occurs presumably through isomerization to nitrite form.

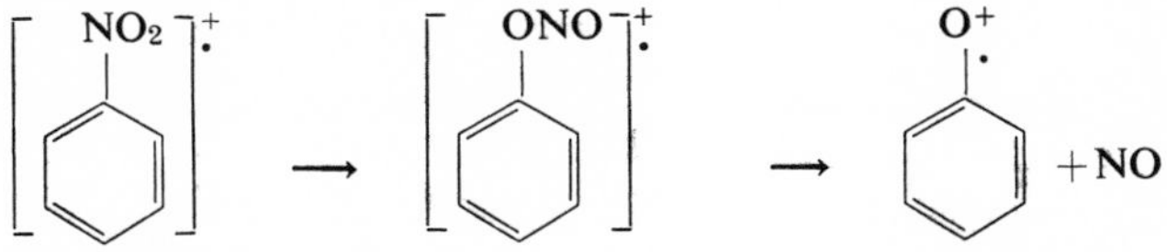

Chapman *et al.* [42] report the photoisomerization of $\beta$-methyl-$\beta$-nitrostyrene

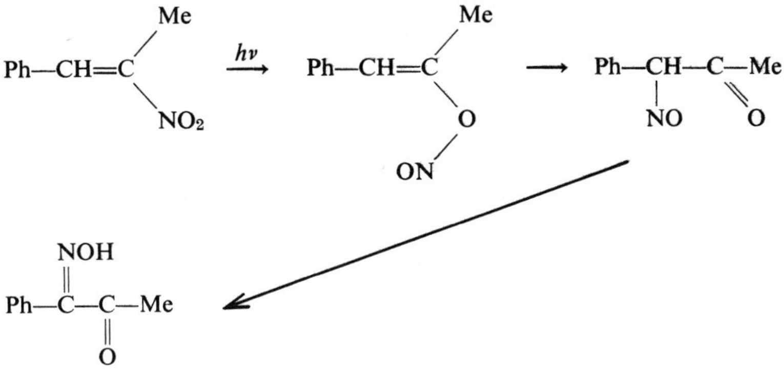

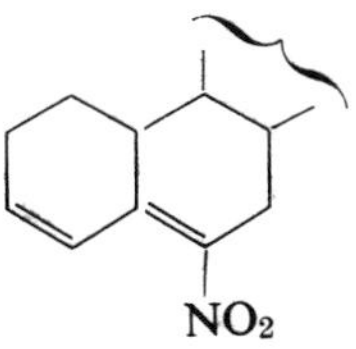

It is interesting to note that in the following cholesterol derivative

a peak occurs at $M$-30, due to loss of NO, presumably after isomerization to a nitrite.

The last example to be discussed is taken from the work of Turro *et al.*[44] on dimethylketene dimer. Photochemically the following processes occur involving the loss of one and then two molecules of carbon monoxide:

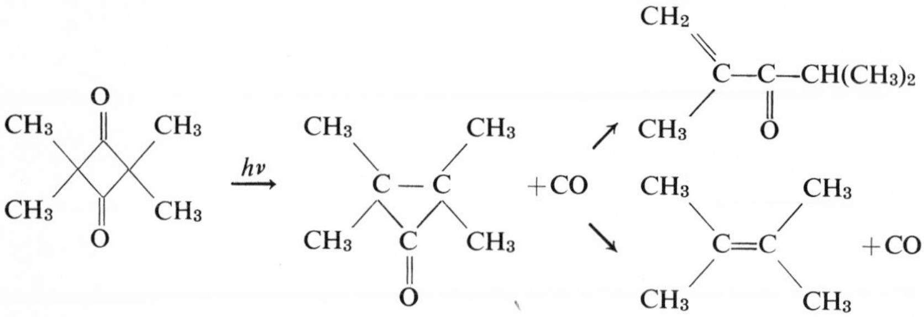

Under electron impact using 70- and 10-V electrons, the following scheme obtains:

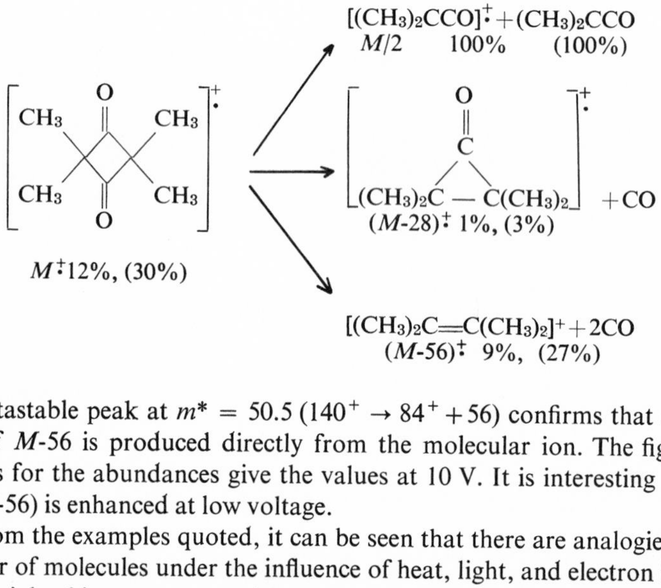

The metastable peak at $m^* = 50.5$ ($140^+ \rightarrow 84^+ + 56$) confirms that at least some of $M$-56 is produced directly from the molecular ion. The figures in brackets for the abundances give the values at 10 V. It is interesting to note that ($M$-56) is enhanced at low voltage.

From the examples quoted, it can be seen that there are analogies in the behavior of molecules under the influence of heat, light, and electron impact. At first sight this may seem rather surprising, since in the three cases vibrationally excited molecules, electronically excited molecules, and ions (either ground state or excited) are involved. An important aspect of the last two cases will be the assignment of a given mode of photodecomposition or of ion fragmentation to a well-defined excited state of the molecule or of the ion. Significantly, alternative pathways are relatively uncommon in thermal reactions, which would be consistent with the involvement in the transition state of only the ground electronic state of the reactant. On the other hand, more and more electronically excited states of molecules and excited states of ions are being recognized, and progress may be expected from a consideration of the fates of these species. Until such a detailed account of the behavior of excited species is achieved, it is still useful to bear in mind the analogy between pyrolysis, photolysis, and electronolysis in predicting the behavior of reacting systems, using this term in its widest sense.

# REFERENCES

1. D. P. Stevenson and J. A. Hipple, *J. Am. Chem. Soc.* **64**:1588, 1942; F. W. McLafferty, *Anal. Chem.* **31**:82, 1959.
2. H. O. Pritchard, R. G. Sowden, and A. F. Trotman-Dickenson, *Proc. Roy. Soc.* **217A**:563, 1953.
3. W. Cooper and W. D. Walters, *J. Am. Chem. Soc.* **80**:4220, 1958.
4. F. W. Schuler and A. W. Murphy, *J. Am. Chem. Soc.* **72**:3155, 1950.
5. A. H. Sehon and M. Szwarc, *Proc. Roy. Soc.* **209A**:110, 1951.
6. A. Fish, *Quart. Rev.* **18**:243, 1964.
7. R. W. Carr, Jr., and W. D. Walters, *J. Phys. Chem.* **67**:1370, 1963.
8. M. Uchiyama, T. Tomioka, and A. Amaro, *J. Phys. Chem.* **68**:1878, 1964; N. E. Duncan and G. J. Janz, *J. Chem. Phys.* **20**:1644, 1952. References to earlier work will be found in these references.
9. A. Maccoll and P. J. Thomas, *Progr. Reaction Kinetics* **4**:119, 1966.
10. A. Maccoll and E. S. Swinbourne, *Proc. Chem. Soc.*, p. 409, 1960; *J. Chem. Soc.*, p. 149, 1964.
11. E. S. Lewis and W. C. Herndon, *J. Am. Chem. Soc.* **83**:1961, 1961.
12. R. C. L. Bicknell and A. Maccoll, *Chem. Ind. (London)*, p. 1912, 1961; R. C. L. Bicknell, Ph.D. Thesis, University of London, London, England, 1962.
13. A. Davis and J. H. Goulden, paper presented at the Chemical Society Meeting, Brighton, 1966.
14. C. K. Ingold and G. W. King, *J. Chem. Soc.*, p. 2725, 1953.
15. J. C. D. Brand, *J. Chem. Soc.*, p. 858, 1956.
16. H. J. F. Angus, J. M. Blair, and D. Bryce-Smith, *J. Chem. Soc.*, p. 2003, 1960; D. Bryce-Smith and H. C. Longuet-Higgins, *Chem. Commun.*, p. 593, 1966.
17. R. Srinivasan and S. Cremer, *J. Am. Chem. Soc.* **86**:4197, 1964.
18. B. A. Thrush, *Proc. Roy. Soc.* **243A**:555, 1958.
19. R. Schindler and M. H. J. Wijnen, *Z. Phys. Chem. (Frankfurt)* **34**:109, 1962.
20. R. W. G. Norrish and M. Appleyard, *J. Chem. Soc.*, p. 874, 1934.
21. J. Momigny, L. Brakier, and L. D'or, *Bull. Acad. Roy. Belg. (Classe Sci.)*, *Ser. 5*, **48**:1002, 1962.
22. G. C. Macdonald and J. S. Shannon, *Australian J. Chem.* **15**:771, 1962.
23. Catalogue of Mass Spectral Data, A. P. I. Project 44, National Bureau of Standards, Washington, D.C.
24. J. Collin, *Bull. Soc. Roy. Sci. Liège* **25**:426, 441, 1956.
25. W. H. McFadden and M. Lounsbury, *Can. J. Chem.* **40**:1965, 1962.
26. K. R. Jennings, *J. Chem. Phys.* **43**:4177, 1965.
27. M. C. Flowers, private communication.

28. J. S. Shannon, *Tetrahedron Letters*, p. 801, 1963; H. Budzikiewicz, C. Djerassi, and D. H. Williams, *Interpretation of Mass Spectra of Organic Compounds*, Holden-Day, San Francisco, 1964.
29. F. Daniels and P. L. Veltman, *J. Chem. Phys.* 7:756, 1939.
30. A. Maccoll and P. J. Thomas, *Nature* 176:392, 1955; A. Maccoll in: *Theoretical Organic Chemistry*, Butterworths, London, 1958; C. K. Ingold, *Proc. Chem. Soc.*, p. 279, 1957.
31. M. A. Baldwin, A. M. Kirkien-Konasiewicz, A. G. Loudon, A. Maccoll, and B. Saville, *Chem. Ind. (London)*, p.286, 1966.
32. M. Baldwin, A. Kirkien-Konasiewicz, A. G. Loudon, A. Maccoll, and D. Smith, *Chem. Commun.*, p. 574, 1966.
33. J. W. Kiser, Tables of Ionization Potentials (TID-6142), University of Kansas, 1960, and Supplement, 1962.
34. F. W. McLafferty, *Chem. Commun.*, p. 78, 1966.
35. C. Djerassi and C. Feneslau, *J. Am. Chem. Soc.* 87:5752, 1965.
36. H. Budzikiewicz, C. Feneslau, and C. Djerassi, *Tetrahedron* 22:1391, 1966.
37. C. D. Hurd and F. H. Blunck, *J. Am. Chem. Soc.* 60:2419, 1938.
38. A. G. Loudon and S. K. Wong, private communication.
39. M. A. Baldwin, L. J. Haynes, A. G. Loudon, A. Maccoll, and K. L. Stuart, *J. Chem. Soc.*, p. 1026, 1967.
40. H. Budzikiewicz, J. I. Brauman, and C. Djerassi, *Tetrahedron* 21:1855, 1965.
41. E. K. Fields and S. Meyerson, *Chem. Commun.*, p. 474, 1965.
42. O. L. Chapman, P. G. Cleveland, and E. D. Hoganson, *Chem. Commun.*, p. 101, 1966.
43. J. H. Beynon, R. A. Saunders, and A. E. Williams, *Ind. Chim. Belge* 29:311, 1964.
44. N. J. Turro, D. C. Neckers, P. A. Leermakers, D. Seldner, and P. D'Angalo, *J. Am. Chem. Soc.* 87:4097, 1965.

# DETERMINATION OF HIGH-TEMPERATURE SOLUTION THERMODYNAMICS USING A MASS SPECTROMETER

### R. C. Svedberg*

*Imperial College of Science and Technology*
*London, England*

## INTRODUCTION

A knowledge of solution thermodynamics at high temperatures is necessary for a better understanding of ore reduction and metal refining processes involving equilibria between liquid metal, liquid oxide, or liquid salt solutions. In addition, a knowledge of solution thermodynamics coupled with electrical, magnetic, and X-ray studies can be used to elucidate the structure and constitution of these solutions.

Of the various techniques used to determine these equilibrium solution properties, that of mass spectroscopy is one of the newest and perhaps the most versatile.

The complexity of many of the high-temperature systems, especially the vapor phases in equilibrium with the condensed phases, has been vividly demonstrated [1]. This complexity makes the utilization of many classical techniques for measuring the equilibrium properties of solutions difficult. For example, the use of Knudsen weight loss and torsion effusion methods for measuring vapor pressure requires a knowledge of the molecular weight of each of the vaporizing species.

The mass spectrometer, on the other hand, can be used to determine the pressure of, as well as to separate and identify, the vapor species. When the vapor pressures of the gaseous species in equilibrium with the condensed phases are measured as a function of temperature and composition, the thermodynamics of a solution can be studied by use of the mass spectrometer.

---

* Present address: Materials Dept., Westinghouse Astronuclear Laboratory, Large, Pennsylvania.

## FACTORS INVOLVED IN EQUILIBRIUM STUDIES

A study of equilibrium thermodynamics utilizing the mass spectrometric technique involves: (1) the equilibration and sampling of the vapor phase over a solution; (2) the ionization of the vapor in the ion source of the mass spectrometer; and (3) a careful analysis of the data recorded from the output of the mass spectrometer. The equilibration and sampling relies on the proper Knudsen cell design. A knowledge of ionization by electron impact must be used to determine successfully fragmentation processes, while the ion current measurements from the mass spectrometer must be subjected to a suitable thermodynamic treatment.

### The Knudsen Cell

The Knudsen cell is a crucible with a small, knife-edged orifice from which a vapor phase can be sampled. The purpose of the Knudsen cell is to maintain an equilibrium between the vapor and condensed phases. If a substance is not contained in a Knudsen cell, but is allowed to vaporize freely into a vacuum, the process is known as Langmuir [2] vaporization. Equilibrium vapor pressures are obtained by the Langmuir method only if the rate of vaporization and rate of condensation are equal.

The rate at which the molecules leave the orifice and escape into the vacuum is equal to the number which strike an area of the wall of the vessel equal to the orifice area. This rate, $N$, given by kinetic gas theory is

$$N = \tfrac{1}{4} n\bar{c} \tag{1}$$

where $n$ is the number of molecules/cm$^3$ and $\bar{c}$ is the arithmetical average velocity of the Maxwellian distribution of velocities.

The weight $w$ of material leaving the cell is then given by

$$w = \frac{\tfrac{1}{4} n\bar{c} M a t}{A} \tag{2}$$

where $M$ is the molecular weight of the effusing species, $A$ is Avogadro's number, $t$ is time in seconds, and $a$ is the area of the orifice.

By utilization of the ideal gas law in the form

$$n = \frac{A}{V} = \frac{AP}{RT} \tag{3}$$

(which is valid since this work is generally concerned with pressures below $10^{-3}$ atm and high temperatures) and the value for the average velocity

$$\bar{c} = \sqrt{8RT/\pi M} \tag{4}$$

the pressure of the effusate leaving the cell can be determined from a measurement of the weight loss by the following relationship:

$$p = \frac{w}{at}\sqrt{2\pi RT/M} \qquad (5)$$

This is obtained by a combination of equations (2)–(4) for an ideal Knudsen cell. Knudsen [3] showed that the ratio of the mean free path of the gas to the diameter of the orifice must be greater than 10 in order for the measured pressure to be representative of the real pressure. More recently this has been confirmed by Grieveson et al. [4] and Schadel and Birchenall [5]. Motzfeldt [6] and Speiser and Johnston [7] have derived two separate relationships which show that the ratio of the evaporating surface to the orifice area must be large (of the order of 100 or greater) to ensure accurate pressure measurements. In order to compensate for the assumption made in the derivation of equation (5) that the orifice edges should be infinitely thin, a Clausing factor [8] is introduced. This is a correction factor which accounts for the finite thickness of the material in which the orifice is drilled.

## Ion Production in the Mass Spectrometer Source

Probably the most important part of any mass spectrometric investigation is to determine the precursors of the ions monitored by the mass spectrometer. These ions are produced by bombarding the molecular beam by an electron beam. Listed below are the most probable reactions which can occur during the process of ionization [9].

$$e + XY = XY^- \qquad (6)$$

$$e + XY = X^+ + Y^- + e \qquad (7)$$

$$e + XY = XY^+ + 2e \qquad (8)$$

$$XY^+ = X^+ + Y \qquad (9)$$

What reaction is actually occurring can be established by measuring the appearance potentials of the ions produced, determining the dissociation energies of the molecules, and identifying the precursor ions.

### Appearance Potentials

The first quantity that is measured to determine the origin of the ions is the appearance potential. The appearance potential is that electron energy needed to form an ion by removing an electron from an atom or molecule or by dissociating a molecule. An ionization efficiency curve is a measurement of the ion current of a species as a function of the energy of the bombarding electron beam. The value of the electron energy at which the ion current disappears during the determination of an ionization efficiency curve is called the appearance potential.

A review of the various methods of determining appearance potentials from ionization efficiency curves is presented by Reed [9] and Barnard [10].

Although many methods are described for determining appearance potentials, the two that seem to find most use in thermochemical studies are the vanishing current method and the extrapolated intercept method. In experiments primarily designed to study bonding energies and appearance potentials, methods of eliminating or minimizing the energy spread of the bombarding electron beam are employed [11]. When the energy spread of the electron beam is not eliminated, the ionization efficiency curve approaches the energy axis asymptotically.

The vanishing current method involves determining the electron energy at which the ion intensity vanishes completely. The values obtained by this method are very dependent on machine sensitivity and the magnitude of the pressure of the species being measured. The linear extrapolation method, on the other hand, is based on the assumption that if the energy spread of the electron beam were not present, the tail on the ionization efficiency curve would not occur. The ionization efficiency curve would then continue directly to the energy axis. This is shown in Fig. 1 for several ions. Both methods require calibration to correct for contact potentials and other factors inherent in the ion source of a given instrument. The calibration requires the determination of the appearance potential of several ions whose appearance potentials have been reported in the literature.

### Dissociation Energies

The limiting values of dissociation energies of various molecules can be determined by use of a Born–Haber cycle which can be represented by the following illustration:

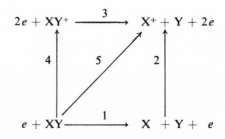

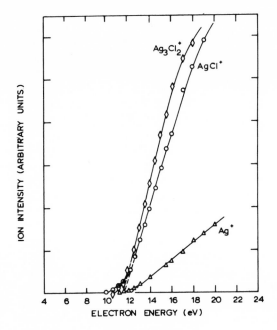

ELECTRON ENERGY (eV)

Fig. 1. Example of appearance potential determination.

Combination of reaction paths 1, 2, and 5 gives the thermochemical relationship

$$A(X^+) = I(X) + D(X-Y) \tag{10}$$

where $A(X^+)$ is the appearance potential ion of X, $I(X)$ is the ionization potential of the radical X, and $D(X-Y)$ is the bond dissociation energy of the X–Y bonds in the neutral molecule.

However, equation (10) is only the simplified form of a complete equation which accounts for other possible sources of energy associated with the formation of the $X^+$ ion. The complete equation is given by

$$A(X^+) = I(X) + D(X-Y) - EA + \sum EE + VE + \sum KE + h\gamma \tag{11}$$

where $EA$ is the electron affinity, $EE$ is the electronic excitation energy, $VE$ is the vibrational and rotational excitation energy, $KE$ is the kinetic energy, and $h\gamma$ is the energy of any photons emitted. Other dissociation processes can be measured by combining other paths of the Born–Haber cycle.

Because of the difficulty in determining the kinetic energies and excitation energies of the ionization processes, relationship (10) is usually used to calculate a limiting dissociation energy rather than to calculate an exact value.

## Precursor Identification

Precursor ions are generally identified by considerations of appearance
potential and the variations of ion current ratios with phase changes, thermodynamic activity changes, and temperature changes. If the appearance
potential is several electron volts higher than the reported ionization potential
for the particular ion under study [12], it can generally be assumed that the
ion results from the simple dissociation of a molecule. If there are no excited
states present in the product ions and no additional kinetic energy is produced,
the difference between the appearance potential and the ionization potential,
given by equation (10), is the bond dissociation energy of the molecule.

If the intensities of two ions are measured as a function of temperature [13] and the ratio does not depend upon temperature, then the ions are
fragmenting from the same precursor unless the separate precursors have
identical heats of sublimation or vaporization. If the ratio varies as a function
of temperature, then the ions can be assumed to originate from different
precursors.

Should a phase change be encountered when measuring the ratios as a
function of temperature, the ions which have the same parent will not reflect
a change in ratio at this phase change. If the ions have separate parent
molecules, the phase change will be indicated by a change in the slope of
the ratios. This change in slope would also reflect the magnitude of the heat
associated with the phase change.

By a change in the thermodynamic activity [13, 14] of a component
and measurement of the ratios of several ion currents, the source of the
ions can again be ascertained. If the ratio is a function of the magnitude of
the change in the activity, then the precursor for each ion in the ratio is
different. Again, if the ratio remains constant, the ions have originated
from the same precursor.

A double oven experiment [15], whereby the temperature of the vapors
in equilibrium with a melt is varied with respect to the temperature of the
melt, has been used to determine fragmentation processes. Relative ionization
cross sections can also be determined by this method.

## Utilization of Mass Spectroscopic Data

The information obtained from a mass spectrometer is in the form of
ion currents ($I^+$). These ion currents are related to the pressure $P$ of the
vapor effusing from a Knudsen cell by the relation [16]

$$P = kI^+ T \tag{12}$$

where $k$ is a constant which can be calculated from

$$k = \frac{g}{\sigma_i S_i \alpha_i} \tag{13}$$

where $S_i$ is the collector efficiency of the electron multiplier, $g$ is a geometrical correction factor, $\sigma_i$ is the ionization cross section for electron bombardment, and $\alpha_i$ is the isotopic abundance of the species.

A knowledge of the multiplier efficiency $S_i$ is necessary in order to correct for the rate of emission of secondary electrons caused by the impact of the positive ions with the electron-multiplier cathode. The rate of secondary emission is dependent on such factors as the energy and mass of the incident ion, the chemical and physical composition of the cathode, and the charge of the incident particle [17].

The ionization cross sections for inelastic collisions can be represented by

$$\sigma = \sigma_0 + \sigma_1 + \sigma_i \tag{14}$$

when $\sigma_0$ is the sum of the cross sections for elastic collisions, $\sigma_1$ is the sum of the various cross sections for ionizing collisions, and $\sigma_i$ is the sum of the various cross sections for electronic excitations.

Otvos and Stevenson [18] list the ionization cross sections for some molecules at 75 eV. The cross sections of large molecules are supposed to be obtained by adding the cross sections of the simpler molecules. However, using various techniques to measure relative ionization cross sections and comparing mass spectrometer data with those reported by other techniques, it has been demonstrated that this additivity principle is not entirely correct, especially for low-energy ionization. Lampe *et al.* [19] have criticized the additivity principle and have suggested that there is a relationship between the polarizability and the total ionization cross sections.

Goldfinger and Jeunehomme [20] have shown that the ratio of cross sections for certain homonuclear diatomic molecules compared to those of the atoms is about 1.5. Berkowitz *et al.* [15] have obtained values of 1 to 1.4 for the dimer/monomer cross section ratios of the lithium halides. There is a need for more experimental and theoretical work in this area of ionization cross sections before these uncertainties can be eliminated.

The geometric factor $g$ accounts for the effusate percentage which enters the mass spectrometer source and the number of ions, created in the source, which are actually sampled and measured by the mass spectrometer. The first consideration is a function of cell position, and this can be handled if care is taken to ensure that the location of the Knudsen cell orifice with respect to the ion source is constant. The second consideration is a machine characteristic and can be measured by calibration of the instrument.

If the value of the cross sections, multiplier efficiencies, and geometric factors could be known exactly, the absolute vapor pressure of any substance, measurable by the mass spectrometer, could be obtained. As explained above, many uncertainties pertaining to these quantities still remain. However, should it be necessary to know the absolute pressure of a substance, it is possible to calibrate the mass spectrometer by several methods [21].

The first method involves the quantitative vaporization of a known weight of the substance being studied. By measuring the integrated ion current, the number of atoms effusing per second per square centimeter of orifice area, which yield one unit of intensity after ionization, is known. From the Knudsen equation (5), the pressure responsible for this unit of intensity can then be determined.

A second method involves the quantitative vaporization of a known amount of standard material [22]. The ion current is then integrated and the relative ionization cross sections and multiplier efficiencies of the standard and unknown are used to calculate the relative pressure through use of the following expression:

$$\frac{P_1}{P_2} = \frac{I_1 T_1 \sigma_2 S_2 \alpha_2}{I_2 T_2 \sigma_1 S_1 \alpha_1} \tag{15}$$

where the subscript 2 refers to the standard. All other quantities have been previously defined.

A nonreactive internal standard of known vapor pressure can also be used [23]. Thus, for a given temperature, the vapor pressure of the standard is known and the relationship given in equation (15) can be used.

If accurate values of the standard heat and entropy of formation of a compound are known, the decomposition pressure of the elements can be calculated and compared with the ion intensities.

The heat of sublimation or vaporization, $\Delta H$, of a pure consensed phase can be obtained by measuring the ion current as a function of temperature and using the Clausius–Clapeyron equation:

$$\frac{d(\ln I^+ T)}{d(1/T)} = -\frac{\Delta H}{R} \tag{16}$$

This quantity is also independent of the ionization cross section and the multiplier efficiencies as these are not generally a function of temperature, but depend only on the vapor species being investigated.

The heat of a gaseous phase reaction can be determined by measuring an equilibrium constant $K$ for the reaction as a function of temperature. By use of the van't Hoff equation

$$\frac{\partial(\ln K)}{\partial(1/T)} = -\frac{\Delta H_r}{R} \tag{17}$$

the heat of reaction can be calculated from the slope of the line $\ln K$ vs. $1/T$. Note that the $K$ shown above is not a true thermodynamic equilibrium expression because the absolute vapor pressures are not known and thus cannot be used to calculate free energies.

The values of the vapor pressures are only as accurate as the values of the ionization cross sections and multiplier efficiencies used to calculate them. It is possible, however, to determine many quantities using the mass spectrometer ion currents directly, without the need for an accurate determination of the vapor pressure. The usefulness of knowing the pressures of the various substances studied should not, however, be minimized. If accurate pressures of the products and reactants of an equilibrium reaction are known, a calculation of the thermodynamic equilibrium constant and free energy of the reaction is possible. This quantity, along with a reliable knowledge of the heat of formation, yields entropy changes for the reaction under consideration.

## SOLUTION PROPERTY MEASUREMENTS

It is possible to measure solution thermodynamics without having to determine absolute vapor pressures. Some of the methods which have been suggested and employed will be briefly discussed.

### Salt Solutions

Berkowitz and Chupka [23] reported the possibility of using the equilibrium monomer/dimer ratio of the vapor over a condensed salt to determine the thermodynamic properties of the condensed phase. Since there is at least 1% of the dimer present in a great majority of the salt vapors, it is theoretically possible to apply this technique to a large number of systems.

By measurement of the equilibrium

$$MX_{(s)} + MX_{(g)} = M_2X_{2(g)} \tag{18}$$

and the respective equilibrium constant

$$K = p_{M_2X_2}/a_{MX}\,p_{MX} \tag{19}$$

for a pure salt and for a series of compositions of a salt mixture containing the pure salt, the activity of the salt system can be measured. At a constant temperature, the equilibrium constants can be equated:

$$K = \left(\frac{p_{M_2X_2}}{a_{MX}\,p_{MX}}\right)_{pure} = \left(\frac{p_{M_2X_2}}{a_{MX}\,p_{MX}}\right)_{mixture} \tag{20}$$

Since the activity of the pure salt is equal to one, solving for $a_{MX}$ in the mixture gives

$$a_{MX} = \frac{(p_{MX}/p_{M_2X_2})_{pure}}{(p_{MX}/p_{M_2X_2})_{mixture}} \tag{21}$$

The pressure in a Knudsen cell is related to the ion current $I^+$, measured with the mass spectrometer, by $p = kI^+ T$, where $k$ is a constant for any machine and vapor species.

Substitution of this into equation (21) gives the activity in terms of the ion currents shown in equation (22):

$$a_{MX} = \frac{(I^+_{MX^+}/I^+_{M_2X_2^+})_{pure}}{(I^+_{MX}/I^+_{M_2X_2})_{mixture}} \tag{22}$$

The temperature and constant $k$ cancel in this expression and a direct measurement of the respective ion currents yields an activity which is completely independent of ionization cross sections, multiplier efficiencies, and geometrical considerations.

Büchler and Stauffer [24] used a different technique to measure the activities of the LiF–BeF$_2$ system. An examination of the vapor species present in this system indicated that a great deal of the monomer and dimer ions Li$^+$ and LiF$^+$, measured over the mixture, came from the fragmentation of the BeLiF$_3$ molecule. This precluded the use of the monomer/dimer method. Instead a twin crucible method was developed.

The activity of BeF$_2$ was measured by comparing the BeF$_2$$^+$ ion current over pure BeF$_2$ with the ion current of BeF$_2$$^+$ coming from a mixture of LiF–BeF$_2$. Both samples were measured during the same experiment, each being contained in adjacent compartments of the twin crucible.

The equilibrium constant $K$ was calculated for the reaction

$$\text{LiBeF}_{3(g)} = \text{LiF}_{(s)} + \text{BeF}_{2(g)} \tag{23}$$

when the activity of LiF was equal to 1, that is, by equilibrating the solution with solid LiF. $K$ was then calculated from the measured ion currents of BeF$_2$$^+$ and LiBeF$_2$$^+$ using expression (24):

$$K = \frac{(a_{LiF})(I^+_{BeF_2^+})}{I^+_{LiBeF_2^+}} \tag{24}$$

The activity of LiF could then be determined by measuring the ion currents over a mixture of different compositions and calculating the activity of LiF from the known value of $K$.

## Liquid Alloy Systems

The determination of thermodynamic properties of liquid alloy mixtures using the mass spectrometer has recently been demonstrated by Ginsberg [25], Fruehan [26], and Norman et al. [27].

Ginsberg [25] used a method employing an internal standard to calibrate the mass spectrometer. Initially, attempts were made to measure the activity of an Ag–Au system by measuring the ion current of the Ag in the mixture and comparing it to the ion currents measured for pure Ag. However, small variations in machine parameters caused by such factors as slight differences in the position of the Knudsen cell, aging of the electronics, small changes in vacuum within the mass spectrometer, and contamination of the operating components in the ion source and electron multiplier prevented this method from being very useful. In the case of the Ag–Au system, $BaF_2$ served as a suitable standard. It did not react with the Ag–Au alloy, it had the proper vapor pressure in the temperature range of interest, and it could be pressed and sintered into a crucible.

The ratio of the ion current of $Ag^+$ to the ion current of $BaF^+$ was then measured as a function of composition and temperature. Since the activity of $BaF_2$ was always unity, the ratio of the ion intensities of $Ag^+$ to $BaF^+$ was a function only of the Ag activity. Therefore, by comparison of this ratio for pure Ag with that over an Ag–Au mixture, the activities could be determined. Machine changes which would affect the absolute ion current would not change the ratio as both would be subjected to the same machine variables.

Fruehan [26] developed the following expression from the Gibbs–Duhem relationship utilizing Dalton's law of partial pressures:

$$\ln \gamma_2 = - \int_{N_2=1}^{N_2=N_2} N_1 \, d \left( \ln \frac{I_1^+}{I_2^+} - \ln \frac{N_1}{N_2} \right) \tag{25}$$

The equation is derived by subtracting $d \ln a_j$ from the Gibbs–Duhem equation and solving the resulting equation for $\ln a_i$. This integral makes it possible to determine the activities of a system by measuring only the ratio of ion currents of two components in a system which are directly dependent on the activity. The activity coefficient can then be calculated by graphically integrating the above expression.

Norman et al. [27] have used the mass spectrometer to measure the Henry's law activity coefficients in the Zn–Sn–In system.

The method used to determine the coefficient involves measuring the rate of change of the number of moles of Zn leaving the cell per unit time $dn/dt$ and using the expression

$$\frac{dn}{dt} = pA/K \sqrt{MT} \tag{26}$$

where $p$ is the partial pressure of the species, $M$ is the molecular weight,

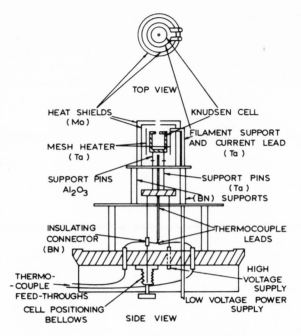

Fig. 2.   Knudsen cell assembly.

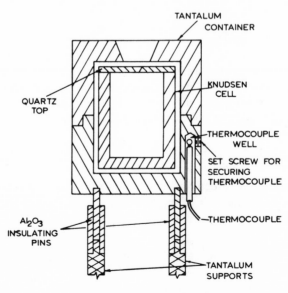

Fig. 3.   Knudsen cell design.

$A$ is the effective orifice area, $T$ is a temperature, and $K$ is a constant. If the solution species is sufficiently dilute, the partial pressure $p$ can be used to describe the Henry's law coefficient,

$$p = P\gamma(n/\sum_i n_i) \tag{27}$$

where $n \ll \sum_i n_i$, $n$ is the number of moles of the evaporating species in the solution, $\sum_i n_i$ represents the total solution composition, $\gamma$ is the activity coefficient, and $P$ is the vapor pressure of the pure component at the temperature of interest.

By combining equations (26) and (27) and noting that $d(\ln n)/dt = d(\ln I^+)/dt$, the expression

$$\gamma = \left[\frac{d(\ln I^+)}{dt}\right](K\sqrt{MT}\sum_i n_i/PA) \tag{28}$$

is obtained. A measurement of the decrease in pressure of a species with time, combined with a knowledge of the total pressure $P$ for the species of interest and an accurate determination of the Knudsen cell conditions (such as the orifice area), will then yield the Henry's law coefficient.

## APPLICATION OF THE VARIOUS TECHNIQUES

The work which will be reported has been done at the University of Pennsylvania under the supervision of G. R. Belton. The monomer/dimer technique has been applied to the silver chloride–alkali chloride systems [28]. The use of the integral technique will be demonstrated using the Fe–Ni system [26] as well as to confirm the results obtained using the monomer/dimer ratio on the chlorides.

### Experimental

The Knudsen cell assembly in Fig. 2 was used for both the liquid salt and alloy experiments. This assembly is similar in principle to that first used by Chupka and Inghram [29]. However, in the case of the salt system, heating was done solely by radiation from the tantalum mesh heater and the temperature was measured using a platinum–rhodium thermocouple. Figure 3 indicates the placement of the thermocouple and the detailed designs of the Knudsen cell assembly and support. The $Al_2O_3$ support pins and tantalum mesh heater which completely surrounded the Knudsen cell were incorporated to ensure proper temperature distribution in the Knudsen cell.

**Table I**

| System | Ionic species | Appearance potential (eV) | Relative intensity | Temperat. (°C) | Mole fraction alkali chloride | Electron energy (eV) |
|---|---|---|---|---|---|---|
| LiCl–AgCl | $Li^+$ | 11.9 | 153.5 | 625 | 0.545 | 22 |
| | $LiCl^+$ | 10.9 | 231 | | | |
| | $Li_2Cl^+$ | 11.4 | 427 | | | |
| | $Li_3Cl_2^+$ | detected | — | | | |
| | $LiAgCl^+$ | 11.9 | 5.87 | | | |
| | $Li_2AgCl_3^+$ | 11.1 | 2.37 | | | |
| | $LiAg_2Cl_2^+$ | 11.1 | 3.09 | | | |
| | $AgCl^+$ | 11.3 | 18.68 | | | |
| | $Ag^+$ | 11.6 | 2.63 | | | |
| | $Ag_3Cl_2^+$ | 11.1 | 1.00 | | | |
| NaCl–AgCl | $Na^+$ | 11.1 | 209.00 | 728 | 0.556 | 30 |
| | $NaCl^+$ | 10.6 | 56.00 | | | |
| | $Na_2Cl^+$ | 11.1 | 52.30 | | | |
| | $Na_3Cl_2^+$ | detected | — | | | |
| | $NaAgCl^+$ | 10.8 | 6.78 | | | |
| | $Na_2AgCl_2^+$ | 10.3 | 0.88 | | | |
| | $NaAg_2Cl_2$ | 10.8 | 2.12 | | | |
| | $AgCl^+$ | 11.3 | 16.67 | | | |
| | $Ag^+$ | 11.6 | 7.32 | | | |
| | $Ag_3Cl_2^+$ | 11.1 | 1.00 | | | |
| KCl–AgCl | $K^+$ | 10.4 | 3510.00 | 690 | 0.599 | 20 |
| | $KCl^+$ | 10.2 | 244.00 | | | |
| | $K_2Cl^+$ | 10.2 | 226.00 | | | |
| | $K_3Cl_2^+$ | detected | — | | | |
| | $KAgCl^+$ | 10.2 | 123.00 | | | |
| | $K_2AgCl_2^+$ | 13.6 | 1.87 | | | |
| | $KAg_2Cl_2^+$ | 10.0 | 6.96 | | | |
| | $AgCl^+$ | 11.3 | 112.5 | | | |
| | $Ag^+$ | 11.6 | 22.1 | | | |
| | $Ag_3Cl_2^+$ | 11.1 | 1.00 | | | |
| RbCl–AgCl | $Rb^+$ | 10.1 | 1315.00 | 620 | 0.499 | 22 |
| | $RbCl^+$ | 9.8 | 48.3 | | | |
| | $Rb_2Cl^+$ | 9.8 | 29.9 | | | |
| | $RbAg^+$ | 14.8 | — | | | |
| | $RbAgCl^+$ | 10.6 | 95.8 | | | |
| | $Rb_2AgCl_2^+$ | 11.2 | 1.3 | | | |
| | $RbAg_2Cl_2^+$ | 10.3 | 4.63 | | | |
| | $AgCl^+$ | 11.3 | 75.7 | | | |
| | $Ag^+$ | 11.6 | 20.05 | | | |
| | $Ag_3Cl_2^+$ | 11.1 | 1.00 | | | |
| CsCl–AgCl | $Cs^+$ | 10.1 | 669.00 | 666 | 0.529 | 20 |
| | $CsCl^+$ | 10.1 | 9.81 | | | |
| | $Cs_2Cl^+$ | 10.2 | 14.70 | | | |
| | $CsAgCl^+$ | 9.8 | 31.20 | | | |
| | $Cs_2AgCl_2^+$ | 13.0 | 0.34 | | | |
| | $CsAg_2Cl_2$ | 9.8 | 0.82 | | | |
| | $AgCl^+$ | 11.6 | 11.33 | | | |
| | $Ag^+$ | 11.3 | 2.88 | | | |
| | $Ag_3Cl_2^+$ | 11.1 | 1.00 | | | |

The vapor effusing from the Knudsen cell was sampled using a time-of-flight mass spectrometer. A shutter was used in measuring the intensities of all ionic species to compensate for the background in the mass spectrometer.

## Results of Salt Systems

Listed in Table I are the ionic species detected over the various silver chloride–alkali chloride salt mixtures. Also listed are the measured appearance potentials and the relative intensities of the species at the temperature, composition, and ionizing electron energy specified. The appearance potentials were measured using the extrapolated linear intercept method. In all, nine ionic species were measured as a function of temperature for each composition examined.

Over all mixtures the complex ions $MAgCl^+$, $MAg_2Cl_2^+$, and $M_2AgCl_2^+$ were detected (M denotes the alkali metal atom). These are thought to originate from the precursor molecules $MAgCl_2$, $MAg_2Cl_3$, and $M_2AgCl_3$, respectively.

In order to use the monomer/dimer ratio technique, a monomer/dimer ratio of the pure salt must be established as a reference to which the monomer/dimer ratio of the dilute solutions can be compared. Figure 4 shows the monomer/dimer ratios measured for the pure alkali chlorides. The breaks in the straight lines in Fig. 4 indicate the melting points of the various alkali chlorides.

The differences between the slopes of the monomer/dimer ratio over the solid and liquid are the heats of fusion of the alkali chlorides. To decrease

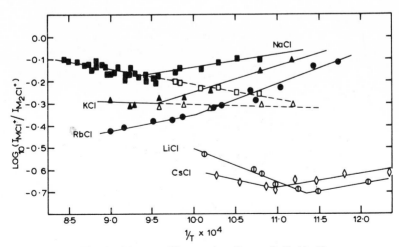

Fig. 4.   Monomer/dimer ratios of pure alkali chlorides.

the uncertainties in the slopes of the monomer/dimer ratio over the liquid, which is the reference state, the points measured over the solid chlorides were referred to the liquid state, thereby increasing the temperature range over which a least-mean-square calculation could be made. This conversion to a liquid standard state is shown by the dotted lines in Fig. 4 for KCl and NaCl. The slopes of the monomer/dimer ratio correspond to differences in the heats of vaporization of the monomer and the dimer molecules.

The ratio of $MCl^+/M_2Cl^+$ was chosen as the ratio indicative of the equilibrium behavior of the melts. Measurements were also made using the $M^+/M_2Cl^+$ ratios as the indicator for the equilibrium monomer/dimer ratio. However, it was found that the ion current of $M^+$ was influenced by some fragmentation effects. The amount of $M^+$ ion measured over the mixtures was greater than could be accounted for by equilibrium considerations [28]. Figure 5 shows the monomer/dimer ratios measured over the mixtures of NaCl–AgCl. The activities derived from these monomer/dimer ratios using equation (22) are shown in Fig. 6 by the continuous line and solid circles. Equation (22) can be expanded to measure activities using a monomer/$n$-mer ratio by use of the equation

$$a_{MX} = \left[ \frac{(I_{MX}^+/I_{M_nX_n}^+)_{\text{pure}}}{(I_{MX}^+/I_{M_nX_n}^+)_{\text{mixture}}} \right] \tag{29}$$

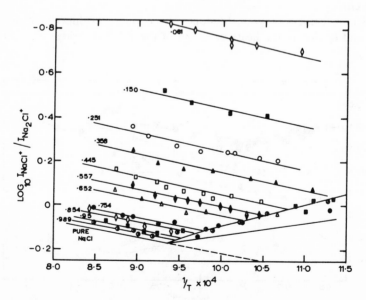

Fig. 5. Monomer/dimer ratios of the NaCl–AgCl system as a function of mole fraction NaCl.

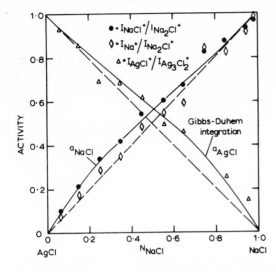

Fig. 6. Activities of NaCl–AgCl system using monomer and dimer and monomer/trimer ratios.

The open triangles in Fig. 6 are the activities of AgCl obtained by using the $AgCl^+/Ag_3Cl_2^+$ ratios and equation (29). The agreement is quite good.

Figure 7 indicates the agreement with existing data for the NaCl–AgCl system. The work by Panish *et al.* [30] and Stern [31], who measured the activity of AgCl using an emf technique, are compared with the activity of AgCl as calculated from the measured monomer/dimer ratios of $NaCl^+/Na_2Cl^+$ and the Gibbs–Duhem equation.

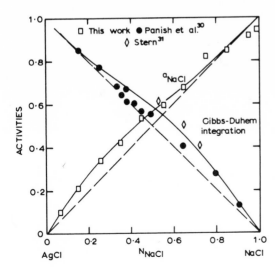

Fig. 7. Activities for the NaCl–AgCl system at 800 °C.

    In Fig. 8 the monomer/dimer ratios of $KCl^+/K_2Cl^+$ are shown as
measured over various mixtures of KCl–AgCl melts. In Fig. 9 the activities
determined from these monomer/dimer ratios are presented along with the
vapor pressure results of Murgulescu and Marta [32] and the emf results of
Murgulescu and Sternberg [33] and Stern [34].

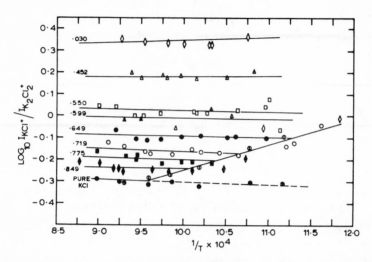

Fig. 8.   Monomer/dimer ratios of the KCl–AgCl system as a function of mole fraction
KCl.

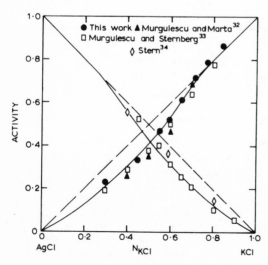

Fig. 9.   Activities for the
KCl–AgCl system at 800 °C.

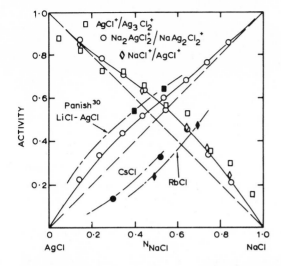

Fig. 10.    Comparison of various methods for determining activities (800°C).

In Fig. 10 the activities measured for several compositions of the LiCl–AgCl, RbCl–AgCl, and CsCl–AgCl systems are presented. In each case, agreement with existing data is good and within the limits of experimental error.

The possibility of observing phase boundaries using the mass spectrometer can be demonstrated. By plotting the composition and temperature of the points where the monomer/dimer ratios over liquid mixtures in Figs. 5 and 8 change slope and become a function of temperature only, the liquidus line of the phase diagram of the NaCl–AgCl and KCl–AgCl system should be obtained. Figures 11 and 12 show these points plotted and compared with the existing phase diagrams [35, 36] of these systems.

It is interesting also to note that the monomer/dimer ratio of the pure solid in Fig. 5 for the NaCl–AgCl is different from that of the invariant monomer/dimer ratio of the liquidus. This indicates a region of solid solubility in the phase system which, in fact, is shown on the phase diagram.

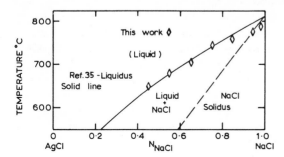

Fig. 11.    Portion of the NaCl–AgCl phase diagram.

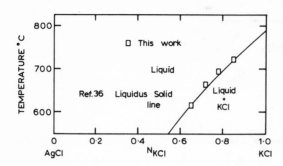

Fig. 12. Portion of the KCl–AgCl phase diagram.

In the case of the KCl–AgCl system, the monomer/dimer ratio determined by the liquid solid phase boundary is, within experimental accuracy, identical with the monomer/dimer ratio of pure solid KCl, indicating that the AgCl–KCl system is in the form of a simple eutectic with no solid solubility.

The difference between the slopes of the monomer/dimer ratios of the pure salt and those of the mixtures is the partial molar free energy of mixing in these systems. Due to the limited temperature range imposed by the experimental system, the uncertainties in the measured heats of mixing were, in many cases, larger than the measured values, being on the order of 300 to 800 cal. However, it was possible to incorporate the calorimetric heats of mixing determined by Hersh and Kleppa [37] with the activities determined by the monomer/dimer ratio to examine the entropy of mixing of the system. From the measured activities, the partial free energy of mixing of the NaCl–AgCl system was determined from

$$\overline{\Delta G_i} = RT \ln a_i \qquad (30)$$

Entropies could then be determined from

$$\overline{\Delta G_i} = \overline{\Delta H_i} - T\overline{\Delta S_i} \qquad (31)$$

making use of the partial free energies calculated for this experiment and the calorimetric heats of Hersh and Kleppa [37].

These partial molar quantities are shown in Figs. 13–15. The entropy of mixing of an ideal solution in Fig. 15 is represented by the continuous line.

The agreement of the activities determined by the monomer/dimer technique with existing data is good. However, it is possible to utilize several alternative approaches for calculating the activities from other ion currents measured in these experiments. These alternative methods provide an independent internal check on the consistency of the data. Thus far, the monomer/dimer ratio for the alkali chlorides and the monomer/trimer ratio for silver chloride have been used.

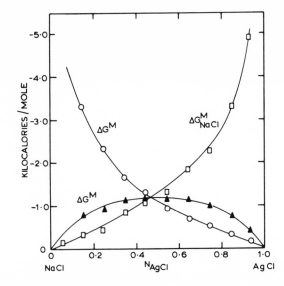

Fig. 13. Free energies of mixing for the NaCl–AgCl system at 800 °C.

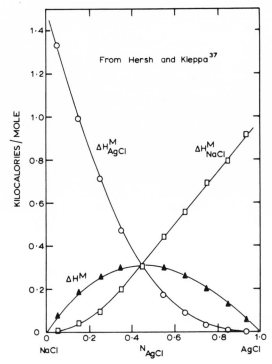

Fig. 14. Enthalpies of mixing for the AgCl–NaCl system at 800 °C.

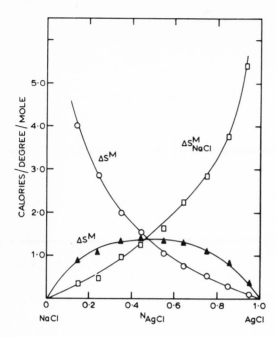

Fig. 15.  Entropies of mixing for the NaCl–AgCl system at 800 °C.

By measurement of the ratio of any two vapor species which can be shown to have a direct dependence on the activity of the components comprising the condensed system and use of expression (25), the activities of these components can be calculated. To illustrate this, the ratios of the ion currents $NaCl^+/AgCl^+$ and $Na_2/AgCl_2^+/NaAg_2Cl_2^+$ were chosen. These are plotted in Figs. 16 and 17, respectively. The activities calculated by graphical integration of Figs. 16 and 17 are shown in Fig. 10 and compared with the activities determined by the monomer/dimer ratio presented as lines. In all, there are more than eight independent methods of calculating the activities of NaCl and AgCl in the NaCl–AgCl system using the ion currents measured in this one experiment.

One decided advantage of using the highest-order species, such as $Na_2AgCl_3$ and $NaAg_2Cl_3$, to determine activities is the elimination of any doubt about what proportion of the ion currents results from fragmentation of higher-order species. These highest-order species are only fragmented to lower-order ions. The probability of forming these ions in the source from ion–molecule reactions under the particular conditions of this experiment is quite small. Thus, the ion current of these large molecules is always representative of their equilibrium concentration.

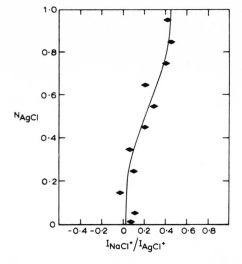

Fig. 16. Plot for integration of NaCl+/AgCl+ ratios.

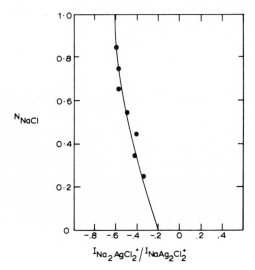

Fig. 17. Plot of the integration of Na₂AgCl+/NaAg₂Cl+ ratios.

## Alloy Systems

The problem of measuring the activities of liquid alloys whose vapor phase contains only monatomic gaseous species is very straightforward when using equation (25). Fruehan [26] has measured the activities in the Fe–Ni, Fe–Co, and Fe–Cr binaries and in the Fe–Cr–Ni ternary. A special form of equation (25) is used for the ternary investigation. The Fe–Ni system has been chosen to illustrate the application of this technique to determine activities. Figure 18 shows the Fe/Ni ratios as a function of composition and temperature. Figure 19 shows the ratio at 1600 °C plotted as a function of the mole fraction of Fe, which was integrated graphically to derive the activities presented in Fig. 20 and compared with existing data [38].

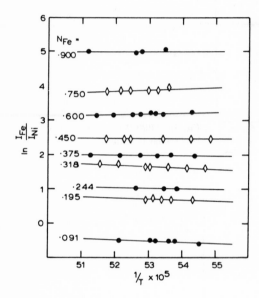

Fig. 18.   Plot of ln $I_{Fe}/I_{Ni}$ vs. $1/T$ for Fe–Ni [26].

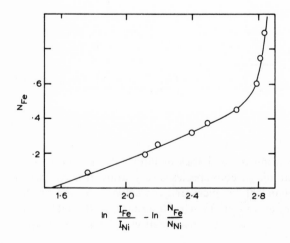

Fig. 19.   Plot of $N_{Fe}$ vs. ln $[(I_{Fe}/I_{Ni}) - (N_{Fe}/N_{Ni})]$ for Fe–Ni at 1600 °C [26].

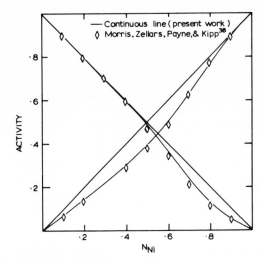

Fig. 20.    Plot of the activities of Fe and Ni vs. $N_{Ni}$ for Fe-Ni at 1600 °C [26].

## CONCLUSIONS

Several methods of determining thermodynamic properties of solutions using a mass spectrometer have been demonstrated. It has been shown that these thermodynamic properties can be measured without a knowledge of absolute vapor pressures. These techniques thus eliminate the uncertainties in the values of absolute vapor pressures measured with a mass spectrometer which must rely on existing data for ionization cross sections and multiplier efficiencies.

## REFERENCES

1. P. W. Gilles, *J. Pure Appl. Chem.* **5**:543, 1962.
2. I. Langmuir, *Phys. Rev.* **2**:329, 1963.
3. M. Knudsen, *Ann. Physik* **28**:999, 1909.
4. P. Grieveson, G. W. Hooper, and C. B. Alcock, *Physical Chemistry of Process Metallurgy*, Part I, Interscience, New York, 1961, p. 341.
5. H. M. Schadel, Jr., and C. E. Birchenall, *Trans. AIME* **188**:1134, 1950.
6. K. J. Motzfeldt, *J. Phys. Chem.* **59**:139, 1955.
7. R. Speiser and H. L. Johnston, *Trans. Am. Soc. Metals* **42**:283, 1950.
8. J. Clausing, *Ann. Phys.* **12**:961, 1932.
9. R. I. Reed, *Ion Production by Electron Impact*, Academic Press, London, 1962, p. 31.
10. G. P. Barnard, *Modern Mass Spectrometry*, Institute of Physics, New York, 1953, p. 243.
11. R. E. Fox, W. M. Hickam, T. Killkaos, and D. J. Grove, *Phys. Rev.* **84**:859, 1951.
12. J. Berkowitz and W. A. Chupka, *J. Chem. Phys.* **29**:653, 1958.
13. M. G. Inghram, R. F. Porter, and W. A. Chupka, *J. Chem. Phys.* **25**:498, 1956.
14. T. A. Milne, *J. Chem. Phys.* **32**:1275, 1960.
15. J. Berkowitz, H. Tasman, and W. A. Chupka, *J. Chem. Phys.* **36**:2170, 1962.

16. R. E. Honig, *J. Chem. Phys.* **22**:129, 1954.
17. M. G. Inghram, R. J. Hayden, and D. C. Hess, *Mass Spectrometry in Physics Research,* Natl. Bur. Std. Circ. 522, Washington, D. C., 1953, p. 257.
18. J. W. Otvos and D. P. Stevenson, *J. Am. Chem. Soc.* **78**:546, 1956.
19. F. H. Lampe, J. L. Franklin, and F. H. Field, *J. Am. Chem. Soc.* **79**:6129, 1957.
20. P. Goldfinger and M. Jeunehomme, *Trans. Faraday Soc.* **59**:2851, 1963.
21. M. G. Inghram and J. Drowart, in: N.K. Heister (ed.), *Proceedings of an International Symposium on High Temperature Technology,* McGraw-Hill, New York, 1960, p. 219.
22. J. Drowart, G. De Maria, R. P. Burns, and M. G. Inghram, *J. Chem. Phys.* **32**:1366, 1960.
23. J. Berkowitz and W. A. Chupka, *Ann. N. Y. Acad. Sci.* **79**:1073, 1960.
24. A. Büchler and J. L. Stauffer, *Thermodynamics,* International Atomic Energy Agency, Vienna, 1966, p. 271.
25. M. Ginsberg, private communication.
26. R. Fruehan, thesis, University of Pennsylvania, Philadelphia, Pennsylvania, 1966.
27. J. H. Norman, P. Winchell, and H. G. Staley, *J. Chem. Phys.* **41**:60, 1964.
28. R. C. Svedberg, thesis, University of Pennsylvania, Philadelphia, Pennsylvania, 1966.
29. W. A. Chupka and M. G. Inghram, *J. Phys. Chem.* **59**:100, 1955.
30. M. B. Panish, F. F. Blankenship, W. R. Grimes, and R. F. Newton, *J. Phys. Chem.* **62**:1325, 1958.
31. K. J. Stern, *J. Phys. Chem.* **62**:385, 1958.
32. I. G. Murgulescu and L. Marta, *Rev. Chim. Acad. Rép. Populaire Roumaine* **7**:1105, 1962.
33. I. G. Murgulescu and S. Sternberg, *Rev. Chim. Acad. Rép. Populaire Roumaine* **2**:251, 1957.
34. K. J. Stern, *J. Phys. Chem.* **60**:679, 1956.
35. S. Zhemchuzhnui, *Z. Anorg. Allgem. Chem.* **153**:53, 1926.
36. S. Zhemchuzhnui, *Anorg. Chem.* **57**:276, 1908.
37. L. S. Hersh and O. J. Kleppa, *J. Chem. Phys.* **42**:1309, 1965.
38. G. R. Zellars, S. L. Payne, J. P. Morris, and R. L. Kipp, *Trans. AIME* **215**:181, 1959.

# A SURVEY OF THE APPLICATION OF SPARK SOURCE MASS SPECTROMETRY TO THE ANALYSIS OF SOLIDS

## R. Brown

*Scientific Apparatus Department*
*Associated Electrical Industries Limited*
*Urmston, Manchester, England*

In many fields of science and technology, it is becoming more essential to have a full knowledge of the chemical composition of high-purity materials. Advances in certain branches of science such as solid-state physics, reactor technology, studies in superconductivity, and many other fields are dependent upon the abilities of available analytical techniques to give information on trace element concentrations in a host of matrices.

Spark source mass spectrometry has proved to be a valuable ally of the research scientist in a great many diverse branches of science. Consequently the diversity of classes of materials subjected to analysis by spark source mass spectrometry is very wide. This paper describes but a few of the applications in the form of some of the problems encountered.

It is important to consider several of the features of mass spectrometry which, when taken together, set apart mass spectrometry from any other analytical technique.

## LINEARITY

It has been shown that ion intensity is proportional to concentration over at least $10^5:1$. Hannay and Ahearn [1] investigated the linearity by analyzing a series of boron-doped silicon samples. Figure 1 shows that ion intensity is proportional to concentration over more than three orders of magnitude concentration ratio. Later, Halliday *et al.* [2] carried out an analysis on a series of gold-doped titanium standards; this work showed that the technique is linear over a concentration range in excess of $10^5:1$. The

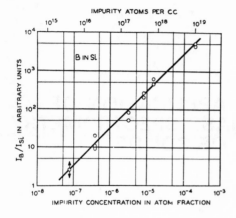

Fig. 1. Impurity concentration ion intensity for boron-doped silicon.

results are shown in Fig. 2. Subsequently, analysis of other standards on a routine basis has corroborated these findings.

## SENSITIVITY

It has been determined that an element which is monoisotopic, or has one particularly abundant isotope, may be detected when present at a concentration of approximately 1 ppb using an exposure of $10^{-6}$ C.

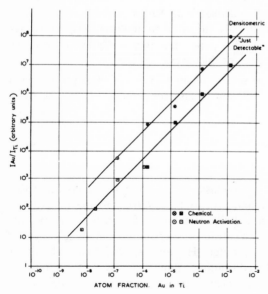

Fig. 2. Atom fraction *vs.* ion intensity for Au in Ti.

## OVERALL ELEMENTAL COVERAGE

The mass range of the Associated Electrical Industries mass spectrometer, AEI MS702, is 45:1; this enables the analyst to detect elements simultaneously within the mass range from lithium at $m/e$ 7 through uranium at $m/e$ 238. A mass range of $m/e$ 1 to $m/e$ 45, i.e., from hydrogen to calcium, may be encompassed by decreasing the magnetic field. A choice of mass scale dispersion is made simply by adjustment of the magnetic field.

### Simplicity of Spectrum

Essentially, the mass spectra of mixtures or compounds of inorganic material are atomic rather than molecular. The principal lines of the spectra are due to ions of the major component having one positive charge; in the general case, the higher the number of positive charges, the lower the intensity. Less important features of the spectrum are molecular and complex lines; quite unlike organic mass spectrometry these lines may constitute a nuisance rather than an aid to analysis. At very low intensity are lines from charge exchange due to collisions of ions with residual gas molecules in the vacuum system. A detailed examination of inorganic mass spectra is given by Craig et al. [3].

### Relative Sensitivities of Elements

Compared with many other physical techniques it is apparent that in spark source mass spectrometry there is little variation in the sensitivities between elements. Table I shows the relative sensitivities of various elements in copper, iron, and aluminum. All the listed sensitivities are measured against iron which is assumed to have unit sensitivity. Relative sensitivities of various elements must be established by analysis of a suitable standard containing the elements of interest, before any fully quantitative analysis is undertaken.

Table I.   Relative Sensitivities Referred to Fe $= 1.0$ in Various Matrices

| Impurity | Cu matrix | Fe matrix | Al matrix |
|----------|-----------|-----------|-----------|
| Cr | 1.5 | 1.5 | 1.4 |
| Ni | 0.61 | 0.57 | 0.69 |
| Co | 0.93 | 0.80 | — |
| Mn | 1.5 | — | 1.5 |
| Sn | 1.08 | 0.70 | — |
| Pb | 1.17 | 1.60 | — |
| Zn | 2.0 | 3.1 | 0.9 |

It must be pointed out that the relative sensitivities of elements are affected by variation of instrument parameters. Honig and Woolston [4,5] have investigated this effect; later Halliday et al. [2] carried out similar investigations of the effect of varying each of the instrument spark parameters. The conclusion is that relative sensitivities must be established using rigidly controlled instrument parameters, and these parameters must be reproduced for the analysis of samples, otherwise correction for relative sensitivity is invalidated. More recently, it has been found possible to fix the spark conditions and keep them constant throughout the analysis [6].

Mass spectrometry has been applied successfully to problems in the fields of metallurgy, solid-state physics, nuclear reactor technology, powders analysis, geology, and biological studies.

## METALLURGY

### High-Duty Alloys

Metals are probably the most straightforward class of materials to analyze by spark source mass spectrometry, since they usually are easy to form into electrodes and are electrically conducting.

A typical problem encountered is a comparison of two samples of steel or high-duty nickel alloy, one of which has satisfactory properties while the other one does not. Conventional methods of analysis usually have failed to reveal any differences in chemical composition. Such a problem was encountered in the analysis of two apparently chemically identical samples of high-duty nickel alloy, one sample having markedly inferior properties to those of the other. This type of material is used in the fabrication of blades in a jet engine where failure of such components can be disastrous.

Table II shows a comparison of the values obtained for the two samples. It was observed that the lead content of the unsatisfactory material is higher than that of the good sample. It was concluded that lead was the cause of the failure in this particular case. Many elements have a deleterious effect on the physical properties of high-duty alloys. In addition to lead, it has been found that bismuth, tellurium, and silver also affect the stress–rupture properties of these alloys. The use of the spark source mass spectrometer in this application and the effect of various impurities is reported in the literature [7-9].

### Refining of Metals

The overall coverage of elements in one analysis is particularly useful in monitoring purification techniques. The efficiency of zone refining processes may be conveniently and rapidly checked. Mass spectrometry also

**Table II.   Analysis of Special Nickel Alloys (elements detected ppm atomic)**

| Element | Sample A | Sample B |
|---|---|---|
| Bismuth | 0.2 | 0.2 |
| Lead * | 24 | 110 |
| Mercury † | Detected | Detected |
| Holmium | 0.03 | 0.03 |
| Dysprosium | 0.4 | 0.4 |
| Terbium | 0.3 | 0.3 |
| Gadolinium | 3 | 3 |
| Europium | 0.2 | 0.2 |
| Neodymium | 40 | 40 |
| Praseodymium | 30 | 30 |
| Cerium | 300 | 300 |
| Lanthanum | 100 | 100 |
| Molybdenum | 10 | 10 |
| Niobium | 0.3 | 0.3 |
| Yttrium | 2 | 2 |
| Selenium | 2 | 10 |
| Arsenic | 10 | 10 |
| Gallium | 2 | 2 |
| Zinc | 20 | 20 |
| Copper | 50 | 50 |
| Cobalt | 300 | 300 |
| Iron | 2,000 | 2,000 |
| Manganese | 3,000 | 3,000 |
| Vanadium | 50 | 100 |
| Titanium | 10 | 10 |
| Calcium | 200 | 400 |
| Chlorine | 10 | 10 |
| Sulfur | 100 | 100 |
| Silicon | 10,000 | 10,000 |
| Aluminum | 3,000 | 3,000 |
| Magnesium | 30 | 30 |
| Fluorine | (1 | — 10) |
| Boron | 3 | 3 |

\* Estimated accurately by microdensitometer.
† Detected in both samples, but it is not a
homogeneous impurity; apparent concentration not greater than 3 ppm in both samples.

provides a convenient method to check the efficiency of electrolytic refining of metals. Table III shows a comparison of anode and cathode copper; analyses of this kind may be carried out routinely [10] and the relative concentrations of 70 or more elements may be established within two hours, even down to concentrations in the ppb range. It is of critical importance to know the concentration of elements in copper, particularly for the electrical industry, since trace quantities of elements such as arsenic, selenium, and bismuth in copper can seriously affect its maleability and conductivity.

Table III shows the large reduction in the concentration of these particular elements during electrolytic refining.

### Table III.   Analysis of Copper Before and After Refining

| Element | (A) Anode | (B) Cathode |
|---|---|---|
| Bismuth | 9.6* | 0.01 |
| Lead | 29.0* | 0.4 |
| Thallium | 0.1 | <0.03 |
| Mercury | <0.1 | <0.1 |
| Gold | 10 | <0.1 |
| Tantalum † | 3 | 6 |
| Tellurium | 28 | <! |
| Antimony | 91.0* | 0.2 |
| Tin | 0.5* | <0.03 |
| Indium | 0.1 | <0.01 |
| Cadmium | 0.1 | <0.03 |
| Silver | 670* | 1.2* |
| Selenium | 600 | <1 |
| Arsenic | 300 | 0.1 |
| Zinc | 7 | <0.2 |
| Nickel | 400 | 10 |
| Cobalt | 1 | <0.03 |
| Iron | 50 | 3 ‡ |
| Manganese | 0.1 | <0.03 |
| Chromium | 0.56* | 0.3 ‡ |
| Titanium | <0.3 | <0.1 |
| Calcium | <3 | 0.3 |
| Potassium | <3 | 0.1 |
| Chlorine | 30 | 10 |
| Sulfur | 50 | 10 |
| Silicon | 1 | 1 |
| Aluminum | 10 | 6 |
| Sodium | <0.03 | 0.1 |
| Fluorine | <0.1 | 0.2 |
| Boron | 0.1 | 0.1 |

* More accurate determinations using micro-densitometer.
† Source parts made of tantalum.
‡ Nonlinear spectrum.

Mass spectrometry is currently being used to monitor the purity of aluminum and its alloys, copper and its alloys, high-duty nickel alloys, steels, and pure noble metals, rare earth elements and their oxides, superconducting metals including tantalum, niobium, and tungsten, and many other materials where high purity is a prerequisite in attaining the required physical properties.

## SOLID-STATE PHYSICS

### Semiconductors

The immediate needs of the semiconductor industry in the 1950's dictated that a method of analysis having a sensitivity of one or two orders of magnitude greater than the existing routine physical methods should be established. Mass spectrometry was applied to the problem of the analysis of III–V semiconductors, such as gallium arsenide, indium antimonide, gallium phosphide, etc; some of this earlier work is described in the literature by Brown et al. [11].

Several of the large producers and users of semiconductors have gone into spark source mass spectrometry, and the technique has yielded a great amount of information on the zone refining process used in the purification of semiconductors. However, more recently a great deal of interest has arisen in the analysis of thin films, rather than bulk impurity estimations.

### Thin Films

Associated Electrical Industries has carried out a number of analyses of thin films, and the results of this work have not been published previously. One such analysis was carried out on four silicon wafers, 1 in. in diameter and 0.0085 in. thick; the samples were submitted with the following description: (1) boron diffused in surface, (2) boron deposited on surface, (3) phosphorus deposited on surface, (4) phosphorus diffused in surface.

#### Analysis

Each wafer was divided into six separate segments and one of these segments was mounted in the instrument source, with a gold wire counter electrode mounted opposite the thin film. Two experiments were conducted on each sample.

1. A penetration experiment consisting of consecutive exposures of $10^{-11}$ C on the same spot on the surface was performed to estimate the depth of crater produced by a $10^{-11}$ C exposure. It was found that 26 single sparks each producing a $10^{-11}$ C exposure were required to penetrate the 0.0085-in.-thick wafers. This represents a penetration of 8.3 $\mu$ per $10^{-11}$ C exposure.

2. A surface analysis was accomplished by recording a series of graduated exposures from $3 \times 10^{-13}$ to $6 \times 10^{-12}$ C, sparking at several points on the surface.

The depth of the surface analysis craters was estimated to be about 6 $\mu$, which is lower than the penetration experiment craters. This was due to the fact that lower excitation conditions were employed. The equivalent depths of the layers of boron and phosphorus were calculated using the "just detectable" exposures [3] to determine the concentration of impurity, assuming the usual plate sensitivity of 100 ppm per $10^{-11}$ C exposure.

With knowledge of the depth of the crater and the concentration of surface element within the material consumed, the equivalent depth, or concentration of atoms per atoms per unit surface area, can be estimated. If we consider the surface layer consumed to be $d$ cm deep, the number of atoms per square centimer can be shown to be

$$Z_{Si} = \frac{d \times D_{Si} \times N}{A_{Si}} \quad atoms/cm^2$$

where $D_{Si}$ is the density of silicon, $N$ is Avogadro's number, and $A_{Si}$ is the atomic weight of silicon.

For boron,

$$Z_B = \frac{d \times D_{Si} \times N \times C_B}{A_{Si}} \quad atoms/cm^2$$

where $C_B$ is the concentration of boron in silicon. Converting to depth of boron in centimeters, we have

$$\text{depth of boron} = \frac{d \times D_{Si} \times N \times C_B \times A_B}{A_{Si} \times N \times D_B} \quad cm$$

$$\therefore \text{depth of boron} = d \times \frac{D_{Si}}{A_{Si}} \times \frac{A_B}{D_B} \times C_B$$

*Sample 1.* Substituting the values for a crater 6 $\mu$ deep, we have $d = 6 \times 10^{-4}$ cm, $C_B = 0.02\%$ since the boron isotope 11 is 80% abundant and gave a just detectable line at an exposure of $6 \times 10^{-12}$ C.

$$\therefore \text{depth of boron} = 6 \times 10^{-4} \times \frac{2.33}{28.1} \times \frac{10.8}{2.34} \times \frac{0.02}{100} = 4.7 \,\text{Å}$$

*Sample 2.*   Concentration of boron is 0.4%. Depth of boron is 94 Å.

*Sample 3.*   Concentration of phosphorus is 3.3%. Depth of phosphorus is

$$6 \times 10^{-4} \times \frac{2.33}{28.1} \times \frac{31}{1.82} \times \frac{3.3}{100} = 2904 \text{ Å}$$

The results quoted are semiquantitative in view of the lack of information on the relative sensitivities of boron and phosphorus in silicon. Experience has shown that boron and phosphorus do have approximately unit sensitivity, but to put the method on a fully quantitative basis, it would be necessary to analyze samples of silicon containing known amounts of boron and phosphorus in order to evaluate their relative sensitivity.

Another assumption implicit in the calculation is that the area of the crater increases in proportion to the exposure, up to some reasonable limit; measurements of craters produced by exposures of $3 \times 10^{-13}$, $6 \times 10^{-13}$, $10^{-12}$, $3 \times 10^{-12}$, and $6 \times 10^{-12}$ C indicate that this is so. Careful optical examination of a series of craters produced by various exposures strengthens the belief in the validity of this assumption.

### Analysis of Surfaces

The use of a rotating electrode system has proved to be a valuable method for the examination of thin films: Hickham and co-workers [12,13] have demonstrated that when a disk sample is rotated and sparked against a counter electrode it is possible to achieve a resolution on single spark discharges of approximately 1 $\mu$. The depth of penetration of each spark is about 2000 Å. Using this system it is convenient to carry out surface analysis on thin films, avoiding excessive contribution to the spectrum from the support substrate.


## NUCLEAR REACTOR TECHNOLOGY

### Determination of Cobalt in Stainless Steel

In the construction of a nuclear reactor, stainless steel is used to fabricate certain components of the fuel channel. It is essential at this time to vet the purity of the stainless steel to ensure that the concentrations of elements which produce radioactive isotopes are sufficiently small. Cobalt is a case where the maximum permissible concentration is specified by many health physics departments in various countries. Under conditions of high neutron flux, $^{59}$Co is converted to $^{60}$Co, which is $\beta$- and $\gamma$-active and has a half-life

Fig. 3.   Mass spectrum of stainless steel.

of 5.15 yr. Figure 3 shows a spectrum of a typical sample of stainless steel. In this particular sample, the contribution of $^{118}Sn^{++}$ ions to the spectrum of $^{59}Co^{+}$ had to be evaluated. The method of correcting for direct overlap of this type has been described by Brown [14].

Table IV shows the comparison of mass spectrographic results with emission spectrographic values, when correction for relative sensitivities is taken into account. The method is described by Halliday *et al.* [2]. The values listed in the table show good agreement where element concentrations are sufficiently high to obtain accurate values from other methods of analysis. However, by virtue of the linearity of the method, it is equally feasible to obtain accurate values in the 1–100 ppm range of concentration, or even lower concentration levels.

### Table IV.   Accuracy of Analysis After Calibration*

| Impurity | Concentration (wt. %) | | |
|---|---|---|---|
| | MS7 average of eight analyses | MS7, corrected using SS12 | Given spectrographic value |
| Cr | 0.26 | 0.18 | 0.185 |
| Co | 0.19 | 0.18 | 0.19 |
| Ni | 0.10 | 0.13 | 0.13 |
| Cu | 0.047 | 0.029 | 0.04 |
| Zr | 0.017 | 0.007 | 0.005 † |
| Nb | 0.072 | 0.025 | 0.05 † |
| Mo | 0.053 | 0.060 | 0.07 |
| Sn | 0.019 | 0.017 | 0.02 |
| Pb | 0.018 | 0.007 | 0.0075 † |

* Bureau of Analysed Samples Limited, Mild Steel Residual Series, Spectrographic Standard SS14. Pulse length, 100 μsec; 300 pulses/sec; 30 kV RF; 19.5 kV accelerating voltage.
† Not certified — approximate.

## Analysis of Graphite

It is necessary to analyze graphite to monitor the concentration of elements having a high neutron capture cross section. Elements such as boron and the rare earths come into this category. Carbon is particularly prone to produce molecular ions by spark source excitation; molecular species up to $C_{24}^+$ have been observed; therefore, it may be anticipated that this causes an analytical problem. It is fortunate, however, that the spectral overlap in the case of carbon is quite small. Figure 4 is a histogram diagram showing limits of detection of impurity elements in four materials—graphite, copper, aluminum, and indium arsenide. It can be seen that the majority of elements have a detection limit of 0.001 ppm in spite of its prolific production of molecular species. Fortunately, the effect of overlap by $C_n^+$ ions is minimal, since in the majority of cases of overlap of the major impurity isotopes of the various elements, other isotopes are available having an appreciable abundance.

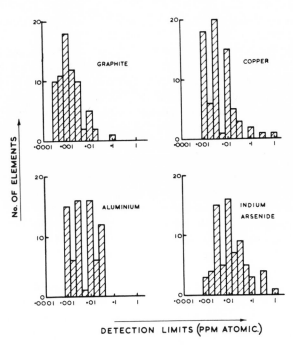

Fig. 4. Detection limits of impurity elements in four materials.

## Analysis of Beryllium

In beryllium analysis, there are two major problems to overcome—spectral interference and sample preparation.

### Spectral Interference

Beryllium, like carbon, produces many molecular species; in many cases, $^9Be_n{}^+$ ions occur at the same nominal mass as many of the impurities, e.g., $Be_3{}^+$ occurs at nominal mass $m/e$ 27, which is the same as that for the sole isotope of aluminum $^{27}Al^+$. However, when one calculates the resolving power required to separate $^9Be_3{}^+$ and $^{27}Al^+$, considering the mass defects on these ions, it is seen that it is possible to resolve them into a doublet. Beryllium has a positive mass defect of 12.2 mmu; aluminum has a negative mass defect of 18.5 mmu. Hence

$$\text{Mass of } ^9Be_3{}^+ \quad = 27.0366$$
$$\text{Mass of } ^{27}Al^+ \quad = 26.0815$$
$$\therefore \Delta M \qquad\quad = 55.1 \text{ mmu}$$

The resolving power required to separate $^9Be_3{}^+$ and $^{27}Al^+$ is

$$RP = \frac{M}{\Delta M} = \frac{27}{0.0551} = 490$$

Most commercial double-focusing mass spectrometers are capable of at least 1000 at $m/e$ 27; therefore, the determination of aluminum in beryllium presents no problem. The ease by which elements are resolved is increased as elements of higher atomic number are sought, up to thorium, atomic number 90, where a positive mass defect is observed. However, at this point there is no coincidence of $Be_2{}^+$ ions.

### Preparation of Sample

It is essential to clean the surface of beryllium prior to analysis by spark source mass spectrometry. The usual chemical etches have been found to change the chemical composition of the surface due to selective etching or redeposition of elements onto the surface. This problem has been overcome by bombarding the sample with argon ions in a discharge tube. The surface of the sample thus being cleaned by a physical process appears to show no change in composition.

Blosser [15] has reported the routine analysis for all elements in beryllium including gases and carbon. He reports that he can determine the concentration of oxygen in beryllium down to concentrations lower than 10 ppm.

Analyses of many other elements concerned with reactor technology have been carried out; these include zirconium, thorium, uranium, and plutonium [16].

## ANALYSIS OF POWDERS

The analysis of insulating powders by spark source mass spectrometry posed several problems, mainly confined to the presentation of the sample to the instrument source. The problem was very largely overcome by mixing the sample with a conducting powder. This work was reported by Brown and Wolstenholme [17]. They listed the requirements for the analysis of powders as follows:

1. The materials must be electrically conducting.
2. The physical strength must be sufficient for clamping in the ion source.
3. There must be minimum interference from the mass spectrum of the support material.
4. Impurities in the support material must be at low and known concentration.

It has been found that graphite mixtures satisfy the above requirements, although it is sometimes advantageous to use silver or gold as the support material. The interference from $C_n{}^+$ ions on the spectrum of the sample material is acceptably small, and Fig. 5 shows a plot of the resolving power

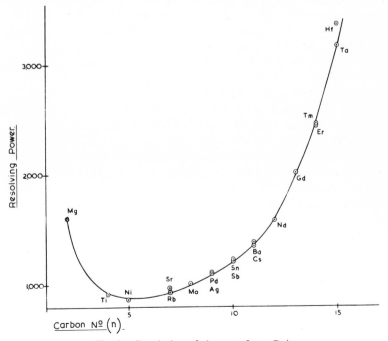

Fig. 5.   Resolution of elements from $C_n{}^+$.

requirements $M/\Delta M$ against carbon number ($n$). It can be seen that where coincidence occurs, the resolving power requirements in the majority of cases are small.

The method of mixing the sample and subsequently pressing the powder into electrodes was first applied to the analysis of titanium dioxide, and as soon as the potential of the method was appreciated it was applied to a whole range of powder samples. The method, which was reported by Errock [18], is still probably the most widely used technique, as the ratio of ions from the sample and the support material is usually constant. One factor which can affect the accuracy of analysis is the degree of homogeneity of the electrodes. The most profitable line of development now will be the development of methods to overcome nonhomogeneity. Nicholls and collaborators [19] describe a method of fusing a mixture of the sample and a low melting point flux, incorporating an internal standard of rhenium. This technique has enabled an accuracy down to $\pm 5\%$ or less to be obtained on the analysis of rocks.

## Analysis of Titanium Dioxide

The use of titanium dioxide as a pigment in paints and as an opaquing agent in synthetic fibers has grown to large proportions in the last few years.

It is essential to know the concentrations of various elements in titanium dioxide, since many elements, such as vanadium and chromium, can markedly affect the color of pigment material. Certain elements may undergo photocatalytic oxidation, and if a pigment containing an excess of these elements is used as an opaquing agent in synthetic fibers, it would cause physical degradation of the fiber.

Recent work reported by Jackson and Whitehead [20] shows that an accuracy of 10–20% is obtained using the MS7 mass spectrometer. The work describes the preparation of the sample and compares the relative merits of graphite, silver, and gold as the choice of support material. Up to eight samples may be analyzed on a fully quantitative basis in an 8-hr day, with quantitative determinations down to 5 ppm.

An ion beam chopper has been developed which allows the analyst to maintain constant excitation conditions and greater consumption of sample weight per unit exposures. Using this device, Jackson et al. [21] have reported a marked improvement in the accuracy which they have been able to obtain; in fact, titanium dioxide analysis routinely yields a standard deviation average of 5%, which is now almost at the limit of accuracy imposed by the photographic plate.

The usual procedure is to mix equal weights of the titanium dioxide and pure graphite, and then to compress the mixture into electrodes. Figure 6 shows the spectra of three synthetic standards where the concen-

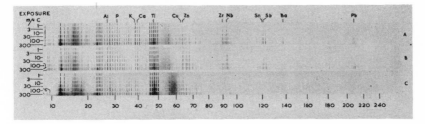

Fig. 6.   Mass spectra of three titanium dioxide samples.

tration of various elements is higher than in pigment materials; the spectra shown, however, indicate the ease with which the differences in element concentration are observed.

Of particular note are the differences of concentration of Pb, Ba, Sn, Sb, Zr, Nb, Cu, Zn, Ca, K, P, and Al. A rapid visual inspection of the plates from samples under comparison frequently yields a lot of useful information since semiquantitative analysis may be carried out by eye [3].

For accurate quantitative analysis, it is necessary to measure the spectral line densities with a microdensitometer; Fig. 7 shows a typical microdensitometer scan of a synthetic standard for titanium dioxide analysis. It should be noted that the background at masses 50 and 60 is fairly high; in this case, a background correction is required on the peak height. The peak heights are then plotted against the log relative exposure required to produce the lines, and a calibration curve is drawn for each element under analysis.

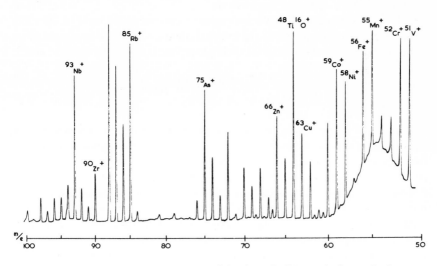

Fig. 7.   Microdensitometer scan of titanium dioxide synthetic standard.

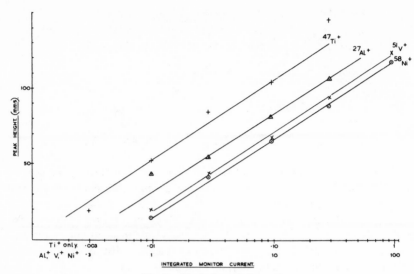

Fig. 8.  Typical analysis curves.

Figure 8 shows some typical calibration curves for titanium (internal standard), aluminum, vanadium, and nickel. In early work on titanium dioxide
analysis, titanium was used as internal standard. The recent work by Jackson
has shown that there is a marked increase in quantitative accuracy when
niobium is used as internal standard. Niobium is always present in a pigment
sample, and its concentration may be determined very rapidly and with high
accuracy by X-ray fluorescence analysis.

The basis of a quantitative analysis is to determine the ratio of intensity
of the impurity element against the internal standard. The concentration of an
impurity is calculated from the following expression derived by Craig *et al.* [3]:

$$C_i = \frac{E_s}{E_i} \cdot \frac{C_s}{100} \cdot \frac{I_s}{I_i} \cdot \frac{S_s}{S_i} \cdot \frac{A_i}{A_s} \cdot \frac{M_i}{M_s} \times 10^6 \text{ ppm atomic}$$

where $E_s$ and $E_i$ are the log relative exposures required to produce lines of a
density $D$ in the linear portion of response of the photographic emulsion
for the internal standard and impurity isotope, respectively; $C_s$ is the atomic
percentage concentration of the element chosen as internal standard;
$I_s$ and $I_i$ are the natural abundances of the isotopes of the standard and
impurity elements, respectively, chosen for the estimates; $S_s$ and $S_i$ are the
relative sensitivities of the singly charged ions of the internal standard and
impurity isotopes, respectively (these values are determined in a separate
analysis of a standard); $A_s$ and $A_i$ are the relative areas of the spectral lines
of the internal standard isotope and the impurity element isotope, respec-

tively; and $M_s$ and $M_i$ are the ratios of the intensities of the singly charged ions to those of the particular multiply charged ions on which the estimate is based (it is normal to use singly charged ions where possible, so rarely does this factor apply).

When the above method is used for the determination of elements in titanium dioxide, even without considering relative line areas, an accuracy of $\pm 5\%$ may be achieved when using the most refined instrumental techniques available.

## ANALYSIS OF GEOLOGICAL SAMPLES

The determination of isotope ratios by mass spectrometry has long been an accepted technique; this is accomplished by using a thermal ionization source. However, it is only in the past five years or so that chemical analysis of geological materials by spark source mass spectrometry has been investigated.

Brown and Wolstenholme [22] reported data on the analysis of the two standard samples, granite $G_1$ and diabase $W_1$, but the work was only semi-quantitative and the values for several elements disagreed with other reported values owing to the fact that no standards were available to establish relative sensitivity coefficients.

Later, Taylor [23] carried out a more detailed study of the problem and established reliable relative sensitivity values. Initially, like Brown and Wolstenholme, he used silicon as the internal standard element, but realized its limitation due to its high concentration. Finally he chose lutecium as internal standard and he quotes a precision of $\pm 10\%$ on analysis of $G_1$ and $W_1$.

Nicholls and collaborators [19] have worked on a method to improve sample homogeneity and accomplished this by fusing the sample and a rhenium internal standard with a low melting point flux. The fusion procedure is repeated three times and the fused sample is ground after each fusion. It is apparent that sample homogeneity and choice of a suitable internal standard are the critical factors influencing attainable analytical accuracy. Nicholls reports a standard deviation of approximately $\pm 5\%$ on the analysis of silicate rocks.

An important class of elements to the geologist consists of the rare earths and, for the purpose of dating rocks, rubidium, strontium, and lead. Figure 9 shows the regions of the mass spectrum containing the above elements. In order to evaluate the concentration of the rare earths, it is best to make sample electrodes with silver powder rather than graphite; this eliminates the production of $XC_n^+$ ions which may interfere with the rare earths of higher atomic number. Such interference could be serious because

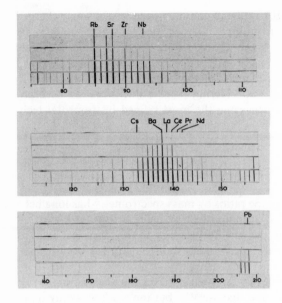

Fig. 9. Part spectra of powdered granite $G_1$.

usually the natural abundance of the rare earth elements decreases with increase in atomic number.

Table V, which is reproduced from the paper by Taylor [23], shows a comparison of results obtained by spark source mass spectrometry and other

**Table V.　Analytical Data, as Parts per Million (weight ppm)**

| Element | Mass number | $G_1$ | | $W_1$ | | Andesite | | Crustal average |
|---------|-------------|-------|-------|-------|-------|----------|------|-----------------|
| | | MS7 | Other | MS7 | Other | MS7 | Spec. | |
| Cs | 133 | 1.45 | 1.5$^g$ | 0.75 | 1.1$^g$ | 1.0 | — | 3 |
| Rb | 85 | 245 | 220$^g$ | 19 | 22$^g$ | 27 | | 90 |
| Tl | 205 | 1.3 | 1.3$^g$ | 0.19 | 0.13$^g$ | 0.45 | | 0.45 |
| Ba | 137 | 1275 | 1220$^g$ | 200 | 225$^g$ | 315 | 295 | 425 |
| Pb | 208 | 50 | 49$^g$ | 8.0 | 8$^g$ | 8.2 | — | 12.5 |
| Sr | 86 | 250 | | 190 | | 200 | 227 | 375 |
| La | 139 | 110 | 102$^a$ | 14 | 12$^a$ | 9.8 | | 30 |
| Ce | 140 | 140 | 134$^a$ | 18 | 24$^a$ | 18 | | 60 |
| Pr | 141 | 16 | 21$^a$ | 2.5 | 3.7$^a$ | 2.6 | | 8.2 |
| Nd | 146 | 40 | 55$^a$ | 11 | 15$^a$ | 10.3 | | 28 |
| Sm | 147 | 7.4 | 8.6$^a$ | 3.3 | 3.8$^a$ | 2.4 | | 6.0 |
| Eu | 153 | 1.4 | 1.0$^a$ | 0.95 | 1.1$^a$ | 0.77 | | 1.2 |
| Gd | 158 | 6.5 | 4.9$^a$ | 3.0 | 4.2$^a$ | 2.7 | | 5.4 |
| Tb | 159 | 0.95 | 0.50$^a$ | 0.66 | 0.75$^a$ | 0.55 | | 0.90 |

## Table V (cont.)

| Element | Mass number | G$_1$ MS7 | G$_1$ Other | W$_1$ MS7 | W$_1$ Other | Andesite MS7 | Andesite Spec. | Crustal average |
|---|---|---|---|---|---|---|---|---|
| Dy | 163 | 4.4 | — | 2.6 | — | 2.3 | | 3.0 |
| Ho | 165 | 0.70 | 0.50[a] | 0.77 | 1.35[a] | 0.76 | | 1.2 |
| Er | 167 | 1.7 | 1.40[a] | 1.8 | 2.6[a] | 2.2 | | 2.8 |
| Tm | 169 | 0.28 | 0.20[a] | 0.31 | 0.36[a] | 0.33 | | 0.48 |
| Yb | 172 | 1.10 | 0.63[a] | 1.6 | 1.55[a] | 2.2 | | 3.0 |
| Y | 89 | 13 | 12[a] | 29 | 24[a] | 17 | 19 | 33 |
| Th | 232 | 36 | 42[b] | 2.2 | 2.2[b] | 4.7 | | 9.6 |
| U | 238 | 3.7 | 3.1[b] | 0.46 | 0.55[b] | 1.4 | | 2.7 |
| Zr | 91 | 210 | 240[c] | 95 | 104[b] | 103 | 108 | 165 |
| Hf | 178 | 6.0 | — | 2.0 | — | 3.0 | — | 3 |
| Sn | 118 | 1.7 | 2.3[g] | 1.5 | 2.3[g] | 0.44 | | 2 |
| Nb | 93 | 20 | 20[g] | 4.0 | 10[g] | 2.6 | — | 20 |
| Mo | 98 | 7.7 | 7[g] | 1.0 | 0.5[g] | 0.58 | — | 1.5 |
| W | 184 | 0.40 | 0.4[g] | 0.30 | 0.45[g] | 0.40 | | 1.5 |
| Ti | 47 | | | | | 5300 | | 5700 |
| Mn | 55 | | | | | 910 | 930 | 950 |
| Cu | 65 | | | | | 25 | 26 | 55 |
| Co | 59 | | | | | 30 | 27 | 25 |
| Ni | 62 | | | | | | | 75 |
| Sc | 45 | | | | | | | 25 |
| V | 51 | | | | | 160 | 142 | 135 |
| Cr | 53 | | | | | 58 | 70 | 100 |
| B | 11 | | | | | 19 | — | 10 |
| Tl | 205 | 1.3 | 1.3[g] | 0.19 | 0.13[g] | 0.45 | | 0.45 |
| Ag | 109 | | | | | Trace | — | 0.07 |
| Pb | 208 | 50 | 49[g] | 8.0 | 8[g] | 8.2 | | 12.5 |
| Cd | 111 | | | | | 1.3 | — | 0.2 |
| Bi | 209 | 0.10 | 0.2[g] | 0.25 | 0.17[g] | | | 0.17 |
| In | 115 | 0.10 | 0.03[g] | 0.35 | 0.08[g] | 0.15 | — | 0.1 |
| Sb | 121 | 0.35 | 0.1[f] | 0.89 | 0.3[f] | 0.18 | — | 0.2 |
| Cu | 65 | | | | | 25 | 26 | 55 |
| As | 75 | 1.2 | 3[f] | 1.8 | 3[f] | — | — | — |
| S | 32 | | | | | | | 160 |
| P | 31 | | | | | 170 | | 1400 |
| F | 19 | | | | | 19 | | 130 |
| Cl | 35 | | | | | 100 | | 625 |
| I | 127 | | | | | 0.12 | | 0.5 |

Table references: [a] L. Haskin and M. Gehl, *J. Geophys. Res.* **68**:2037, 1962. [b] J. W. Morgan and J. F. Lovering, *Anal. Chim. Acta* **28**:405, 1963. [c] M. Kaye, *Geochim. Cosmochim. Acta* **29**:139, 1965. [d] R. H. Filby, *Geochim. Cosmochim. Acta* **29**:49, 1965. [e] G. W. Reed, *Geochim. Cosmochim. Acta* **28**:1729, 1964. [f] R. Brown and W. A. Wolstenholme, *Nature* **201**:598, 1964. [g] M. Fleischer and R. E. Stevens, *Geochim. Cosmochim. Acta* **26**:525, 1962.

values obtained by other methods. In addition, the crustal averages are listed. It is interesting to note the good agreement obtained, particularly on the rare earths, which are notoriously difficult to separate by other techniques.

Apart from the analysis of powder samples for academic interest, the mass spectrometer has been used to solve practical problems involved in production. One such problem reported by Brown and Wolstenholme [17] involved the analysis of two magnesium oxide samples. The samples represent the material used as the refractory in "redring heaters." One sample had been heated in the electrical heater for 2000 hr and had failed. The other sample was unused material. Figure 10 shows the relevant part of the spectra of the two samples. It is apparent that in the "bad" sample, the chromium and manganese levels are significantly higher than in the good samples. The heater comprises an Inconel tube containing a nichrome filament and magnesium oxide refractory. Both Inconel and nichrome contain chromium but only nichrome has a high manganese content; it was, therefore, concluded that the refractory magnesium oxide had probably failed due to migration of material from the nichrome filament. Table VI gives the analysis of the two samples.

The methods available for the analysis of powders by spark source mass spectrometry make possible the analysis of virtually any refractory powder, provided that the particle size is sufficiently small to allow the preparation of homogeneous electrodes. Particles of less than 200 mesh represent a suitable size; where the particle size is greater, the technique of fusion reported by Nicholls [19] may be applicable in many cases.

**Table VI.  Analysis of Magnesium Oxide Results in ppm (atomic)**

| Element | Unused sample | Used sample |
|---|---|---|
| Nickel | 50 | 50 |
| Cobalt | 30 | 30 |
| Iron | 100 | 100 |
| Manganese | 4 | 50 |
| Chromium | 15 | 1800 |
| Vanadium | 1 | 2 |

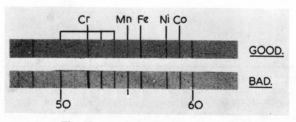

Fig. 10.  Analysis of magnesium oxide.

## BIOLOGICAL MATERIALS

There has been a growing awareness that mass spectrometry would be a useful addition to the analytical techniques available for the analysis of biological samples where only very small amounts of material are available.

Ahearn [24] reported a method for the analysis of liquids. The method involves the evaporation of the liquid sample onto a pure substrate in the form of an electrode. Figure 11 shows the apparatus that Ahearn used to ensure that the liquid drop is held onto the end of the rod. A variable voltage is applied to the field plate, the voltage depending upon the size of the drop. The field is varied so that it prevents the effect of surface tension from spreading the drop up the side of the rod. To achieve evaporation, the rod may be heated by infrared radiation. Figure 12 shows how the drop evaporates while being "pulled" by the electrostatic field. Ahearn reports that it is possible to detect very small concentrations of elements when analysis is carried out by sparking the deposited sample against a pure counter electrode. Work carried out by Chastagnier [25] on the analysis of moderator water confirms Ahearn's statement on sensitivity. Work that we have carried out on geological waters indicates that elements in the $10^{-11}$ to $10^{-12}$ g/ml concentration range may be detected by this method.

In pediatrics, where only too frequently very small samples are available, this method should be very valuable for the analysis of biological fluids. It might be used to check the uptake of various elements in the bloodstream from prescribed treatment involving inorganic elements. Also in many cases, it is important to know the concentration of elements in urine or faeces; such analyses may be routinely carried out by spark source mass spectrometry.

Wolstenholme [26] has reported a technique for the analysis of dried blood plasma. The results reported are semiqualitative only because no standards were available to establish relative sensitivity coefficients. Figure 13 shows the spectra of ignited and unignited plasma. It can be seen that in the case of unignited plasma there is a large contribution of hydrocarbon lines

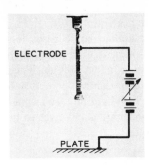

Fig. 11.   Apparatus to hold the liquid drops at the end of the rod.

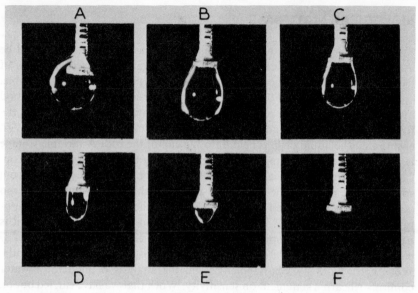

Fig. 12.   Step-by-step evaporation of the drop.

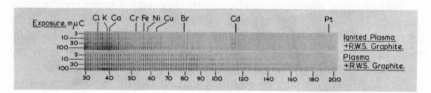

Fig. 13.   Mass spectra of dried blood plasma.

to the spectra which might increase the detection limits. On igniting the sample by conventional means there is a risk that volatile elements may be lost. However, a low-temperature ashing technique[27] is now available which should largely preclude these losses. Further work using this device* is to be carried out, and the results will be reported in the near future.

Many biological samples have been analyzed and in some cases less than a milligram of sample has been available. Techniques for handling such small samples have been developed, involving the use of a specially designed moulding die. Analyses of human hair, dental plaque, dental enamel, and ashed tissue have been carried out. This is a field in which handling techniques will prove to be of critical importance, and many techniques have yet to be developed to handle this rather special class of samples.

* Low Temperature Asher, manufactured by Tracerlab, Richmond, California.

Hickham and Sweeney [28] have found that by using a specially formed counter electrode it is possible to examine very small areas of sample. In Fig. 14 a system for the analysis of niobium wire is illustrated. However, the method should lend itself to the analysis of mounted microtome slices of tissue, although it was used primarily for analysis of inclusions in metal samples.

## ANALYSIS OF SPECIAL SAMPLES

In many cases, the material for analysis is far from ideal in terms of size or physical character. The sample may be too small for mounting directly into the source of the mass spectrometer, it may have an extremely low melting point, or it may be an insulator. Frequently, samples of this type are encountered, and at this point it is of value to illustrate how this type of problem is overcome.

### Small Samples

Often the analyst may be called upon to examine samples such as a semiconductor disk having a diameter of less than 1 mm, or perhaps a single crystal of cadmium sulfide, tin oxide, or ruby. In these cases, the sample must be mounted in some suitable support material. Pure indium has been chosen as a mount for such samples [29]. Indium may be obtained in a very pure state, since it is used in the preparation of III–V semiconductors. It is very malleable, so it may be formed into whatever shape is required. To mount a single crystal, an indium rod is cut at one end with a clean scalpel and the end of the rod is opened out so that the crystal may be inserted into the slit. The indium rod is etched prior to insertion of the sample. The sample is held rigid simply by crimping the end of the indium rod over it. Figure 15 shows two crystals mounted in this way. Table VII shows a comparison of analytical values by emission spectroscopy and mass spectrography on CdSe crystals.

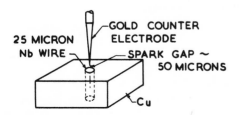

25 MICRON Nb WIRE — GOLD COUNTER ELECTRODE — SPARK GAP ~ 50 MICRONS — Cu

Fig. 14. Apparatus for analysis of niobium wire.

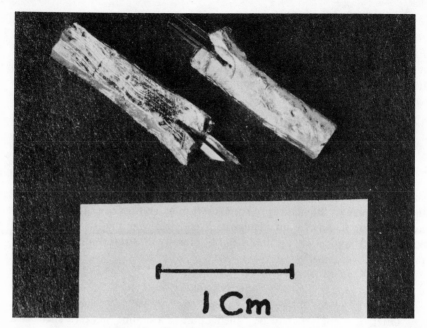

Fig. 15. Crystals mounted on indium rods.

**Table VII. Analysis of Cadmium Selenide Crystals [results in ppm (atomic)]**

| Element | Mass spectrography | Emission spectroscopy |
|---|---|---|
| Boron | 1 | 1 |
| Chromium | 5 | 6 |
| Zinc | 100 | 60 |
| Silicon | 150 | 120 |
| Copper | 10 | 6 |
| Phosphorus | 2 | <300 |
| Barium | 1 | <10 |

Another method is to attach the sample onto a metal rod using a silver epoxy resin; this is chosen because of its low vapor pressure.

Robin et al.[30] have analyzed crystals of ruby by tying them into a conducting substrate with gold wire.

## Low-Melting-Point Materials

Work on the analysis of gallium (MP, +29.8 °C) at Associated Electrical Industries Limited led to the development of a method of refrigerating samples during sparking. Wolstenholme[31] has reported the method employed for the analysis of gallium and states that the sample is held in the solid state throughout the analysis. This has the effect of reducing errors in the determination of volatile elements which would normally be distilled from a molten sample. Figure 16 shows a diagram of the refrigeration system designed by AEI and reported by Wolstenholme.

Nalbantoglu[32] has reported an improved method for refrigerating samples, and although the principle is essentially the same as the earlier design, reported by Wolstenholme, more efficient cooling is achieved by the use of solid silver as the conducting material. Figure 17 shows a photograph of Nalbantoglu's system. Using the system as illustrated, Nalbantoglu has analyzed mercury with a remarkable degree of success. Table VIII shows a comparison of a relatively pure and an impure sample of mercury. It is apparent that a limit of detection down to 0.0004 ppm weight is attainable for chlorine and down to the $10^{-8}$ range for other elements. Analysis of reagents may be carried out using this system, and Table IX shows a comparison of two samples of phosphoric acid.

The scope of this method should prove to be very wide, and it provides a valuable addition to existing methods of analysis of reagents.

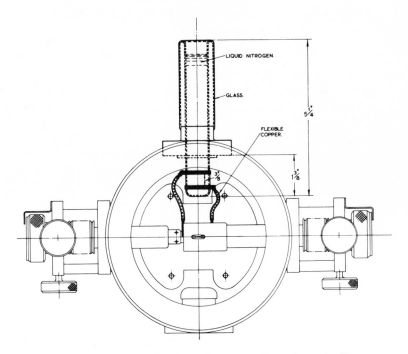

Fig. 16.   AEI refrigeration system used for the analysis of gallium.

Fig. 17.   Improved refrigeration system using solid silver as a conductor.

**Table VIII.   Analysis of Mercury (results in ppm weight)**

| Element | Sample 1 | Sample 2 |
|---------|----------|----------|
| Bi | 30 | <0.05 |
| Cd | 30 | 1 |
| Ag | — | — |
| Ga | 1.5 | 0.1 |
| Zn | 9 | 0.2 |
| Cu | 2.5 | 0.15 |
| Fe | 5.6 | 0.6 |
| Mn | 0.08 | <0.01 |
| Ca | 0.4 | 0.2 |
| K | 0.4 | 0.1 |
| Cl | 0.25 | 0.0004 |
| Al | 0.4 | <0.1 |
| Na | 0.8 | <0.1 |

## Insulators

Analysis of insulators may be carried out by grinding them to powders and using the method of Brown and Wolstenholme [17], described earlier in this chapter. However, in doing this, the risk of contamination of the sample is high. James and Williams [33] described a method of mounting an insulating sample and a conductor side by side in an electrode holder, so that the spark may be initiated on the conductor and then transferred to the insulating sample. The method is very useful but suffers from the disadvantage that the ratio of ions produced from the insulator and the conductor is variable.

**Table IX.   Analysis of Phosphoric Acid (results in ppm weight)**

| Element | Sample 1 | Sample 2 |
|---------|----------|----------|
| Bi | 170 | — |
| Pt | 800 | 2 |
| Co | 140 | 5 |
| Ni | 165 | 0.2 |
| Fe | 10 | 6 |
| Mn | 160 | — |
| Cr | 3 | 2 |
| Ca | 13 | 8 |
| K | 40 | 20 |
| Cl | 4600 | 1.2 |
| Al | 4 | 2.5 |
| Na | 450 | 420 |
| B | 90 | 0.01 |

Ahearn [34] has described a method of examining steatite by sparking against a counter electrode of a pure metal. The bulk impurities may be determined using this method but the sensitivity of the method is dependent upon the "blank" values from the counter electrode. Figure 18 shows a diagram of electrode arrangements which may be employed for the analysis of insulators.

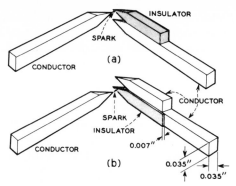

Fig. 18.   Two electrode arrangements used for analysis of insulators.

## Gases in Solids

The determination of interstitial gases in metals may be carried out by spark source mass spectrometry. Evidence suggests that the problems involved in this analysis are not instrumental but are in the handling and preparation of the sample. The cleaning of a sample surface with chemical reagents introduces complications in that a film of surface oxide is almost certainly produced. Physical methods of preparation have been used, and turning a metal sample with a clean diamond-tipped tool appears to be satisfactory.

It has been found that an extensive pre-spark prior to analysis aids in decreasing the contribution from surface-adsorbed or reacted gases. Indeed the normal practice of making exposures of gradually increasing length should be abandoned in favor of a reverse sequence and the longest exposures should be taken first.

It is possible to determine the concentration of gases down to 1 ppm or less, but it is difficult to establish how quantitative the results are, since no reliable standards are available for gases at this level of concentration. Considerable work on the determination of gases has been carried out by Blosser [35], who has carried out most of his work on beryllium, and Bourguillot et al. [36] and Stefani et al. [37], who have reported on the determination of gases in copper and beryllium.

## CONCLUSION

Spark source mass spectrometry has been applied to problems of analysis over a wide field. As an analytical technique, it appears to have very great potential since analysis is not dependent upon the limitations of the instruments themselves, but rather on the technique of sample preparation, handling, and presentation to the instrument.

The analyst is presented with problems, the solution of which are largely in his own hands. In these circumstances, it is only a matter of time before spark source mass spectrometry will be used in every field where chemical analysis requiring high sensitivity is essential. The problems of sample handling are very real and cannot be dismissed lightly—they are not, however, insurmountable.

## ACKNOWLEDGMENT

This paper is published with the permission of Dr. J. D. Waldron, General Manager, AEI Scientific Apparatus Department.

# REFERENCES

1. N. B. Hannay and A. J. Ahearn, *Anal. Chem.* **26**:1056, 1954.
2. J. S. Halliday, P. Swift, and W. A. Wolstenholme, *Advances in Mass Spectrometry*, Vol. 3, Inst. Petroleum, London, 1965.
3. R. D. Craig, G. A. Errock, and J. D. Waldron, *Advances in Mass Spectrometry*, Vol. 1, Pergamon Press, 1959.
4. R. E. Honig and J. R. Woolston, *Appl. Phys. Letters* **2**:138, 1963.
5. R. E. Honig and J. R. Woolston, *Appl. Phys. Letters* **3**:8, 1963.
6. AEI Tech. Inform. Sheet, No. A2006, Associated Electrical Industries Limited, Manchester, England.
7. AEI Tech. Inform. Sheet, No. A160, Associated Electrical Industries Limited, Manchester, England.
8. D. R. Wood and R. M. Cook, *Metallurgia* **67**:109, 1963.
9. T. A. Davies, *Proc. Feigl Anniversary Symposium*, Birmingham, England, 1960.
10. AEI Tech. Inform. Sheet, No. A134, Associated Electrical Industries Limited, Manchester, England.
11. R. Brown, R. D. Craig, J. A. James, and C. M. Wilson, *Proc. Conf. Ultrapurification Semicond. Mater.*, Boston, April 1961.
12. W. M. Hickham and Y. L. Sandler, in: J. I. Bregman and A. Dravnieks (eds.), *Surface Effects in Detection*, Spartan Books, Washington, p. 192, 1965.
13. W. M. Hickham and G. G. Sweeney, in: A. J. Ahearn (ed.), *Mass Spectrometric Analysis of Solids*, Elsevier, Amsterdam, 1966.
14. R. Brown, Analysis of Stainless Steel, *Joyce Loebl Rev.*, Spring 1963.
15. E. R. Blosser, private communication, Battelle Memorial Institute, 1964.
16. A. J. Johnson, A. Kozy, and R. N. Morris, *Proc. 14th Ann. Conf. Mass Spectrometry Allied Topics*, Dallas, 1966, pp. 154–159.
17. R. Brown and W. A. Wolstenholme, Analysis of Insulating Powers, *ASTM E14 Meeting Mass Spectrometry*, San Fransisco, 1963, Paper No. 75.
18. G. A. Errock, *10th Intern. Conf. Spectroscopy*, College Park, Maryland, June 1962.
19. G. D. Nicholls, A. L. Graham, E. Williams, and M. Wood, Precision and Accuracy in Trace Element Analysis of Geological Materials Using Solid Source Spark Mass Spectrography, *Anal. Chem.* **39**(6): 584, 1967.
20. P. F. S. Jackson and J. Whitehead, *Analyst* **91**:418–427, 1966.
21. P. F. S. Jackson, P. G. T. Vossen, and J. Whitehead, The Use of an Ion Beam Chopper for Improved Precision in Spark Source Mass Spectrography, *Anal. Chem.* **39**(14): 1737, 1967.
22. R. Brown and W. A. Wolstenholme, *Nature* **201**:598, 1964.
23. S. R. Taylor, *Geochim. Cosmochim. Acta* **29**:1243–1261, 1965.
24. A. J. Ahearn, *J. Appl. Phys.* **32**:1197, 1961.
25. P. Chastagnier, *ASTM E14 Meeting Mass Spectrometry*, Montreal, 1964, Paper No. 55.
26. W. A. Wolstenholme, *Nature* **203**:1284–1285, 1964.
27. C. E. Gleit and W. D. Holland, *Anal. Chem.* **34**:1454–1457, 1962.
28. W. M. Hickham and G. G. Sweeney, in: A. J. Ahearn (ed.), *Mass Spectrometric Analysis of Solids*, Elsevier, Amsterdam, 1966.
29. AEI Tech. Inform. Sheet, No. A172, Associated Electrical Industries Limited, Manchester, England.
30. A. M. Robin, J. C. Brun, A. Cornu, and R. Stefani, CENG, Grenoble Report CENG/DPC/SIS/SSM No. 65-303 AMR/JG.
31. W. A. Wolstenholme, *Appl. Spectr.* **17**:5, 1963.
32. M. Nalbantoglu, Analysis of Metals with Low Melting Point by Spark Source Mass Spectrometry, *ASTM E14, GAMS, Brit. Inst. Pet. Meeting*, Paris, September 1964.

33. J. A. James and J. L. Williams, in: J. D. Waldron (ed.), *Advances in Mass Spectrometry*, Vol. 1, Pergamon Press, Oxford, 1959, p. 157.
34. A. J. Ahearn, *J. Appl. Phys.* **32**:1195, 1961.
35. E. R. Blosser, private communication, Battelle Memorial Institute, 1964.
36. R. Bourguillot, A. Cavard, A. Cornu, A. M. Robin, and R. Stefani, *Bull. Chem. Soc. France* **430**(8):2621–2623, 1966.
37. R. Stefani, R. Bourguillot, and A. Cornu, *Intern. Conf. Metallurgy Beryllium*, Grenoble, May 1965.

# MASS SPECTROMETRY IN NUCLEAR PHYSICS RESEARCH

## H. W. Wilson

*Scottish Research Reactor Centre*
*East Kilbride, Scotland*

In this chapter we can of necessity deal only briefly with the applications of mass spectrometry in the nuclear physics field [1, 2]. The emphasis will be on measurements of importance in the areas of reactor and fission physics.

Solid, gas, and spark source machines, time-of-flight instruments, and high-resolution equipment all play a part. However, the discussion that follows deals mainly with solid and gas source machines since these are most common.

The criteria of importance are the following:

1. *Sensitivity:* Very often rather small amounts of material are available from, e.g., nuclear reactions. Thus, sensitivity is often important. It is possible in solid source machines to measure $10^{-12}$ g or even less total sample of many elements and in gas machines as little as, for example, $2 \times 10^{-14}$ cc of xenon, i.e., $5 \times 10^5$ atoms.

2. *Abundance Sensitivity:* This is the ability to measure small peaks adjacent to very large ones. Double magnetic stage instruments offer a big advantage over single-stage ones although other techniques, such as retardation of ions, also improve this aspect of performance. For example, if one is trying to measure the small amount of daughter product formed by the $(n, \gamma)$ or $(n, 2n)$ reactions, abundance sensitivity is most important. It is possible with the use of a two-stage machine operating in the tantalum region to measure an isotope whose abundance is only $10^{-7}$ of an isotope one mass removed. The addition of an electrostatic stage further improves this performance. A single-stage machine would have an abundance sensitivity of about 1 part in $10^4$ to $10^5$ depending on radius, accelerating voltage, and other factors.

3. *Resolution:* The resolution required depends on the problem. For

most of the measurements to be described, a resolution of $\Delta m/m = 1/500$ would be adequate. A very much higher resolution is required, of course, for nuclear mass measurements; for example, the mass of the neutron is now known to 1 part in $10^7$ or 0.1 keV, of $O^{16}$ (relative to $C^{12}$) to 1.5 parts in $10^8$.

## ISOTOPE DILUTION

Isotope dilution is a most important technique, applicable to many types of measurement. To take just one example, it is difficult to measure very small amounts of $U^{235}$ on accelerator targets. Alpha counting is not accurate because of interference from $U^{234}$ alphas. But by adding a small and known amount of $U^{233}$ and measuring the ratio of $U^{235}$ to $U^{233}$, the amount of $U^{235}$ can be deduced. The $U^{233}$ usually is known as the "spike," and a correction must be made for any $U^{235}$ (and $U^{234}$, $U^{236}$, $U^{238}$) it may contain. This correction normally would be small. The $U^{233}$ can be measured by alpha counting since its half-life is short compared to that of $U^{235}$. In principle, this technique can be applied to any element which has more than one stable isotope and even to cases where only radioactive isotopes are available, provided these are sufficiently long-lived (see Fig. 1).

## CROSS-SECTION MEASUREMENTS

An important application is to the measurement of nuclear cross sections. Mass spectrometry can play a part in a number of ways. As an example of how it can be used directly, suppose we wish to measure the thermal neutron capture cross section of $U^{235}$:

$$U^{235} + n \rightarrow U^{236} + \gamma$$

The $U^{235}$ is irradiated for a time $t$ and by a total flux of neutrons $\phi \times t$, where $\phi$ is the number of neutrons/cm$^2$-sec. The irradiation should be not so long that the parent material is appreciably burned up. Then from a measurement of the ratio $U^{236}/U^{235}$ the cross section $\sigma_c$ can be calculated:

$$\text{number of atoms of } U^{236} = \text{number of atoms of } U^{235} \times \sigma_c \, \phi t$$

The mass spectrometry method is especially useful when the daughter is stable or too long-lived to be measured by radioactive methods. It should be pointed out that other methods of measuring this cross section exist, and also that $\phi$ must be accurately known. Clearly, high abundance sensitivity is important here.

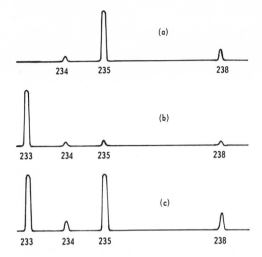

Fig. 1. (a) Mass spectrum of unspiked $U^{235}$ sample. (b) Mass spectrum of spike. (c) Mass spectrum of spike plus sample.

Another example is the measurement of the cross section of the fission product $Pm^{147}$ for the reaction $Pm^{147} (n, \gamma) Pm^{148}$. $Pm^{147}$ decays with a half-life of 2.65 years to form $Sm^{147}$ [3]. $Pm^{148}$ is formed partly in an isomeric state, decaying to form $Sm^{148}$ with a half-life of 42 days, and partly in the ground state, decaying to $Sm^{148}$ with a half-life of 5.3 days.

One might in principle measure the ratio $Pm^{148}/Pm^{147}$ by mass spectrometry but, because of half-life considerations, only a relatively short radiation would be possible; the ratio $Pm^{148}/Pm^{147}$ would be small and, therefore, difficult to measure. However, by allowing the irradiated sample to decay and separating the samarium formed, one can measure the ratio $Sm^{148}/Sm^{147}$. This is enhanced by the long half-life of $Pm^{147}$ relative to that of $Pm^{148}$. Also by separating the samarium at several intervals following the irradiation, one can obtain the cross section to form the isomeric and the ground states of $Pm^{148}$.

An important cross-section measurement in the reactor field is that of $\alpha$, which is the ratio of capture cross section to fission cross section for fissile isotopes. There is a well-known "four factor formula" in reactor physics,

$$k = \eta pf\varepsilon$$

which is a measure of the criticality of a reactor system. It is important to know the factors as accurately as possible for calculation purposes. If one could design a reactor purely by calculation, this would, in principle, save the costs of zero energy and prototype experiments, which run to millions of dollars. This is not yet possible, but what has been written serves to emphasize the importance of accurate measurements of the four constants. The term $\eta$ is the ratio of thermal neutrons captured in fuel causing fission to the total number captured and can be written

$$\eta = \frac{v}{1+\alpha}$$

Now, at least for important fissile isotopes, $\alpha$ is less than unity and, for example, is about 0.1725 for $U^{235}$. Thus, if $v$ is known accurately (which it is in this case), one can calculate $\eta$ to an accuracy some six or seven times better than the accuracy to which $\alpha$ is known. There are different ways of carrying out the measurement of $\alpha$. For example, Cabell and Slee [4], at Harwell, have measured $U^{235}$ and $U^{236}$ relative to $U^{238}$ in an enriched sample of $U^{235}$. Since $U^{238}$ has a much smaller neutron cross section than does $U^{235}$, the measurement of these two ratios allows one to measure both the fission *and* capture burnup of $U^{235}$ and, therefore, the cross sections.

Of course mass spectrometry can often play a subsidiary role in cross-section measurements as, for example, in the measurement of isotopic ratios in enriched targets for beam experiments.

## ISOTOPIC RATIOS

In the reactor field, accurate measurement of the isotopic ratios of uranium and plutonium is of considerable importance both for economic and for reactor physics reasons. With highly enriched uranium costing of the order of £4,000 per kilogram, it is clearly necessary to be able to measure accurately both the initial enrichment of reactor fuel and the degree of burnup. Reactor physicists and engineers are interested also in the change in Pu and U ratios in different parts of a reactor.

## FISSION PRODUCT YIELDS

Gas and solid source instruments have been used in fission yield measurements following the work of Thode and Graham [5] who used gas instruments to measure krypton and xenon isotope fission yields. These are produced with high yield in the fission process. This and other work showed fine structure in the shape of the yield curve and, in particular, that $Mo^{100}$, $Xe^{133}$, and $Xe^{134}$ fission yields lay well above the curve. The nuclear shell model provides an explanation of this phenomenon, the effect being due to the stability of "magic" number groups of nucleons. This work has been reviewed by Thode, McMullen, and Fritze [6].

## HALF-LIFE MEASUREMENT AND IDENTIFICATION
## OF ACTIVE ISOTOPES

A classic example of the use of the mass spectrometer in this field was to elucidate the decay of rubidium which was shown to be radioactive as long ago as 1906 by J. J. Thomson [7]. Mass spectrometric analysis of strontium extracted from minerals containing rubidium was made by Mattauch [8] and showed that the strontium did not have the normal isotopic composition but that the mass 87 isotopic abundance was enhanced. Thus, the radioactivity of rubidium, which consists of two isotopes masses 85 and 87, was due to $Rb^{87}$. If one knows the age of a rubidium-rich mineral from other measurements, e.g., by $K^{40}$ or U–Pb dating, the half-life of $Rb^{87}$ can be determined as was done first by Strassman and Walling [9]. Or, if the half-life is known, the measurement of $Sr^{87}$ and rubidium in a sample can be used to measure the age of the mineral. However, isotope geology is outside the scope of this chapter.

Nevertheless the measurement of the half-life of $Rb^{87}$ affords another example of how the mass spectrometer can play a part. McNair and Wilson[10] measured the half-life by radioactive counting methods, using rubidium enriched in $Rb^{87}$ to enhance the counting rate. To make a thin and uniform source, vacuum sublimation was employed. Mass spectrometry was used both to measure the enrichment of the rubidium and also, by isotope dilution, to determine the quantity of rubidium in the source.

An accurate knowledge of the half-life of $C^{14}$ is important for dating purposes, and one method recently employed in several laboratories [11] is to measure accurately the isotopic composition of $CO_2$ with a high $C^{14}$ content, dilute the sample by a factor of $10^7$ or more, and then count the radioactivity of an aliquot of the gas by proportional counting methods.

## RADIATION EFFECTS

The effect of nuclear and, in particular, reactor radiation on organic materials has important biological and reactor operational consequences. A few experiments have been made analyzing, by mass spectrometry, the products of such irradiations over rather long periods, but in an experiment at present under way at the Reactor Centre it is hoped to measure shorter-lived products and also to distinguish between primary and secondary irradiation effects.

## OTHER APPLICATIONS

Mention might be made of the use of mass spectrometers in isotope separator programs, elucidation of nuclear decay schemes, identification of fissile nuclides, accurate mass measurements, isotopic ratios of rare gases in meteorites, spallation studies, and so on, but space does not permit. We have not discussed spark source machines, but they can play an important part in many investigations in the identification and measurement of trace quantities of elements in materials. However, if further information is required, reference may be made to the two articles of Hintenberger [1] and Wilson and Daly [2], which can also be used to guide further reading.

## REFERENCES

1. H. Hintenberger, High Sensitivity Mass Spectroscopy in Nuclear Studies, *Ann. Rev. Nuclear Sci.* **12**:435, 1962.
2. H. W. Wilson and N. R. Daly, Mass Spectrometry of Solids, *J. Sci. Instr.* **40**:273, 1963.
3. N. C. Fenner and R. S. Large, *J. Inorg. Nucl. Chem.* **29**:2147, 1967.
4. M. J. Cabell and L. J. Slee, *J. Inorg. Nucl. Chem.* **24**:1493, 1962.
5. H. G. Thode and R. L. Graham, *Can. J. Research* **A25**:1, 1947.
6. H. G. Thode, C. G. McMullen, and K. Fritze, *Advan. Inorg. Chem. Radiochem.* **2**:315, 1960.
7. J. J. Thomson, *Phil. Mag.* **10**:584, 1906.
8. J. Mattauch, *Naturwissenschaften* **25**:189, 1937; *Physik. Z. Sowjetunion* **38**:951, 1937.
9. F. Strassman and E. Walling, *Ber. Deut. Chem. Ges.* **71**:1, 1938.
10. A. McNair and H. W. Wilson, *Phil. Mag.* **6**:563, 1961.
11. W. B. Mann, W. F. Marlow, and E. E. Hughes, *Intern. J. Appl. Radiation Isotopes* **11**:57, 1961; D. E. Watt, D. Ramsden, and H. W. Wilson, *Intern. J. Appl. Radiation Isotopes* **11**:68, 1961; I. U. Olssen, I. Karlen, A. H. Turnbull, and N. J. Prosser, *Arkiv Fysik* **22**:237, 1962.

# VALIDITY OF SELECTION RULES IN EXCITATION AND IONIZATION COLLISION PROCESSES

## Jacques E. Collin

*Laboratoire de Spectrométrie de Masse*
*Institut de Chimie*
*Université de Liège*
*Liège, Belgium*

## INTRODUCTION

The amount of information obtained in recent years on the excitation, ionization, and dissociation processes of atoms and molecules shows the interest that has arisen in the subject, but emphasizes the discrepancies and the difficulties which appear when an attempt is made to provide a general and consistent scheme for the description of the interaction of particles and of the evolution of the excited species which are observed. Two recent conferences [M8 ,Q1] on the physics of atomic and electronic collisions give a good idea of the nature and importance of the research currently undertaken in that field.

Theoretical approaches have been restricted mostly to conditions where the Born (BO) approximation is valid, but little experimental evidence, except for atoms, has been found to justify it, and we should like to review the present status of the question. We shall therefore discuss the BO approximation, in relation with experimental results, and consider to what extent experimental circumstances lead to different interaction laws and possibly to a violation of selection rules. We shall try, if possible, to obtain general information on these selection rules with regard to the nature and relative importance of the effectively observed transitions, when different kinds of impact particles are used.

Obviously, these questions depend on the collision interaction time, and they might bring an answer regarding the nature of the resulting excited neutral or ionized states of the atoms or molecules.

Different, but at least as important, is the problem of predicting the behavior of the produced excited species; in particular, the case of ions is important, since the selection rules on which this behavior depends should be at the basis of an explanation of mass spectra. The general theory known as the "quasi-equilibrium statistical theory" was developed some fifteen years ago by Rosenstock and collaborators (for a good review of the theory see [R2]) and has been used many times in semiquantitative calculations of mass spectra. As such, it is useful mainly in explaining the basic features of the mass spectral patterns for molecules large enough to allow a statistical treatment on the basis of the evolution of the ground state of the molecular ion. It is, however, not immediately applicable to small molecules, where discrete electronic levels of ions have to be considered separately, and where symmetry properties of ions may induce particular selection rules. This important problem has been particularly considered recently by Lorquet and his collaborators [L17-L20] at the University of Liège, and great promises have appeared in this field.

The case of the superexcited neutral species brought into the ionization continuum range is also important, particularly when it leads, through preionization or predissociation, to the appearance of ions. The very general occurrence of these phenomena is just beginning to be realized and has opened a new field of intense research [M14].

## EXCITATION AND IONIZATION OF ATOMS AND MOLECULES BY COLLISION PROCESSES

### Introduction

The interaction of electrons with atoms and molecules and the variation of excitation and ionization cross sections with the impinging particle's energy have been discussed thoroughly by different authors. Particularly interesting are the chapters on this subject to be found in several excellent books [B4, F3, G2, H3, M4, M5, M6, M22, R3, S17]. More specific aspects were discussed by Wannier [W3], Geltman [G3], Watanabe [W4], and Cottrell and Walker [C12]. In all cases, quantum-mechanical calculations have been performed using, of necessity, approximations for the resolution of the many-body problems involved. The most widely used is the Born approximation, which we shall briefly discuss.

Since the interaction problem and the involved simplifying approximations relate to the time allowed for the impinging particle to interact with the target atom or molecule, it may be anticipated that the relative speeds of the particles and also, therefore, their kinetic energy will be of utmost importance. It follows that impinging particles of different masses having the same kinetic energy may induce different transitions, owing to their different velocities.

# The Born Approximation
# and Its Application to Impact Processes

## *Excitation and Ionization Cross-Section Laws*

A general discussion of the BO approximation is given in the well-known book of Massey and Burhop [M5], and a good résumé recently has been published by Schram [S5].

The classical treatment of binary collisions leads to an expression for the variation of cross sections very different from the experimental results and will not be considered here. On the other hand, the quantum-mechanical treatment requires the solution of the correct expression of the Schrödinger equation. Even the simplest case of a hydrogen atom and an electron is a three-body problem, and approximate solutions will have to be found.

The BO approximation has been introduced for that purpose. It assumes that there is practically no interaction between the bombarding particle and the target, i.e., the wave of the incident particle is undistorted by the force field of the target species, and the wave function of the interested atomic or molecular electron is not disturbed by the projectile. At equal speeds, this assumption is likely to be better verified for neutral particles than for electrons or ions.

It may be shown that these hypotheses are practically valid if the energy transferred through the collision complex to the target is small compared to that of the incident particle; more precisely, it should be valid when the impinging particle's energy is such that its velocity is at least five to seven times that of the orbital electron, of which the energy is of the order of 10 to 15 eV. From that point of view, the BO approximation should hold for electrons having energies of the order of 200 eV or more.

When these conditions are met, only the electric field of the projectile influences the target particle at long distances, and a weak perturbation treatment may be followed. In such a case, the differential interaction (excitation or ionization) cross section for atoms and electrons may be shown to follow theoretically the general equation (1), using Massey's notations [M5]:

$$I_{0,n} = \frac{4 \pi^2 m^2}{h^4} \cdot \frac{k_n}{k} \left| \int V_{0,n}(r') \exp \left[ i(k\bar{n}_0 - k_n \bar{n}_1) \, \bar{r}' \right] d\tau \right|^2 \qquad (1)$$

where $2 \pi/k$ is the wavelength of the impinging particle before collision, $2 \pi/k_n$ is the wavelength of the impinging particle after collision, and $\bar{n}_0$ and $\bar{n}_1$ are the vectors in the direction of incidence and scattering.

$$V_{0,n}(r) = e^2 \int \sum_1^N \frac{1}{r_{0s}} \, \Psi_0(\bar{r}_1, \bar{r}_2, ..., \bar{r}_N) \, \Psi_n^* (\bar{r}_1, ..., \bar{r}_N) \, d\tau_1 ... d\tau_N \qquad (2)$$

with $r_{0\ s}$ the distance between impact electron and $s$th atomic electron and $\psi_0$, $\psi_n$ the wave functions for ground and $n$th atom excited state. According to Bethe [B5], this may be simplified by integration over the coordinates of the incident electron in the following manner:

$$I_{0,n} = \frac{4\pi^2 m^2 e^4}{h^4} \cdot \frac{k_n}{k} \left| \frac{4\pi}{K^2} \int \Psi_0 \left( \sum_1^N \exp\left[ i(k\bar{n}_0 - k_n \bar{n}_1) \bar{r}_s \right] \right) \Psi_n^* \, d\tau_1 \ldots d\tau_n \right|^2$$

(3)

with $K^2 = k^2 + k^2_n - 2\,kk_n \cos\theta$ and $\bar{r}_s$ being the multiplicity of the atom.

If a single electron in the atom is involved in the transition, as is generally the case, the summation may be dropped and, to obtain the total cross section, integration should be performed over all values of $\theta$:

$$Q_{0,n} = 2\pi \int I_{0,n}(\theta) \sin\theta \, d\theta$$

(4)

or, by changing the variable,

$$Q_{0,n} = \frac{2\pi}{kk_n} \int_{K_{\min}}^{K_{\max}} I_{0,n}(K) \, K \, dK$$

(5)

It may be shown that a good approximation to this equation is

$$Q_{0,n} \cong \frac{4\pi m^2 e^4}{k^2 \hbar^6} |z_{0,n}|^2 \log \frac{2\,mv^2}{E_n - E_0}$$

(6)

where $|z_{0,n}|^2 = \int \psi_0(\bar{r}) |Z| \psi_n^*(\bar{r}) \, d\tau$ is the dipole moment matrix element for the transition. This expression is valid only for $|z_{0,n}| \neq 0$, i.e., for optically allowed transitions.* In such a case, the cross section is thus proportional to $1/v^2 \cdot \log v^2$.

For an optically forbidden transition, $|z_{0,n}| = 0$ and another approximate expression is found:

$$Q_{0,n} \cong \frac{2\pi m^3 e^4}{k^2 \hbar^6} |(z^2)_{0,n}|^2 |E_0|$$

(7)

where $|(z^2)_{0,n}|$ is the quadrupole matrix element. In this case, the cross section should be proportional to $1/v^2$.

Equations (6) and (7) (Bethe's equations) are valid only for transitions between the ground state and the excited state $n$. Therefore, the true cross

---

* A good discussion of optically allowed and forbidden transitions may be found in the review papers of Garstang [G2] and Nicholls and Stewart [N2].

section should take into account a summation of such expressions over all possible transitions in the energy range considered. Obviously, this complicates the problem considerably, particularly in the case of molecules, where the number of accessible states within a small energy range may be important.

The extension of Bethe's equations (6) and (7) to ionization may be obtained similarly, and must take into account the kinetic energy of the ejected electron. In this way, Bethe [B5] obtained the following relation for the electron-impact ionization cross section, for removal of an electron having quantum numbers $n$ and $l$:

$$Q_{nl}^+ \cong \frac{2\pi e^4}{m_e v_0^2} \cdot \frac{c_{nl}}{|I_{nl}|} \cdot Z_{nl} \log \frac{2 m_e v_0^2}{C_{nl}} \tag{8}$$

with

$$c_{nl} = \frac{Z_{eff}^2}{n^2 a_0^2} \int |z_{nl,k}|^2 \, dk \tag{9}$$

where $Z_{eff}$ is the effective nuclear charge; $Z_{nl}$ is the number of electrons in the $n$, $l$-shell; $I_{nl}$ is the ionization energy for the $n$, $l$-electron; $C_{nl}$ is the energy of the order of $I_{nl}$; and $k$ is the kinetic energy of the ejected electron. In the same way, one obtains [M4, M21] for the cross section of ionization by a fast ion of charge $+Z'e$

$$Q_{nl}^+ \cong \frac{2\pi Z'^2 e^4 c_{nl} Z_{nl}}{m_e v_0^2 |I_{nl}|} \log \frac{2 m_e v_0^2}{C_{nl}} \tag{10}$$

As given, this relation applies strictly to completely stripped nuclei, such as $H^+$ or $He^{++}$, so that for heavy ions used as bombarding particles, generally having a single positive charge, an effective charge $Z'_{eff}$ must be used in equation (10). For instance, a value of $1.2e$ must be used for $Z'_{eff}$ in $He^+$, which is considerably less than the effective charge $1.69e$ deduced from theoretical calculations for the ground state wave function for helium [M22].

In addition, the calculation of the ionization cross sections may be in error, particularly for molecules, because of the possibility of excitation to superexcited states, located in the ionization continuum energy range. If such is the case, the probability of preionization may be of importance and possibly will contribute to the resultant total ionization cross section, inasmuch as the lifetime of these superexcited states is not too long. (This will generally be the case, most lifetimes ranging between $10^{-10}$ and $10^{-14}$ sec.)

## Multiplicity—Allowed and Forbidden Transitions

According to equation (3), the probability for a transition accompanied by a change of multiplicity $\bar{r}_s$ of the atom or molecule should be zero, if spin-orbit coupling is neglected. Therefore, the total spin of the target cannot change during the collision. This is in part due to the different symmetry properties of the wave functions for different multiplicity states, since the integral $\int \psi_0 \psi_n{}^* \, d\tau$ vanishes, when $\psi_0$ and $\psi_n{}^*$ have different multiplicities [M5]. This rule is the same as for optical transitions.

The situation may be different for electron bombardment. It is indeed the total spin of the electron-target system which should be conserved. For a target of spin $s$, and multiplicity $2s+1$, and an electron of spin $\frac{1}{2}$ (in $h/2\pi$ units), the total spin will be $s \pm \frac{1}{2}$. If the excitation brings the target to a state $n'$ of multiplicity $s'$, the total spin becomes $s' \pm \frac{1}{2}$, and for a spin-allowed transition one must have $s' \pm \frac{1}{2} \leqslant s \pm \frac{1}{2}$, i.e., $s' = s-1$, $s$, or $s+1$, so that the multiplicity of the state may change by $\pm 2$, if the spin of the impinging electron and of that electron leaving the collision complex have opposite directions. Since spin-orbit coupling is neglected, this implies an exchange of electrons. Therefore, it might be expected to occur if the bombarding particle's speed is low enough to allow for an exchange during the collision time.

In fact, for slow electrons, the collision cross sections for spin-forbidden transitions become quite large [M5], and we shall examine later the experimental evidence now available.

## Experimental Consequences of Selection Rules

### Excitation and Ionization Cross Sections

An obvious test for the theory which we have briefly outlined is to verify experimentally the adequacy of the equations referring to the cross-section variation with the energy and speed of the bombarding particle.

As has been seen, equations (6) and (7) should give a fairly good description of this variation for both optically allowed and forbidden transitions, in the case electron bombardment. This is an interesting case, because the energy of the electrons may easily be varied within a wide range; from such a study, one should be able to determine the range of validity of the BO approximation, and, as a consequence, the range of energies where forbidden transition may play a role in the collision processes. *

---

* It may be useful to recall here that ionization cross sections should have approximately the same value for electrons and protons of equal velocities, as soon as their speed is greater than $10^9$ cm/sec [M22], i.e., as soon as the BO approximation is valid.

In the case of photon-impact cross sections, for which an equivalent expression to equation (6) has been developed [S5, M15], the problems are different, since the speed of the particle is now independent of its energy. Therefore, the cross section should also be independent of the wavelength, as soon as the photon energy is greater than the threshold value of the process which is considered.

Most interesting are the cases of excitation and ionization cross sections by heavy particles, charged or not, such as protons, $\alpha$ particles, ions, atoms, and molecules. The experimental evidence, unfortunately, is not very abundant to date.

## Transition Probabilities and Critical Processes

The second type of information one may look for is the transition probability for a given process. Optical transition probabilities may be calculated and determined experimentally by spectroscopy. The equivalent measurements for other types of projectiles than photons are by no means as easy to obtain.

One good method is to study the energy loss of a scattered electron beam after passage through the gas, as a function of the scattering angle, and particularly at low scattering angles. Many new results have recently been obtained in that way and have been greatly improved by the use of monoenergetic electron beams [C7] as a source of excitation. The amount of scattered electrons having lost the critical energy corresponding to a given excitation (and/or ionization) process is proportional to the so-called "generalized oscillator strength" as defined by Bethe [B4, B5] and is analogous to the oscillator strength used by spectroscopists. An expression for this generalized oscillator strength is the following [S5]:

$$f_n(K) = \frac{E_n}{R} \left| \frac{1}{Ka_0} \int e^{iKz} \, \Psi_0(r) \, \Psi_n^* \, d\tau_r \right|^2 \tag{11}$$

where $K$ is defined as in equation (3), $a_0$ is the Bohr radius in the hydrogen atom, and $R$ is the Rydberg constant.

A careful analysis of the observed generalized oscillator strengths in photon and electron excitation should allow detection of forbidden transitions. The comparison of the critical processes induced by both types of projectiles by threshold techniques might also bring complementary information, particularly within the first ionization continuum range, since they imply the use of low-energy electrons, i.e., slow electrons; this is the general situation in ionization and appearance potential work in mass spectrometry. This is unfortunately a simplified view of the real situation, for many complications generally arise and blur the effects, among others vibrational (and rotational) excitation, preionization, predissociation, etc.

*Comparison of Mass Spectra Obtained with Various Projectiles*

In the particular case of the excitation to higher levels than the first ionization limit, at least a fraction of the target molecules will appear as ions, at the end of the collision process. If the target particles are polyatomic molecules, the subsequent evolution will be mainly the consequence of the particular excited (and/or ionized) state to which they have been brought. It is to be expected that molecules in different excited states will show a different behavior; this is true, in particular, for the molecular ions brought into different ionic electronic states, for both energy and symmetry reasons.

This is the third source of information. Since the BO approximation's validity seems dependent mainly on the velocity of the incident particle, the mass spectra obtained with different types of particles should be the same, when these particles have the same speed (and, of course, enough energy for the transition to occur). This should be so at least for particles of the same electrical kind, i.e., photons and atoms or molecules; electrons and negative ions; protons, $\alpha$ particles, and other positive ions.

However, decreasing the speed should result in increasing the probability for transition to forbidden states.

These questions will be discussed in a separate section.

## Violation of Selection Rules in Photon Impact Processes

Even for photon impact, selection rules do not apply rigorously; this has been known for a long time, since the first example of violation of selection rules was found 40 years ago, when $^2D \rightarrow ^2S$ transitions in the alkali atoms were found by Datta [D1]. Many other forbidden atomic transitions were found in the 1920's, mostly in astrophysical studies on auroral
• light and on gaseous nebulae spectra [B7, M20]. Generally speaking, spin-forbidden transition laws are less strictly obeyed than momentum-forbidden laws [C9, G2]. Many examples have been found in laboratory experiments and in astrophysical observations [B7]. The theory of forbidden transitions, worked out as a perturbed state problem, has been given by Condon and Shortley [C9].

An interesting case is that of transitions induced by external fields. This is a particular Stark effect [B8, J1], which might be of importance in certain mass spectrometry experiments, when intense fields around the ionization chamber are prevalent.

Violation due to two-quantum processes cannot be discarded and has indeed been observed in the case of the hydrogen atom. It might be effective when high ionizing fluxes are used, as would be the case if short-wavelength lasers could be used as source of ionization.

When dealing with molecules, various perturbation causes arise, notably spin-orbit coupling, so that multiplicity-forbidden transitions may be found [H7]. The Lyman–Birge–Hopfield bands of nitrogen are well known and correspond to the dipole-forbidden transition [H8, W8] $a^1\Pi_g \to X^1\Sigma_g^+$. Lichten [L23] showed that the $a^1\Pi_g$ state is metastable and has a lifetime of $1.7 \times 10^{-4}$ sec.

Oxygen is another interesting case. According to Mulliken [M17], a low-lying $^1\Delta_g$ state exists, to which a transition from the ground $X^3\Sigma_g^-$ triplet state is clearly forbidden. It was however found and identified in the telluric spectrum and in the liquid oxygen spectrum by Herzberg and Herzberg [H9].

Other spin-forbidden transitions have been reported for CO, GaF, $N_2$, and GeH [G2].

Obviously, even in the case of photon-impact processes, selection rules may be violated for perturbation reasons other than insufficient BO approximation. It is, therefore, expected that still more forbidden transitions are likely to occur with slow incident particles.

## A DISCUSSION OF AVAILABLE EXPERIMENTAL DATA

### Forbidden Transition Probabilities in Inelastic Collisions

#### Atoms

*Atomic Hydrogen.* This is the simplest case, but unfortunately the difficulties involved in an experimental study of the ionization or excitation of hydrogen atoms by various means are enormous, due to the problem of obtaining a beam of atomic hydrogen intense enough to be submitted to bombardment and detected, either spectroscopically (for neutral excitation) or electrically (for ionization), so that there are practically no data available for transition to forbidden states nor for allowed states, the atomic spectrum being excepted. The only experimental evidence refers to ionization or excitation cross sections and will be discussed later.

*Rare Gases.* Although less simple, theoretically speaking, than hydrogen atoms, the rare gases have attracted researchers for obvious reasons: being inert gases, they do not give strong adsorption phenomena, they are easily obtained in pure form, and they are monatomic and well known spectroscopically.

Fortunately enough, results have been obtained not only for electrons and photons, but also for proton, α-particle, and hydrogen-molecular ion bombardment. Table I summarizes those forbidden transitions which were observed; 18 such transitions have been detected, of which at least eight are spin-forbidden, whereas about 70 various transitions, including allowed ones, were observed in all.

## Table I.  Forbidden Transitions in Rare Gases

| Atom | Transition | Type* | Method† | Particle Nature | Particle Energy (eV) | Particle Speed‡ | Reference |
|---|---|---|---|---|---|---|---|
| He | $1^1S \rightarrow 2^3S$ | s | b | $e^-$ | 25–100 | 3.6–5.9 | K1, K2 |
| | | | a | $e^-$ | 50 | 4.2 | C2 |
| | | | b | $e^-$ | 22–55 | 3.6–4.3 | C10 |
| | $\rightarrow 2^3P$ | s | b | $e^-$ | 25–100 | 3.6–5.9 | K1, K2 |
| | | | a | $e^-$ | 50 | 4.2 | C2 |
| | $\rightarrow 3^3S$ | s | a | $e^-$ | 50 | 4.2 | C2 |
| | $\rightarrow 2s2p, {}^3P$ | s | c | $H_2^+$ | 75.000 | 2.7 | R1 |
| | $\rightarrow 2^1S$ | m | b | $e^-$ | 25–100 | 3.6–5.9 | K1, K2 |
| | | | b | $e^-$ | 511 | 13 | L4 |
| | | | a | $e^-$ | 50 | 4.2 | C2 |
| | | | b | $e^-$ | 22–55 | 3.6–4.3 | C10 |
| | $\rightarrow 3^1S$ | m | b | $e^-$ | 25–100 | 3.6–5.9 | K1, K2 |
| | | | a | $e^-$ | 201.9 | 8.3 | L9 |
| | | | a | $e^-$ | 50 | 4.2 | C2 |
| Ne | 42.1: $\rightarrow {}^3P$ | s | | | | | |
| | $(2s^22p^43s^2)$ | | c | $H_2^+$ | 75.000 | 2.7 | R1 |
| | 43.6: $\rightarrow {}^1S$ | m | c | $H_2^+$ | 75.000 | 2.7 | R1 |
| | $(2s2p^63s)$ | | d | $e^-$ | 90–100 | 5.9 | S8 |
| | 46.5: $\rightarrow {}^1S$ | m | c | $H_2^+$ | 75.000 | 2.7 | R1 |
| | $(2s2p^64s)$ | | d | $e^-$ | 90–100 | 5.9 | S8 |
| | 47.5–47.8: $\rightarrow {}^1S$ | m | c | $H_2^+$ | 75.000 | 2.7 | R1 |
| | $(2s2p^65s)$ | | | | | | |
| | $(2s2p^66s)$ | | | | | | |
| Ar | 11.55: $\rightarrow {}^3P_2$ | s | e | $He^+$ (α) | ? | ? | H2 |
| | 11.72:     $^3P_0$ | s | | | | | |
| | 11.62:     $^3P_1$ | s | | | | | |
| | 13.12 | | a | $e^-$ | | | C2 |
| | 13.28 $\rightarrow 3p^54p$ | p | | | | | |
| | 13.48 | | | | | | |
| | 14.09: $\rightarrow {}^3P_1$ | s | e | $He^+$ (α) | ? | ? | H2 |
| | 27.54: | s | a | $e^-$ | 90–100 | 5.9 | S8 |
| | | | c | $H_2^+$ (not $H^+$) | 75.000 | 2.7 | R1 |
| Kr | 25.8: ? | ? | a | $90–100 e^-$ | 90–100 | 5.9 | S8 |
| Xe | 21.3: ? | ? | a | $e^-$ | 90–100 | 5.9 | S8 |

* Notation: s, spin-forbidden; m, momentum-forbidden; p, parity-forbidden.
† Notation: a, low-angle scattering; b, high-angle scattering; c, analysis of ejected electrons KE; d, energy loss of scattered electrons; e, ionic yield; f, Penning ionization.
‡ In $10^8$ cm/sec units.

Helium is the most studied atom. At least 17 papers have been published; most of them pertain to electron scattering experiments, chiefly at near zero angles [C2, L1, L2, L9, S2, S8, S9, S13], and some experiments as a function of the scattering angle [L4, L5, S1] or at great angles only [K1, K2]. Very good energy resolution has been obtained in the most recent researches (see Fig. 1, for example) thanks to the use of monoenergetic electron beams and of electrostatic energy analyzers of the Clarke and Marmet type [C8] or of the hemispherical type [S8]. Many of the experiments were performed in the research group of Lassettre.

A new and ingenious technique for the investigation of such phenomena has been recently proposed by Cermàk [C10]. It is based on the observation of the Penning ionization effect, which results from ionization by metastable atoms. For instance, ionization of argon atoms may be obtained by collision with helium atoms in metastable states, such as $2^1S$ and $2^3S$, according to the reaction

$$\text{He}\,(2^3S, 2^1S) + A \rightarrow A^+ + \text{He}\,(1\,{}^1S) + e$$

The released electrons, in such processes, have kinetic energies differing by the energy difference between the $2^3S$ and $2^1S$ states of helium, i.e., 0.8 eV, and may be analyzed in a Lozier retarding potential device such as is used notably in photoelectron spectroscopy [T4].

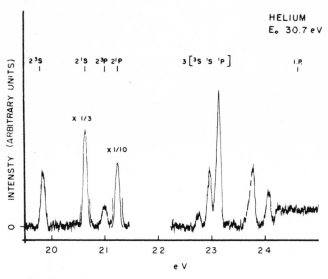

Fig. 1. Electron energy loss spectrum for 30.7-eV electrons in helium. I.P. indicates the first ionization potential. (After Chamberlain *et al.* [C2].)

The energies of the electrons will be, in the above-mentioned example, 4.06 eV and 4.86 eV, according to which of the helium metastable states is concerned in the ionization process. Therefore, the dependence of the relative abundances of electrons having these kinetic energies on the energy of the primary exciting beam (in this case it was an electron beam) will be directly related to the relative individual cross sections for excitation of the helium atoms brought into the forbidden $2^1S$ and $2^3S$ states.

In very difficult but also extremely interesting experiments, Rudd and Lang [R1] have analyzed the kinetic energy distribution of electrons ejected under the impact of 75-keV protons and hydrogen molecular ions obtained with a Cockroft–Walton accelerator; these results are discussed below. Simpson and Mielczarek [S9] have cast some doubt on the high-angle scattering results of Kuppermann and Raff [K1, K2]; the careful studies of the former seem to indicate very different probabilities for the forbidden transitions, according to the scattering angle; it has indeed been shown theoretically that zero-angle measurements should yield results more similar to the optical ones. However the most recent results [C2] have definitely confirmed the occurrence of forbidden transitions at low electron energies (see Table I).

Except for one observation with 511-V electrons by Lassettre et al. [L4] on a momentum-forbidden transition (He, $1^1 S \rightarrow 2^1 S$), all data were obtained by use of electrons or positive ions of speeds never exceeding $6 \times 10^8$ cm/sec, i.e., about one fiftieth of the speed of light, whereas in all experiments where no forbidden transitions were observed, the speed was at least of the order of $10^9$ cm/sec. A striking example is the case of argon, recently reported by Boersch [B3] for 25-keV electrons (speed $0.9 \times 10^{10}$ cm/sec). In this case, and using an energy resolution of 0.04 V, Boersch measured the energy loss of the electron beam and obtained almost exactly the equivalent of the emission spectrum of argon, the coincidence of energy levels being practically perfect. The same author reported other remarkable data for ethylene (see below).

As can be seen from Table I, forbidden transitions are found in all rare gases, as long as the impinging particles are slow enough. The results suggest that for speeds below $10^9$ cm/sec, the BO approximation is no longer valid for these atoms.

A very good example of spin exchange interaction between the projectile and the target, previously discussed in the theoretical introduction, is found in the experiments of Rudd and Lang mentioned above [R1]. These authors observe that 75-keV $H_2^+$ ions (speed, $2.7 \times 10^8$ cm/sec) induce a transition around 58.4 V, in helium, which is not observed with 75-keV $H^+$ ions (speed, $3.8 \times 10^8$ cm/sec) and which they ascribe to the spin-forbidden transition to the $2s\,2p$, $^3P$ state. This is shown in Fig. 2. Such a transition is thus only accessible by electron exchange and, since the

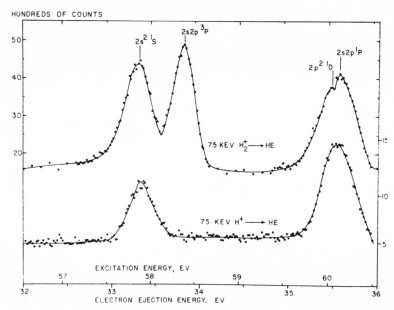

Fig. 2. Energy spectrum of electrons ejected from helium under bombardment of 75-keV molecular hydrogen ions and protons. (After Rudd and Lang [R1].)

$H^+$ ions have no electron to exchange, they cannot induce the transition. The same is true for the 27.54-V transition in argon, observed with $H_2^+$ ions, but not with $H^+$ ions; it must thus be a spin-forbidden transition; this transition was also found in scattering experiments by Simpson et al. [S8].

### Diatomic Molecules

The four molecules $H_2$, $N_2$, $O_2$, and CO have been studied, and the results are summarized, for forbidden transitions, in Table II. Only experiments with electrons have been performed and may be compared to spectroscopic results. In experiments with electrons of energies equal to or higher than 200 eV, all the observed transitions correspond remarkably well to spectroscopically known energy levels. *

In the case of hydrogen [B3, K3, L1, L3, S20] the transitions to the $B^1\Sigma_u^+$, $C^1\Pi_u$, and $D^1\Pi_u$ states were observed. The experiments of Boersch [B3] were particularly interesting; thanks to a resolution better than 0.01 V, obtained with a Wien energy filter, he could resolve not only the vibrational but also the rotational structure, corresponding to these states.

For $N_2$ [L12, L11, M2, M3] the optically well-known transitions [H5] were observed, including the dipole-forbidden but spectroscopically detected

---

* References for spectroscopic data may be found in the papers discussed and will generally not be given here.

## Table II. Forbidden Transitions in Diatomic Molecules

| Molecule | Level (eV) | Transition | Type* | Method† | Particle Nature | Particle Energy (eV) | Particle Speed‡ | Reference |
|---|---|---|---|---|---|---|---|---|
| $H_2$ | 0.2–0.3 | $v = 0 \to v = 1$ | d | d | $e^-$ | 0–15 | 0–1.5 | E2, S20 |
| | 9.2 | $1^1\Sigma_g^+ \to 1^3\Sigma_u^+$ | s | b | $e^-$ | 60 | 4.7 | K2 |
| $N_2$ | 0.2–3.5 | vibrat. excitat. | d | c | ($e^-$ monochr.) | 2.1–3.2 | 0.8–0.9 | H1 |
| | | | | e | $e^-$ | 2.1–3.2 | 0.8–0.9 | S19 |
| | 7.8 | $A^3\Sigma_u^+$ (vibr. str.) | s | e | $e^-$ | 0–15 | 0–1.5 | S19 |
| | | | | f | $e^-$ | 0–25 | 0–3.6 | W1 |
| | 8.5 | $X^1\Sigma_g^+ \to a^1\Pi_g$ (Lyman–Birge–Hopfield) (vibr. struct.) | d | c | $e^-$ monochr. | 2.1–3.2 | 0.8–0.9 | H1 |
| | | | | a | $e^-$ | 200 | 8.4 | L11 |
| | 11.04 } 11.2 } | $C^3\Pi_u$ | s | f | $e^-$ monochr. | 0–25 | 0–3.6 | W1 |
| | | | | e | $e^-$ monochr. | 0–15 | 0–1.5 | S19 |
| | | | | c | $e^-$ monochr. | 15–35 | 1.5–4 | H1 |
| $O_2$ | 0.2–0.4 →2.0 | vibrat. excitat. $\to v = 9$ $(^3\Sigma_g^-)$ | d | e | $e^-$ | 1–5 | 0.5–1 | S10 |
| | 1.0 | $1\Delta_g$ | s, m | e | $e^-$ | 1–5 | 0.5–1 | S10 |
| | 1.6 | $1\Sigma_g^+$ | s, sym | e | $e^-$ | 1–5 | 0.5–1 | S10 |
| CO | 6.2 | $a^3\Pi$ | s | e | $e^-$ | 1–15 | 0.5–1.5 | S19 |

* Notation: d, dipole-forbidden; s, spin-forbidden; m, momentum-forbidden; sym, symmetry-forbidden.
† Notation: a, zero-angle scattering; b, high-angle scattering; c, energy loss, energy scattering; d, energy loss analysis; e, trapped-electron current; f, secondary emission of metastable molecules.
‡ In $10^8$ cm/sec units.

Lyman–Birge–Hopfield transition [H6] $X^1\Sigma_g^+ \to a^1\Pi_g$. Vibrational structure is observed and the relative transition intensities were found to be in agreement with the theoretical Franck–Condon factors [M2, L11].

The Lassettre team has also studied the electron scattering at zero angle for electrons of 200 eV in CO [L7, M1, S3] and obtained an exceptionally good agreement with the spectroscopic results, for both electronic and vibrational transitions, as may be seen from Table III. Just as good results were obtained with 518 eV electrons for $O_2$ [L8].

**Table III.    Excitation Potentials of CO (eV) ***

| State | $v'$ | Electron impact | | Ultraviolet |
|-------|------|-----------------|---|-------------|
| $A^1\Pi$ | 0 | 8.03 $\pm$ 0.00 | | 8.03 |
| | 1 | 8.21 | 0.00 | 8.21 |
| | 2 | 8.39 | 0.00 | 8.39 |
| | 3 | 8.57 | 0.01 | 8.57 |
| | 4 | 8.74 | 0.01 | 8.74 |
| | 5 | 8.90 | 0.01 | 8.90 |
| | 6 | 9.06 | 0.00 | 9.06 |
| | 7 | 9.22 | 0.00 | 9.22 |
| | 8 | 9.38 | 0.01 | 9.38 |
| $B^1\Sigma^+$ | 0 | 10.78 | 0.00 | 10.78 |
| | 1 | 11.04 | 0.01 | 11.04 |
| $C^1\Sigma^+$ | 0 | 11.40 | 0.01 | 11.395 |
| $E^1\Pi$ | 0 | 11.52 | 0.01 | 11.52 |
| | 1 | 11.76 | 0.01 | — |
| $F^1\Pi$ | 0 | 12.37 | 0.01 | 12.37 |
| ... | ... | 12.58 | 0.01 | 12.58 |
| ... | ... | 12.79 | 0.00 | 12.79 |
| $G^1\Pi$ | 0 | 13.050 | — | 13.049 |
| | 1 ? | 13.17 | — | 13.172 |
| | | 13.29 | — | 13.285 |
| | | 13.41 | — | 13.390 |

* V. D. Meyer, A. Skerbele, and E. N. Lassettre, *J. Chem. Phys.* **43**:805, 1965; *J. Chem. Phys.* **44**: 4069, 1966.

At low electron energies, however, at least ten forbidden transitions are again observed, for those diatomic molecules; four are dipole-forbidden and six are at least spin-forbidden. The dipole-forbidden transitions are observed for the homonuclear molecules $H_2$, $N_2$, and $O_2$. Schulz [S10, S19] has developed a trapped-electron technique for analyzing the electron energy loss in inelastic collisions, by measuring the electron current variation to a suitable collector, due to the trapping in a potential well of those electrons having lost part of their initial energy in the collision. He could show that $N_2$ [S7, S19] and $O_2$ [S10] in their ground electronic state are vibrationally excited, although the transition is obviously dipole-forbidden. A hypothetical temporary negative molecular ion is supposed to be the intermediate means of energy transfer (compound state theory). The results obtained for $O_2$ are shown in Fig. 3. By energy loss measurements with an electrostatic selector, Schulz [S20] also investigated the ground electronic state vibrational excitation of hydrogen. In all cases, a possible theoretical approach has been recently proposed by Bowman and Miller [B1] (see also Engelhardt and Phelps [E2]), which emphasizes the importance of polarization interaction in such processes.

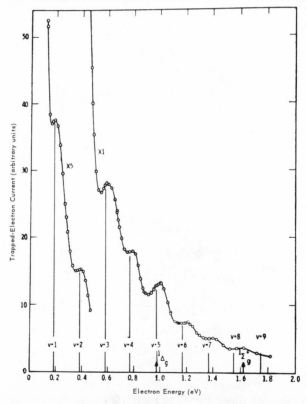

Fig. 3. Vibrational and electronic excitation of oxygen by electron impact, as observed by the trapped-electron method. Electronic transitions are spin-forbidden. (After Schulz and Dowell [S10].)

Spin-forbidden singlet-triplet transitions have been observed for the four molecules. Kuppermann and Raff [K2] attribute the 9.2-V absorption in $H_2$, which they found in high-angle scattering experiments, to the $1^1\Sigma_g^+ \to 1^3\Sigma_u^+$ transition. Kuyatt et al. [K3], however, have not found this transition at zero-angle scattering, although the energy of the electrons was half that used by Kuppermann and Raff and, therefore, have cast doubt on these authors' results.

In nitrogen, two spin-forbidden transitions have been reported. One, around 7.8 V, is attributed to the transition $^1\Sigma_g^+ \to A^3\Sigma_u^+$ and was observed by the trapped-electron method by Schulz [S19] and by a study by Winters [W1], of the secondary electron emission of a nickel surface hit by metastable nitrogen molecules, using a monoenergetic electron beam. The second transition, at 11.2 V, was found by Schulz [S19] and by Heideman and co-workers [H1] at the National Bureau of Standards; in this latter case, where the energy loss of scattered electrons was measured, it was observed that this transition appears for 15.7-eV electrons, but disappears with 35 eV electrons. It was attributed to the transition to the $C^3\Pi_u$ state.

For carbon monoxide, Schulz [S19] reported the $^1\Sigma_g \to A^3\Pi$ transition in trapped-electron experiments.

We shall finally consider the interesting case of oxygen. The ground state of this molecule is a triplet state ($^3\Sigma_g^-$). Schulz and Dowell [S10] have shown by the trapped-electron method that two forbidden transitions seem to be produced. They correspond to the low-lying $^1\Delta_g$ and $^1\Sigma_g^+$ electronic states; the first one is momentum- and spin-forbidden whereas the second one is momentum-, symmetry-, and spin-forbidden. The overlap of vibrational excited states of the ground electronic state $^3\Sigma_g^-$ ($v = 5$ and $^1\Delta_g$; $v = 8$ and $^1\Sigma_g^+$) did not allow the separation of these transitions with the energy resolution used (0.07–0.10 V), but their occurrence seemed to be definitely established (see Fig. 3).

## Polyatomic Molecules

Data exist for three triatomic molecules ($H_2O$, $CO_2$, and $N_2O$) and for $NH_3$. Unfortunately, only high-energy electron experiments were done. Lassettre and co-workers [L1, M16, S3, S25] have used 300–400-eV electrons and observed in $H_2O$ nine spectroscopically known transitions. Three more transitions were observed, above the ionization potential, but could not be compared to spectroscopic data; it seems likely, however, that they refer to allowed superexcited states [P1]. The same is true for $CO_2$, for which the ten observed transitions have their analog in UV spectra [T1]. In ammonia, six transitions [S3] closely correspond to spectroscopic values, whereas six presumably superexcited allowed states have been detected above the ionization limit.

Very high-energy electron experiments were performed by Geiger and

Wittmaack [G1] on $CO_2$ and $N_2O$. They showed that collision of 33-keV electrons induces pure vibrational excitation of the ground electronic state of these molecules and that only those transitions are observed which are optically allowed, i.e., IR active unsymmetric stretching and bending modes for $CO_2$, and the symmetric stretching, unsymmetric stretching, and bending modes for $N_2O$. This is shown in Fig. 4.

The only conclusion that may be drawn is that when electrons of energy higher than 150–200 eV are used, the collision results in a series of transitions which can all be correlated with optically allowed transitions, observed either in UV or IR spectroscopy. An urgent need for further experiments is evident, particularly at low energies and with particles other than electrons.

Although the transitions in hydrocarbon molecules have also been studied only by means of electrons, the amount of experimental information obtained is important; a great range of energies has been investigated, as well as many different experimental techniques. As a consequence, at least eight transitions have been attributed to spin-forbidden transitions.

Methane, ethane, acetylene, ethylene, propyne, 1-butyne, and benzene have been examined. Lassettre and co-workers have studied methane, ethane, and ethylene [L1] with 390-eV electrons, and benzene [S3] with 300 eV-electrons, but could not always compare their observed transitions to spectroscopic data, these being sometimes nonexistent. Exceptions are

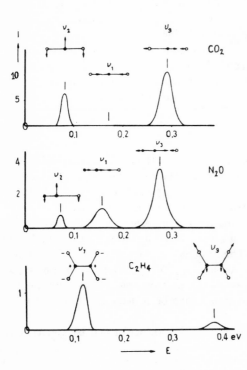

Fig. 4. Electron energy loss spectra for 33-keV electrons in $CO_2$, $N_2O$, and $C_2H_4$. Only IR dipole-allowed vibrational excitations are observed. (After Geiger and Wittmaack [G1].)

observations for the 10.12-V transition in methane, the 7.66-V and 9.03–9.95-V transitions in ethylene, and the five transitions below the ionization potential in benzene, which all have their spectroscopic analog (see Table IV).*

Most interesting are the cases of acetylene and ethylene. Acetylene has been studied by Lichten [L13, L14], Bowman and Miller [B1], and the author [C4, C5]. Lichten has analyzed the secondary-electron current produced by metastable acetylene molecule deactivation on a platinum surface. He concluded that an excited metastable state is obtained by electron bombardment for an energy of about 8.5 V and is a triplet state. Its lifetime is very long (of the order of a millisecond). Another transition was observed around 14 V. Bowman and Miller [B1] used the trapped-electron technique and a monoenergetic electron beam and detected seven transitions, below the ionization potential, of which four are known spectroscopically. Of the three others, the lowest (2.0 V) is attributed to a triplet state which was predicted theoretically to be below the first singlet transition (bent state) situated at about 6 V. The two others, at 7.7 and 7.9 V, were not interpreted, but might also be forbidden. Collin [C4, C5, C14] has observed mass spectrometrically, by the RPD method, an ionic state at 13.25 V and at 14.4 V, attributed to preionized states of the neutral molecule. The second value might correspond to the same state as that observed by Lichten around 14–14.5 V; both were attributed to spin-forbidden transitions [C6].

In the case of ethylene, Lichten [L13] found metastable states at 8.8 V and 14.4–15.2 V, whereas Kuppermann and Raff [K1, K2], by a study of scattered electrons, detected with 40-, 50-, and 75-eV electrons spectroscopically unknown states at 4.4–4.8 and 6.4–6.6 V. They assigned the 4.4–4.8 V value to the spin-forbidden $N \to T$ transition $^1A_{1g} \to {}^3B_{1u}$. The intensity of this transition decreases with increasing electron energy, suggesting again that it is spin-forbidden. The 6.4–6.6 V transition was tentatively attributed to the forbidden $n \to \pi^*$ transition. These results have been contested by Simpson and Mielczarek [S9], who did not find the same transitions when doing low-angle scattering experiments with 50 V electrons. The recent trapped-electron measurements of Bowman and Miller, however, have confirmed Kuppermann and Raff's observations and the above proposed interpretation.† There are also UV spectroscopic data, using the oxygen-intensification technique, which are in agreement with this assessment. Bowman and Miller did not find the 6.6-V transition. Collin [C4, C5] has observed, in the RPD‡ curve of $C_2H_4{}^+$, two critical values which he attributed to preionized forbidden states, possibly spin-forbidden; the values are 13.31 and 14.64 V. Here again, the 14.64-V state might be the spin-forbidden metastable state found by Lichten at 14.4–15.2 V.

---

* See "Note 1 Added in Proof," p. 266.
† See "Note 2 Added in Proof," p. 266.
‡ Retarding potential difference (RPD) method for the determination of ionization potentials (see, e.g., [C7]).

## Table IV. Forbidden Transitions in Polyatomic Molecules

| Molecule | Level (eV) | Transition | Type* | Method† | Particle | | | Reference |
|---|---|---|---|---|---|---|---|---|
| | | | | | Nature | Energy (eV) | Speed‡ | |
| $C_2H_2$ | 8.5 | triplet | s | b | $e^-$ | 0–20 | 0–1.8 | L13, L14 |
| | 2.0 | triplet | s | c | $e^-$ | 0–12 | 0–1.3 | B1 |
| | 7.7 | ? | ? | c | $e^-$ | 0–12 | 0–1.3 | B1 |
| | 7.9 | ? | ? | c | $e^-$ | 0–12 | 0–1.3 | B1 |
| | 14–14.4 | triplet | s | b | $e^-$ | 0–20 | 0–1.8 | L13, L14 |
| | | | | eRPD | $e^-$ monochr. | 0–20 | 0–1.8 | C5 |
| $C_2H_4$ | 4.4–4.8 | $^1A_{1g} \to {}^3B_{1u}$ | s | d | $e^-$ | 40–50–75 | 3.8–4.2–6 | K1, K2 |
| | | $(T \leftarrow N)$ | | c | $e^-$ | 0–11 | 0–1.3 | B1 |
| | 6.4–6.6 | $n \to \pi^*$ ? | ? | d | $e^-$ | 40–50–75 | 3.8–4.2–6 | K1, K2 |
| | 8.8 | triplet (metastable) | s | b | $e^-$ | 0–20 | 0–1.8 | L13 |
| | 14.4–14.7 | triplet (metastable) | s | b | $e^-$ | $e^-$ | 0–1.8 | L13 |
| | | | | eRPD | $e^-$ monochr. | 0–20 | 0–1.8 | C5 |
| $C_3H_4$ | 2.8 | triplet $^1X' \to {}^3X$ ? | s | c | $e^-$ | 0–20 | 0–1.8 | B1 |
| $C_3H_6$ | 4.4 | $^1A_{1g} \to {}^3B_{1u}$ | s | c | $e^-$ | 0–20 | 0–1.8 | B1 |
| $C_4H_6$ | 6.3 | $^3X' \to {}^3X$ ? | s | c | $e^-$ | 0–20 | 0–1.8 | B1 |

* Notation: s, spin-forbidden.

† Notation: a, zero-angle scattering; b, secondary emission of metastables; c, trapped-electron technique; d, RPD gun-RP analysis of scattered electrons; e, RPD ionization technique and analysis of threshold laws.

‡ In $10^8$ cm/sec units.

From this discussion, it is clear that in acetylene and in ethylene inelastic collisions with slow electrons may bring the molecule in excited states which do not correspond to known spectroscopic levels and appear to be due to spin-forbidden transitions to metastable triplet states, possibly preionized.

Bowman and Miller [B1] have also found low-energy processes in propylene, propyne, and 1-butyne, at 2.8, 4.4, and 2.4 V, respectively, which they tentatively ascribed to spin-forbidden transitions to triplet states.

However, as soon as the speed of the electrons becomes high enough, the probability of those transitions decreases considerably and finally only the spectroscopically observed levels appear to be excited. The best example of such behavior, and a very striking one indeed, is to be found in the beautiful experiments of Boersch [B3], using very rapid electrons and high resolution energy analysis with a Wien filter. The comparison with the UV spectrum of ethylene obtained by Watanabe and Zelikoff [W7] is really remarkable and proves without any doubt that the same transitions are induced by photons or by 33-keV electrons, the electron-impact energy loss spectrum being almost exactly a duplicate of the UV spectrum, as shown in Fig. 5.

## Mass Spectra Obtained with Various Ionizing Beams

### Introduction

Within the BO approximation's range, one should expect the variation of cross section for a given transition to be very similar, whatever the nature of the bombarding particle. The same is true for the type and the number of

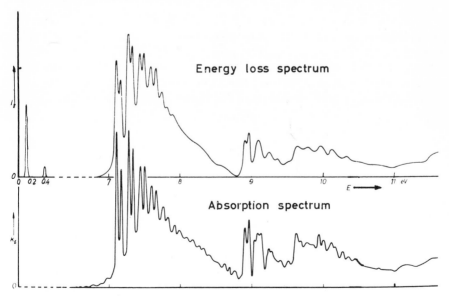

Fig. 5.  Electron energy loss spectrum for 33-keV electron bombardment in ethylene, as compared to the UV absorption coefficient spectrum. (After Boersch [B3].)

those transitions which could be induced during the collision process. It follows that, for bombarding particles of speeds high enough for the BO approximation to be valid, and if, under those conditions, the energy transfer probability function is not too different for different types of particles, the evolution of the produced ion should be the same whenever the collision results in the production of such an ion. This is nothing else than predicting that the mass spectra of a molecule should be the same for electrons, ions, or neutral particle bombardment, as soon as they collide with the same relative speed (referred to the target) and they should tend to be the same as the photon-impact spectrum, once the velocity approaches the velocity of light.

As a corollary, a comparison of the mass spectrum for a given molecule, obtained by various ionizing beams and for various energies and velocities of the impinging particle, should bring new information on the BO approximation conditions as well as on the possibility of violation of selection rules.

With the exception of 50- to 100-eV electrons, however, the experimental data now available are very scarce, although photons, electrons, protons, hydrogen molecular ions, $\alpha$ particles, various ions, atoms, and molecules were used as projectiles.

When ions are used as bombarding particles, the problem arises to know what kind of inelastic collision interaction is going to take place. If the kinetic energy of the ion is low enough, charge transfer is most likely; it is a resonance process in which the amount of energy transferred is in principle dependent on the recombination energy levels for the bombarding ion and the appearance potential or critical ionization potentials of the target molecule. In such processes, a rather well-defined amount of energy is transferred and, knowing the critical potentials, one may deduce the amount of excitation energy with which the newly formed ion is endowed. The behavior of such an excited ion is then well defined and the observed mass spectrum is characteristic of that particular excitation energy. In such experiments, precious information is obtained and has been used as a test for the quasi-equilibrium theory of mass spectra [R2] by means of adequate calculations based on empirical energy transfer functions.

In this field, a great deal of pioneering work was done by Lindholm and his collaborators at the Royal Institute of Technology, in Stockholm (see [C6, G4, K5, K6, L16, L21, L22, P2, S16, S21]). Although these researches are of great interest, they are not directly useful in our present purpose, for the charge transfer process is a very special type of interaction at very low velocities.

For our discussion, it would be more desirable to obtain information on the high-energy process, i.e., the pure ionization by ions, of the type $A^{+*} + B \rightarrow A^+ + B^+ + e$. Unfortunately, it is not clear up to now in what energy range such a process is likely to occur. Massey [M5] has shown that when the resonance charge transfer phenomenon—which takes place only when the energy defect between the ionization energies of the bombarding particle and the target is small—is neglected, the charge transfer process of importance here, i.e., $A^+ + B \rightarrow A + B^+$, will depend mainly on the duration of the interaction time $\tau$ during the collision, as compared to the time of one period (frequency $v$) of the electron to be transferred in the process. The excitation is weak if $\tau v \gg 1$. This is equivalent to expressing the condition $l(\Delta E/hv) \gg 1$, where $l$ is the range of interaction of $A^+$ and $B$, and $v$ is their relative velocity of approach; in this case, $v \ll l\Delta E/h$; if $v$ increases to a value of the order of $l\Delta E/h$, the cross section for the process becomes important and is expected to attain its maximum. It may be shown that this corresponds to an impact energy of the order of $36(\Delta E)^2 ml^2$, where the energy defect $\Delta E$ is expressed in eV, mass of the particle $m$ in atomic units, and range of interaction $l$ in Bohr radius units.

It follows from this discussion that the energy range of charge transfer processes may not be defined uniquely and will depend on the A–B system considered.

Recent experiments by Dufay et al. [D2] show that the cross sections for ionization and charge transfer are approximately the same for 30-keV proton bombardment of methane, ethane, ethylene, and acetylene. These authors consider the ionization process involved to be very different in nature from the usual electron-impact ionization process, as a result of the long interaction time between the colliding particles.

The available evidence suggests that, *below* kinetic energies of the order of 10 to 30 keV (for ions), most processes are likely to be of the charge transfer type, whereas above 30 keV, ionization will be the predominant reaction. There is, however, no clear-cut limit and any generalization would be unjustified.

## Simple Inorganic Molecules

Practically all experiments with particles other than photons or electrons were performed in the charge transfer energy range.

The particular case of molecular hydrogen deserves mention since triplet transition of the $H_2^+$ ion is impossible. The mass spectra, however, might depend partly on transition to triplet neutral preionized states. No information is available, except for slow electrons, where such states have been invoked [B6], and for charge exchange [A2, V2, G4]. The same is true for other molecules which were submitted to ion or molecule bombardment: $D_2$ [M9], $H_2O$ [L22], $N_2O$ [L22, M9], $CO_2$ [L22], $NH_3$ [K8, L7, L15, L22]. For $NH_3^+$, Kupriyanov [K7, K8] found that 1.5- to 80-keV $N_2$ or $O_2$ molecules produced a mass spectrum very similar to that obtained with 60-eV electrons; the same is not true, however, for $CO_2$ bombarded by 1-keV $N_2$ molecules [N1], where the parent ion represents only 46.4% total ionization, instead of 80.5% for 50-V electrons.

## Hydrocarbons

Once more, methane, acetylene, and ethylene were the most widely studied molecules, but the information obtained is very difficult to interpret. There are, however, some interesting results worth discussing. The variation of the stability of the parent ion as a function of the particle speed is interesting, as soon as its energy is high enough to induce all transitions. One should expect that the faster the projectile, the less probable the transition to forbidden states. Therefore, the number of accessible states decreases when the energy increases; the stability should then be increasing with the incident particle's energy (or speed). This seemingly paradoxical behavior is indeed in agreement with the observed phenomena, as we shall see, although the conclusions are not always straightforward.*

*Methane.* Abbe [A1], Wexler [W2], Latypov and Kupriyanov [L15], Melton [M11], von Koch [K6], and Müller-Duysing [M12] have investigated the behavior of methane under various ionizing beams. Table V summarizes, some typical results of those authors.

On the average, there seems to be a definite increase in stability of the molecular ion when the speed of the particle increases, as may be seen when comparing Abbe's data for various ion energies. The case of slow ions (30 keV), however, should not be considered as conclusive evidence, since charge transfer processes are then increasingly important; the fragmentation then is mostly due to a considerable increase in the excitation energy imparted to the molecule or the molecular ion. The trend, however, is well defined. For instance, the fragmentation with 70-V electrons is greater than with 1-keV electrons, which in turn is greater than with high-energy $\alpha$ particles (polonium); as another example, the parent peak has a 54% abundance with 1.2-MeV $He^+$ ions, whereas it falls down to 7.7% for 2-keV $He^+$ ions [A1].

*Acetylene.* A considerable amount of data on acetylene is available; it includes the mass spectra obtained with electrons [A1, M12, S15, W2], $\alpha$ particles [A1, M12, M18], protons [A1, S15, W2],† and other ions [A1, L16, M9].

Direct comparison of the data obtained by various authors and with different instruments is difficult, due to interference of instrumental factors, such as mass discrimination effects; moreover, the similarity and reproducibility of mass spectra, from one instrument to the other, is not so good that small differences may be considered significant. The data for electrons

---

* See "Note 3 Added in Proof," p. 266.
† The results of Schuler and Stuber [S15] have been obtained by means of a $H^+$ ion beam obtained from molecular hydrogen, without mass analysis. It is therefore possible that the beam also contained a nonnegligible percentage of undissociated $H_2^+$ molecular ions.

### Table V.  Mass Spectra of Methane Obtained by Various Means*

| m/e | Electrons 70 eV [A1] | Electrons 70 eV [M12] | Electrons 1 keV [M12] | Electrons 1.225 keV [W2] | C+ [K6] 9 eV | C+ [K6] 30 eV | C+ [K6] 100 eV | C+ [K6] 900 eV | C+ [K6] 2 keV | H+ [A1] 30 keV | H+ [A1] 100 keV | H+ [A1] 1200 keV |
|---|---|---|---|---|---|---|---|---|---|---|---|---|
| 1 | 0.12–0.44 | | 0.15 | — | — | — | — | — | — | 0.55 | 0.2 | 0.21 |
| 2 | 0.30 | | 0.2 | — | — | — | — | — | — | — | — | — |
| 12 | 0.35–0.64 | | 0.2 | 0.95 | — | — | — | — | — | 1 | 0.43 | 0.18 |
| 13 | 1.19–2.04 | | 0.92 | 2.91 | — | 0.7 | 1.2 | 1.2 | — | 2.46 | 1.37 | 0.56 |
| 14 | 3.31–4.88 | | 3.62 | 7.21 | 16.5 | 15.5 | 12.5 | 12.2 | 1.6 | 4.82 | 4.69 | 3.24 |
| 15 | 40.66–40.8 | | 42.93 | 41.1 | 72.4 | 66.6 | 56.0 | 68.8 | 36.4 | 38.8 | 39.2 | 41.73 |
| 16 | 54.4 –49.9 | | 51.06 | 47.8 | 11.1 | 17.2 | 30.3 | 26.6 | 62 | 52.32 | 54.1 | 54.71 |

| m/e | α(Po) [M12] | α(Po) [M11] | He+ [A1] 2 keV | He+ [A1] 30 keV | He+ [A1] 100 keV | He+ [A1] 1200 keV | Ar+ [A1] 900 eV [K6] | Ar+ [A1] 2 keV | Ar+ [A1] 30 keV | Ar+ [A1] 200 keV |
|---|---|---|---|---|---|---|---|---|---|---|
| 1 | — | — | -- | 1.3 | 0.45 | 0.2 | — | — | 0.33 | 0.55 |
| 12 | 0.28 | — | 4.26 | 3.08 | 2.17 | 0.44 | 0.2 | — | 0.42 | 2.54 |
| 13 | 0.61 | — | 21.3 | 6.1 | 2.07 | 1.3 | 0.5 | — | 1.14 | 3.73 |
| 14 | 2.51 | — | 53.6 | 15.39 | 6.92 | 5.16 | 14.8 | 11 | 4.43 | 7.1 |
| 15 | 38.5 | ~30 | 13.2 | 33.83 | 36.38 | 38.7 | 81.6 | 82.3 | 53.35 | 36.81 |
| 16 | 55.8 | ~65 | 7.7 | 40.28 | 51.38 | 54.15 | 2.8 | 6.7 | 40.43 | 49.25 |

\* *Approximate velocities* (in $10^8$ cm/sec)  
   $e^-$    70 eV: 5  
        1 keV: 19  
        1.225 keV: 21

| Atom | 9 eV | 100 eV | 900 eV | 2 keV | 30 keV | 100 keV | 1200 keV |
|---|---|---|---|---|---|---|---|
| $H^+$ | 0.04 | 0.14 | 0.42 | 0.60 | 2.4 | 4.2 | 15 |
| $He^+$ | 0.02 | 0.07 | 0.21 | 0.30 | 1.2 | 2.1 | 7.5 |
| $C^+$ | 0.012 | 0.04 | 0.16 | 0.25 | 1.0 | 1.5 | 4 |
| $Ar^+$ | 0.006 | 0.08 | 0.12 | 0.12 | 0.48 | 0.8 | 2 |

of 70 eV, 250 eV, 750 eV, 1 keV, 2 keV, and 3.5 keV are not really very different: in all cases, the relative percentage of the parent ion is around 80%, and Wexler's results seem to be too low, as compared to other workers' data. The 750-eV electrons and 1200-keV protons have speeds of the same order of magnitude and the corresponding spectra are also very similar (see Table VI). However the trend in stabilities for $H^+$ ion bombardment above 1 MeV is unexpected: the stability seems to decrease from 1.2 MeV (82.8%) to

**Table VI.   Mass Spectra of Acetylene Obtained by Various Means**

| | | | | | Electrons | | | | |
|---|---|---|---|---|---|---|---|---|---|
| m/e | 70 eV | 70 eV | 250 eV | 750 eV | 1 keV | 1 keV | 1 keV | 2 keV | 3.5 keV |
| | [A1] | [M12] | [M12] | [M12] | [M12] | [S15] | [W2] | [M12] | [M18] |
| 1 | 0.12 | 0.31 | 0.23 | 0.24 | 0.16 | 0.24 | — | 0.16 | — |
| 2 | — | 0.15 | — | — | — | — | — | — | — |
| 12 | 0.37 | 0.54 | 0.54 | 0.40 | 0.32 | 0.71 | 1.64 | 0.32 | 0.1 |
| 13 | 2.09 | 3.44 | 3.29 | 2.4 | 2.1 | 2.39 | 3.67 | 1.95 | 2.74 |
| 24 | 3.23 | 3.6 | 3.13 | 2.56 | 2.34 | 2.94 | 3.67 | 2.27 | 3.12 |
| 25 | 13.25 | 13.55 | 14.34 | 14.2 | 14.07 | 13.94 | 16.16 | 13.97 | 15.24 |
| 26 | 80.93 | 78.37 | 78.37 | 80.2 | 80.9 | 79.7 | 74.85 | 81.23 | 77.75 |

| | | | | | $H^+$ | | | | |
|---|---|---|---|---|---|---|---|---|---|
| m/e | 1200 keV | 200 keV | 100 keV | 30 keV | 2 keV | 2.25 MeV | 2 MeV | 0.5 MeV |
| | | | [A1] | | | [W2] | [S15] | |
| 1 | — | — | 0.25 | 0.48 | — | — | 0.29 | 0.31 |
| 12 | 0.35 | 0.46 | 0.72 | 1.11 | 0.24 | 0.24 | 1.9 | 4.07 |
| 13 | 1.4 | 2.86 | 4.07 | 10.53 | 0.38 | 1.5 | 3.66 | 5.77 |
| 24 | 2.2 | 3.16 | 3.82 | 4.98 | 1.8 | 2.38 | 4.16 | 6.4 |
| 25 | 13.2 | 17.63 | 18.41 | 18.55 | 13.01 | 16.44 | 17.1 | 20.64 |
| 26 | 82.8 | 75.9 | 72.67 | 64.24 | 84.5 | 79.43 | 73.1 | 62.75 |

| | | | | | $He^+(\alpha)$ | | | | |
|---|---|---|---|---|---|---|---|---|---|
| m/e | 1200 keV | 200 keV | 100 keV | 30 keV | 2 keV | $\alpha$(Po) | 2 MeV | $\alpha$(Po) |
| | | | [A1] | | | [M12] | [S15] | [M18] |
| 1 | 0.16 | 0.11 | 0.23 | 0.87 | — | — | 0.2 | — |
| 12 | 0.53 | 1.13 | 1.18 | 1.91 | 4.86 | 0.33 | 3.41 | — |
| 13 | 4.48 | 8.53 | 9.11 | 10.23 | 15.8 | 1.99 | 4.42 | — |
| 24 | 3.97 | 6.16 | 6.39 | 10.23 | 47.42 | 2.49 | 5.89 | — |
| 25 | 17.76 | 18.94 | 19.98 | 27.65 | 16.14 | 11.9 | 18.96 | 6.8 |
| 26 | 73.08 | 65.72 | 63.09 | 49.1 | 10.12 | 83.26 | 67 | 93.2 |

| | | | | 200 keV [A1] | | | |
|---|---|---|---|---|---|---|---|
| m/e | $H^+$ | $H_2^+$ | $D^+$ | $D_2^+$ | $He^+$ | $N_2^+$ | $Ar^+$ |
| 1 | — | 0.31 | — | 0.38 | 0.11 | 0.39 | 0.74 |
| 12 | 0.46 | 0.76 | 0.86 | 1.21 | 1.13 | 1.62 | 3.05 |
| 13 | 2.86 | 6.4 | 5.76 | 6.74 | 8.53 | 5.62 | 5.45 |
| 24 | 3.16 | 5.3 | 4.47 | 6.26 | 6.16 | 6.78 | 7.21 |
| 25 | 17.63 | 17.71 | 18.84 | 20.15 | 18.94 | 21.65 | 22.15 |
| 26 | 75.9 | 69.59 | 70.1 | 65.22 | 65.72 | 63.9 | 61.4 |

2.25 MeV (79.4%); but the difference may not be really significant, since, as indicated above, Wexler's data are generally lower for the parent ion.

Lindholm et al. [L16] and Maier [M9] investigated the charge transfer mass spectra of acetylene; according to Maier, there is a definite influence of the kinetic energy of the ion, which also appears clearly from the tables given by Lindholm. It is unfortunately not clear whether this is due to the influence of the kinetic energy itself, or to the increasing interference of the pure ionization phenomena.

Schuler and Stuber [S15] noticed small differences in the fragmentation with the mass of the particle and suggested that this might be the result of a greater contribution of multiple ionization phenomena—these having considerably higher critical potentials, the BO approximation might then be no longer applicable. However, the experiments of Wexler [W2] lead to the opposite conclusion— that more fragments are observed with electrons than with equivalent-speed protons ($2 \times 10^9$ cm/sec). He concluded that the differences with Schuler and Stuber's results are of instrumental origin and might come from discrimination of ions having kinetic energy which would be formed in greater amounts in ion-impact processes.

Kebarle and Godbole [K4] published a systematic study of the mass spectra of some hydrocarbons obtained with electrons of energies varying between 100 eV and 10 keV. Their data for acetylene are consistent with the idea that the higher the electron speed, the lower the probability of transition to various electronic states of the molecular ion, although the increase in stability of the parent ion is very small and occurs practically within the 100–1000 eV range.

Perhaps the best self-consistent set of data is that of Abbe [A1] who investigated the mass spectra obtained by impact of numerous ions, within a wide energy range going from 1 keV to 1.2 MeV. Some of his results are given in Tables V–VII notably for $H^+$ and $He^+$ ions. It may be seen that there is a definite increase of the molecular ion's stability with the speed of the incident particle between 30 keV and 1.2 MeV. It appears, however, that below 30 keV an increase of stability often happens; this might be the result of the relative importance of ionization and charge transfer processes, but no definite explanation has been given up to now.

Table VI also gives Abbe's results at 200 keV for various ions and it is indeed very interesting to note the similarity of the spectra for ions of various natures but of the same $m/e$ ratio, thus of the same speed, for instance, $H_2^+$ and $D^+$, $D_2^+$ and $He^+$; this suggests that, at that energy, the charge transfer processes are negligible. There is a systematic decrease of stability with the decrease in speed of the ion, the order of stability for various ions being as follows:

$$H^+ > H_2^+ \text{ or } D^+ > He^+ \text{ or } D_2^+ > N_2^+ > Ar^+$$

### Table VII.  Mass Spectra of Ethylene Obtained by Various Means

| $m/e$ | Electrons | | | | | | | | |
|---|---|---|---|---|---|---|---|---|---|
| | 70 eV [K4] | 500 eV [K4] | 2 keV [K4] | 70 eV [A3] | 70 eV [M12] | 1 keV [M12] | 1.225 MeV [W2] | 75 eV [M18] | 3.5 keV [M18] |
| 1 | — | — | — | 0.14 | 0.37 | 0.15 | — | — | — |
| 2 | — | — | — | — | 0.37 | — | — | — | — |
| 12 | — | — | — | 0.15 | 0.23 | 0.1 | 0.89 | 0.4 | 0.33 |
| 13 | — | — | — | 0.29 | 0.37 | 0.2 | 1.32 | 0.74 | 0.58 |
| 14 | 2 | 1.4 | 1 | 0.77 | 1.01 | 1.17 | 0.3 | 1.63 | 1.58 |
| 24 | — | — | — | 0.8 | 0.83 | 0.35 | 0.89 | 1.32 | 0.79 |
| 25 | 4.9 | 3.1 | 1.9 | 2.94 | 2.96 | 1.37 | 2.8 | 4.1 | 2.56 |
| 26 | 25.7 | 24.7 | 24.6 | 22.53 | 20.81 | 20.33 | 23.75 | 22.31 | 22.55 |
| 27 | 25.7 | 27.3 | 28 | 25.02 | 26.78 | 25.33 | 28.4 | 26.52 | 26.87 |
| 28 | 38.6 | 41 | 42.1 | 47.33 | 46.25 | 50.96 | 38.9 | 42.70 | 44.49 |

| $m/e$ | Photons | | $N_2$ molecules | Protons ($H^+$) | | | | |
|---|---|---|---|---|---|---|---|---|
| | [S14] | | [N1] | [A1] | | | | [W2] |
| | 18 eV | 22 eV | 1000 eV | 1200 keV | 800 keV | 400 keV | 200 keV | 2.25 MeV |
| 1 | — | — | — | 0.18 | 0.24 | 0.16 | 0.25 | — |
| 2 | — | — | 32.7 | — | — | — | — | — |
| 12 | — | — | — | 0.08 | 0.06 | 0.11 | 0.22 | 0.26 |
| 13 | — | — | — | 0.13 | 0.13 | 0.24 | 0.37 | 0.35 |
| 14 | — | — | — | 0.78 | 0.54 | 0.69 | 0.94 | 1.21 |
| 24 | — | — | — | 0.29 | 0.29 | 0.46 | 0.80 | 0.32 |
| 25 | — | — | — | 1.46 | 1.48 | 1.96 | 2.77 | 1.64 |
| 26 | 18 | 17 | 14.5 | 22.85 | 22.86 | 24.04 | 26.33 | 24.2 |
| 27 | 37 | 26 | 24.8 | 31 | 30 | 31.11 | 29.29 | 28.9 |
| 28 | 28 | 20 | 25.2 | 43.61 | 44.44 | 41.24 | 39.1 | 43.2 |

| $m/e$ | $He^+$ | | | | | | |
|---|---|---|---|---|---|---|---|
| | [A1] | | | | | | [M12] |
| | 1200 keV | 800 keV | 400 keV | 200 keV | 20 keV | 2 keV | $\alpha$(Po) |
| 1 | 0.28 | 0.22 | 0.43 | 0.4 | 1.31 | — | — |
| 12 | 0.23 | 0.28 | 0.58 | 0.74 | 1.44 | 1.66 | — |
| 13 | 0.33 | 0.36 | 0.60 | 0.72 | 1.45 | 2.45 | — |
| 14 | 1.07 | 1.15 | 1.61 | 1.54 | 5.94 | 5.37 | 0.68 |
| 24 | 1.08 | 1.36 | 2.41 | 3.06 | 4.48 | 4.33 | 0.42 |
| 25 | 2.46 | 2.78 | 4.07 | 4.29 | 9.05 | 26.71 | 1.63 |
| 26 | 24.48 | 25.24 | 23.53 | 24.08 | 28.57 | 46.93 | 19.02 |
| 27 | 25.63 | 26.84 | 24 | 22.79 | 16.06 | 7.47 | 25.6 |
| 28 | 44.4 | 41.74 | 43.03 | 42.86 | 31.65 | 5.05 | 52.68 |

*Ethylene.* Table VII summarizes the available data for ethylene These may be compared to the preceding case. Kebarle and Godbole's results [K4] for electrons and Abbe's data [A1, A3] for high-energy ions indicate indeed that the stability of the parent ion increases with the speed, suggesting that the number of transition to excited dissociative states of the molecule or molecular ion decreases with the increase of the speed of the particle. Again, the comparison of different author's results for the same kind of particle is probably not legitimate because of instrumental effects. Abbe's results show again, as for acetylene, that similar spectra are obtained for $D^+$ and $H_2^+$, $D_2^+$ and $He^+$ ions of the same energy (and speeds), or for $D^+$, $H_2^+$ (400 keV) and $H^+$ (200 keV); $D_2^+$, $He^+$ (400 keV) and $D^+$, $H_2^+$ (200 keV).

*Other Hydrocarbons.* High-energy electron-impact spectra have been published for ethane [M18, W2], propane [V1, W2], *n*-butane [K4, W2], various higher hydrocarbons [K1, L15, M10, M19], and benzene [K4, M19]; photon-impact spectra are known for ethane [S14], propane [V1], and various higher hydrocarbons [L15, M10, S14]; ion-impact data may be found for ethane [A3, K5] propane [P2], *n*-butane [C6], and various hydrocarbons [L15]; α-particle spectra were studied for ethane [M11, M12, W2], propane [M12], and *n*-butane [M12]. The results are similar to those discussed above. With the exception of the works of Abbe, Wexler, Müller-Duysing, and Melton on ethane, ion-impact data refer to pure charge transfer conditions and are still difficult to interpret. Obviously, the slow ions used in charge transfer experiments are likely to induce many more transitions to dissociative states than fast particles.

Low-energy electron impact curves have been calculated on the basis of the excitation of only the ground ionic state for propane, within the framework of the quasi-equilibrium theory [V1] and the small differences with the experimental curves were explained by assuming that superexcited states might play a role in the real phenomena.

Particularly interesting conclusions may be drawn from a recent comparative study of photon- and electron-impact mass spectra by Momigny *et al.* [M10] and will be given in the following subsection.

### Comparison of Electron- and Photon-Impact Mass Spectra

Momigny, Wankenne, and Urbain [M10] (MWU) have obtained the electron- and photon-impact mass spectra of some isomers of pentane and hexane with a double-focusing AEI MS9 mass spectrometer, equipped with a rare gas discharge UV resonance lamp; three resonance wavelengths were used. On the basis of the threshold laws for electron- and photon-impact found by Geltman [G3] and generalized by Morrison [M21], MWU have used their results, those of Schoen [S14], and those of Steiner *et al.* [S22] to derive an analytical expression for the variation of the ratio of the parent ion

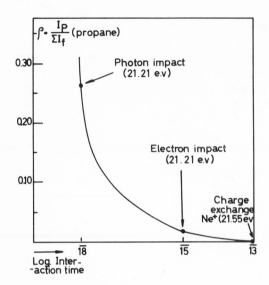

Fig. 6. Ratio of parent-to-fragment ions as a function of the interaction time. (After Momigny et al. [M10].)

abundance to the fragment ions' abundances, as a function of the photon energy. By integrating this relation, they were able to reproduce the electron-impact variation of the same ratio.

However, MWU noted that there is a considerable quantitative difference between the calculated and experimental values of the ratios, and they showed that this ratio is directly dependent on the ionization and fragmentation cross sections. It follows that the quantitative differences observed by these authors are due, at least partly, to a difference between the photon- and electron-impact ionization or excitation cross sections. This fact can be explained only by admitting that optically forbidden transitions take place under slow electron impact. This conclusion is in complete agreement with what has been seen in the preceding sections. MWU noted that the ratio of parent-to-fragment ions seems to be a function of the interaction time between the ionizing particle and the molecule, as is shown by Fig. 6, taken from MWU [M10], in which the ratio $\rho$ was plotted as function of the mean interaction time.

## Excitation and Ionization Cross Sections

As mentioned earlier, a study of the excitation and ionization cross sections as function of the incident particle energy should be useful as a test for the BO approximation and for the possible occurrence of forbidden transitions. Many experiments have been performed in the last 30 years, notably on optical excitation of atoms and molecules by electrons, and we shall not review them here. Comprehensive accounts will be found in the books of Massey and Burhop [M5, M6], Hasted [H3], Bates [B4] (notably the chapter by Seaton and Fite), and McDaniel [M22]. We shall consider here only some recent work related to our present purpose.

### Ionization Cross Sections

A very interesting recent work by Schram and co-workers [S5, S6] deals with the cross sections for the ionization of rare gases and other molecular gases by high-energy electrons.

Schram [S5] has investigated the value of the BO approximation laws for optically allowed and forbidden transitions [expressions (6) and (7)]. Since the product $\sigma_i \times E_{el}$ is a constant or a linear function of ln $E_{el}$ for forbidden or allowed transitions, the test is easy; moreover, the experimental behavior of $\sigma_i$ should indicate the nature of the transition from the point of view of selection rules.

By this method, Schram showed that the first ionization of rare gases follows the BO approximation for optically allowed transitions above 800 eV, but that multiple ionization is due mainly to forbidden transitions involving simultaneous ejection of two or more electrons; it may however happen also through an Auger inner excitation followed by a cascade ionization process. This is exemplified in Fig. 7. Schram also showed that the BO approximation is definitely valid above 600 eV, and this confirms the previous work of Kebarle and Godbole [K4].

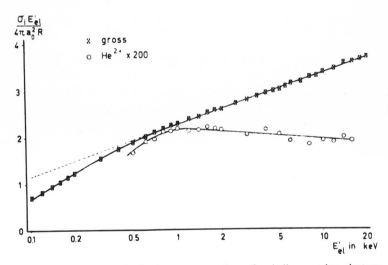

Fig. 7. Variation of ionization cross sections for helium under electron bombardment: plot of $\sigma_i\, E_{el}/4\pi a_0^2\, R$ *versus* ln $E_{el}$, for the gross ionization cross section and the partial double ionization cross section in helium. (After Schram [S5].)

The case of atomic hydrogen deserves special mention, because of its theoretical importance. Fite and Brackmann [F4] have measured the cross section for the reaction

$$e + H \rightarrow H^+ + 2e$$

by a modulated atomic beam method and could confirm the linear threshold law deduced theoretically by Geltman [G3], within the first 5–6 V. Such a law has been verified many times by ordinary electron-impact ionization efficiency curves, obtained with monoenergetic electrons in a mass spectrometer. Fite and Brackmann extended their measurements to 1 keV and found a relation in agreement with the BO approximation treatment above 100 eV, but in quantitative disagreement below 100 eV.

The threshold behavior, however, is far from being definitely known, as is shown by the simple case of the hydrogen molecule, where much controversy has recently arisen [B6].

We have shown above how Momigny et al. [M10] have concluded that different ionization cross sections, in electron- and photon-impact mass spectra, could be explained only by assuming that slow electrons induce transitions to forbidden states not attainable by photon impact.

## Excitation Cross Sections

Excitation has been extensively studied and good reviews may be found elsewhere [B4, H3, M6]. The excitation cross section for atomic hydrogen to the forbidden $2S_{\frac{1}{2}}$ state has been examined by Lichten and Schultz [L14] by a DC cross beam experiment in which an atomic hydrogen beam of thermal origin was bombarded by a crossed DC electron beam; the excited atomic beam was detected by deactivation on a platinum surface electron ejector detector.

Different forbidden excitation processes also have been observed by numerous workers, and cross sections have been determined; the nature of those transitions has been discussed in the preceding sections.

## Ion-Impact Ionization Cross Sections

The simple ionization by ion impact, such as

$$H^+ + H_2 \rightarrow H^+ + H_2^+ + e$$

has been discussed by Massey and Burhop [M5]. Keene [K9] and Fogel et al. [F7] investigated both the positive ion and secondary electron currents, whereas Gilbody and Hasted [G5] measured both the primary and the secondary electron currents, generated by positive ions, between 3 eV and 40 keV.

Charge exchange experiments are of a somewhat different nature, although they probably involve forbidden transitions, owing to the low kinetic energy of the incident ions. Lindholm and co-workers [L16, L21, L22] and Afrosimov and co-workers [A5, A6] have made numerous studies of that kind, but we shall not discuss them here.

Ion-impact excitation has been studied by Kistemaker and his collaborators (see [S23]), who followed the excitation process by spectroscopic analysis in the 3000–5800 Å region. This kind of collision process is important in auroral phenomena.

## SELECTION RULES FOR THE EVOLUTION OF THE MOLECULAR IONS

### Introduction

The previous discussion has been restricted to an examination of the selection rules governing the collisional probabilities for transitions to excited and possibly ionized states. This is but one aspect of the general problem of the appearance of ions, of fundamental importance for mass spectrometry.

The complementary problem, which should also be solved, refers to the evolution of the excited molecular ions formed in the primary collisions How will they decay, and what dissociation paths will they follow ? Very few theoretical approaches have been undertaken up to now, except for the probable evolution of the ground ionic state of molecules large enough for the theory of quasi-equilibrium, mentioned previously [R2], to be applied.

The most general answer, for small molecules in particular, has been given recently by Lorquet and his colleagues, at the University of Liège. We shall briefly outline these developments.

### Positive Charge Distribution

The simplest approach is to admit that all ions derive from the evolution of the ground electronic state of the molecular ion, vibrationally excited. In this case, a first and natural hypothesis is to suppose that the behavior of the molecular ion will depend, in an important way, on the positive charge distribution in the ion, positive holes corresponding to particularly weak bonds. This idea was developed by Thompson [T2, T3], Lester [L27], and Lorquet [L17], who applied it to the particular case of branched paraffins, where the theoretical charge distribution was calculated and correlated in a very satisfactory way to the fragmentation probabilities from the ground state of the ion. It no longer holds for normal paraffins, however, and other factors influencing the dissociation must be looked for, as was recently shown by Lorquet [L19] in an important theoretical paper. For instance, the positive charge density in *n*-butane is 0.43 for the central C–C bond and

0.18 for the external C–C bond, whereas it is well known that, even at low energies, the most important fragment ion in $n$-butane is $C_3H_7^+$. Similarly it may be shown theoretically that most of the positive charge, in $n$-alkylamines, is concentrated on the nitrogen lone pair and on the C–N bond, whereas the most abundant ion is almost always the $CH_2 = NH_2^+$ ion, corresponding to a C–C bond cleavage.

### Vibrationally Induced Transitions

According to Lorquet [L19], these apparent anomalies are due to the fact that such simple reasoning deals with only the Franck–Condon configuration; in reality it would be more appropriate to consider the representation point, on the potential energy hypersurface, within certain bond distance limits, and to examine the possibility of an electronic readjustment in the ion. This electronic relaxation may be treated by theoretical methods, in the case of sufficiently symmetric molecules, where group theory enables one to decide which relaxation matrix elements vanish.

If the discussion is restricted to the consideration of only the first ionic state, the determination of those relaxation processes for which the matrix element is vanishing will indicate those decomposition paths which will be forbidden. This procedure in fact is nothing else than predicting new selection rules governing dissociation processes. Difficulties arise, however, because the ionization process generally will result in a loss of symmetry, so that rigorous application of these selection rules may not be completely appropriate. A recent theoretical treatment of molecular symmetry introduced by Longuet-Higgins [L24] has been applied by Lorquet to some molecules. As a result, for $n$-butane, only the antisymmetric normal modes have nonvanishing matrix elements, so that symmetric normal modes resulting in the appearance of a $C_2H_5^+$ ion are not favored, although the positive charge on the central bond is high; the consequences of this situation are a high probability of bond breaking at the external C–C bond and a high abundance of the $C_3H_7^+$ ion, as is observed.

In the same way, it is shown that for ethylene, the favored motion is a torsional mode; $C_2H_4^+$ twists easily and, in the perpendicular twisted configuration (degenerate $^2E$), Jahn–Teller effects lead to unstability toward twisting or toward the normal modes corresponding to the loss of a hydrogen molecule; the abundance of the $C_2H_2^+$ ion in the ethylene mass spectrum is thus nicely explained.

### Radiationless Transitions and Multiplicity Conservation Rules

*General.* As mentioned earlier, only the ground electronic state has been considered for the molecular ion, and this hypothesis is likely to be rather satisfactory for complex molecules where highly excited ions, thanks to internal conversion within the above restrictions of selection rules, may eventually end up with the ground electronic structure, endowed with strong vibrational excitation.

Since the speed of radiationless transitions is very great ($10^{-12}$–$10^{-13}$ sec) and of the order of the dissociation vibrational time lag, only repulsive levels will bring dissociation, whereas other states will be converted to the ground state, unless they undergo predissociation.

*Spin Conservation and Spin-Orbit Coupling.* Spin conservation rules should hold for ions, as for molecules, and doublet–quartet transitions should be forbidden, or be very slow and thus improbable ($10^{-8}$–$10^{-4}$ sec). Therefore, excited doublet states will normally convert to the ground doublet state, whereas excited quartet states should decay to the ground quartet state.

These rules, however, would not hold any more for heavy-atom-containing molecules, where spin-orbit coupling is known to be important. This is the case in particular for halogenated compounds, where the halogen is bromine or iodine. Therefore, one may consider, with Lorquet, the mass spectrum as the result of the superposition of a number of independent components, corresponding to different electronic states. These may be of various nature. There may be autoionized neutral states transforming to molecular ions, or to a ion pair, or to a fragment ion and fragment radical or molecule; repulsive electronic ionic states leading to fragment ions with kinetic energy; and predissociated molecular ion electronic states, giving rise to metastable ions, as shown notably by Momigny [M14]. One should finally consider the lowest doublet state of the molecular ion and the lowest quartet state (neglecting spin-orbit interaction); the latter will be unimportant if too high in energy to be significantly populated. (Lorquet has shown this probably to be the case for the alkanes.) If, as a first approximation, autoionized, repulsive, and predissociated states are neglected, an interesting case to be considered is that of halogenated alkanes; in particular, the mass spectrum of fluorinated alkanes, because of very weak spin-orbit coupling, should be the result of the decomposition of two independent states, i.e., the lowest doublet state (ground state) and the lowest quartet state. On the other hand, when the halogen is bromine or iodine, spin-orbit coupling is important and the ground doublet state only should be obtained and finally dissociated. Chlorine probably is an intermediate case.

It is remarkable that experimental results seem to confirm this point of view. It has indeed been shown by Lorquet-Julien [L25, L26] that for *n*-pentane and cyclopentane halides, the mass spectrum of the fluoro derivatives (and, to a lesser extent, the chloro derivatives) may be considered as being formed by the superposition of two simple mass spectra, one of which is practically identical to the mass spectra of the bromo or iodo derivatives; this common mass spectral pattern is therefore attributed to the doublet ground state decomposition, whereas the second component, for fluorine (and chlorine), is considered as the contribution of the lowest quartet state. This interesting conclusion can only be considered as tentative because of the simplifying assumptions relative to autoionized, predissociated, and repulsive states.

## ACKNOWLEDGMENTS

We want to express our gratitude to Dr. J. C. Abbe, of C. R. N. Strasbourg, France, for having sent us much precious and important experimental material prior to publication, as well as for his comments and suggestions about this paper. We also acknowledge the criticisms of Dr. J. C. Lorquet, who read the manuscript carefully, and the constant interest of Professor L. D'Or in our work. This research is part of a general program supported by the Fonds de la Recherche Fondamentale Collective, which we thank for its important aid to our laboratory.

## NOTE 1 ADDED IN PROOF

In a very nice and interesting electron scattering experiment at large angles on methane, Ehrhardt and Linder [E3] have recently found that a forbidden transition is taking place above the first ionization limit, at 19.5 eV, as indicated by the angular dependence of the scattering cross section. It was attributed to a superexcited state ($2sa_1 \rightarrow 3sa_1$) and the second ionization potential of methane was deduced from it to be around 24 eV. This superexcited state might be the same as the preionized state around 19 eV discussed by Collin and Delwiche and found in electron impact ionization [C13].

## NOTE 2 ADDED IN PROOF

Recent electron scattering experiments by Doering [D3] have also confirmed the existence of a forbidden transition around 4.6 eV. This author, however, did not find the 6.4–6.6 eV transition.

## NOTE 3 ADDED IN PROOF

Collins and Kebarle [C14] have recently published ionization cross sections, charge transfer cross sections, and ionic fragmentation patterns for many paraffins, olefins, acetylenes, chloroalkanes, and benzene with 40–100 keV protons. These data were discussed notably from the same standpoint as adopted here, but could not be included in the discussion. These authors also conclude that no significant differences should be observed in the mass spectra obtained with particles having speeds higher than $10^8$ cm/sec.

They also published new data on cross sections with 40–100 keV protons not included in this discussion.

# REFERENCES

A1. J. C. Abbe, Private communication, 1966.

A2. J. C. Abbe and J. P. Adloff, *Bull. Soc. Chim. France*, p. 1212, 1964.

A3. J. C. Abbe and J. P. Adloff, *Phys. Rev. Letters* 11:28, 1964.

A4. J. C. Abbe and J. P. Adloff, *Compt. Rend. Acad. Sci.* 258:3003, 1964.

A5. N. V. Afrosimov and N. V. Fedorenko, *Zh. Techn. Fiz.* 27:2557, 1957.

A6. N. V. Afrosimov, R. N. Ilin, and N. V. Fedorenko, *Zh. Eksperim. i Teor. Fiz.* 34:1983, 1958.

B1. C. R. Bowman and W. D. Miller, *J. Chem. Phys.* 42:681, 1965.

B2. E. L. Breig and C. C. Lin, *J. Chem. Phys.* 43:3839, 1965.

B3. H. Boersch, *Proc. 4th Intern. Conf. Phys. Electron. Atomic Collisions, Quebec, 1965*.

B4. D. R. Bates, *Atomic and Molecular Processes*, Academic Press, New York, 1962.

B5. H. Bethe, *Ann. Phys.* 5:325, 1930.

B6. D. D. Briglia and D. Rapp, *J. Chem. Phys.* 42:3201, 1965.

B7. I. S. Bowen, *Astrophys. J.* 67:1, 1928.

B8. H. A. Bethe and E. E. Salpeter, in: S. Flügge (ed.), *Handbuch der Physik*, Vol. 35, 1957, Springer Verlag, Berlin, p. 88.

B9. P. G. Burke and K. Smith, *Rev. Mod. Phys.* 34:458, 1962.

C1. J. C. Y. Chen and J. L. Magee, *J. Chem. Phys.* 36:1407, 1962.

C2. G. E. Chamberlain, H. G. M. Heideman, J. A. Simpson, and C. E. Kuyatt, *Proc. 4th Intern. Conf. Phys. Electron. Atomic Collisions, Quebec, 1965*, p. 378; also G. E. Chamberlain and H. G. M. Heideman, *Phys. Rev. Letters* 15:337, 1965.

C3. J. E. Collin, *J. Chim. Phys.* 57:424, 1960.

C4. J. E. Collin, *Bull. Soc. Chim. Belg.* 71:15, 1962.

C5. J. E. Collin, *Mém. Soc. Roy. Sci. Liège* XIV:1-220, 1967.

C6. W. A. Chupka and E. Lindholm, *Arkiv Fysik* 25:349, 1963.

C7. J. E. Collin, in: R. I. Reed (ed.), *Mass Spectrometry*, Academic Press, London, 1965.

C8. E. M. Clarke, P. Marmet, and L. Kerwin, *Proc. 2nd Conf. Adv. Mass Spectrometry*, 1962.

C9. E. U. Condon and G. H. Shortley, *Theory of Atomic Spectra*, Cambridge Univ. Press, London, 1951.

C10. V. Cermàk, *J. Chem. Phys.* 44:3774, 1966; 44:3781, 1966.

C11. V. Cermàk and Z. Herman, *Collection Czech. Chem. Commun.* 30:169, 1965.

C12. T. I. Cottrell and I. I. Walker, *Quart. Rev.* XX:153, 1966.

C13. J. E. Collin and J. Delwiche, *Can. J. Chem.* 45:1875, 1967.

C14. J. G. Collins and P. Kebarle, *J. Chem. Phys.* 46:1194, 1967.

D1. S. Datta, *Proc. Roy. Soc. (London)* A101:539, 1922.

D2. M. Dufay, M. Dretta, and M. Eidelsberg, *Compt. Rend. Acad. Sci.* 261:1635, 1965; M. Desesquelles, M. Dufay, and G. Docao, *Compt. Rend. Acad. Sci.* 262:B1329, 1966; M. Dufay et al., *Rappt. Activités Fac. Sci. Phys. Nucl. Univ. Lyon*, Jan. 1966.

D3. J. P. Doering, *J. Chem. Phys.* 46:1194, 1967.

E1. H. Ehrhardt and G. Meister, *Proc. 4th Intern. Conf. Phys. Electron. Atomic Collisions, Quebec, 1965*, p. 125.

E2. A. G. Engelhardt and A. V. Phelps, *Phys. Rev.* 131:2115, 1963.

E3. H. Ehrhardt and F. Linder, *Z. Naturforsch.* 22a:11, 1967.

F1. F. Fiquet-Fayard, *J. Chim. Phys.* 63:401, 1966.

F2. J. Franck and H. Grotrian, *Z. Physik* 4:89, 1921 (quoted by Schulz [S11]).

F3. W. L. Fite, Measurement of Collisional Excitation and Ionization Cross Sections, in: Bates [B4].

F4. W. L. Fite and R. T. Brackmann, *Phys. Rev.* 113:1141, 1958.

F5. W. L. Fite and R. T. Brackmann, *Phys. Rev.* **113**:1151, 1958.
F6. W. L. Fite and R. T. Brackmann, *Phys. Rev.* **115**:815, 1959.
F7. Ya. M. Fogel, L. I. Krupnik, and B. G. Safronov, *Zh. Eksperim. i Teor. Fiz.* **28**: 589, 1955.
G1. J. Geiger and K. Wittmaack, *Proc. 4th Intern. Conf. Phys. Electron. Atomic Collision, Quebec, 1965*, p. 354.
G2. R. H. Garstang, Forbidden Transitions, in: Bates [B4].
G3. S. Geltman, *Phys. Rev.* **102**:171, 1956.
G4. E. Gustaffson and E. Lindholm, *Arkiv Fysik* **18**:219, 1960.
G5. H. B. Gilbody and J. B. Hasted, *Proc. Roy. Soc. (London)* **A240**:302, 1957.
G6. R. H. Garstang, *J. Chem. Phys.* **44**:1308, 1966.
H1. H. G. M. Heideman, C. E. Kuyatt, and G. E. Chamberlain, *J. Chem. Phys.* **44**: 355, 1966.
H2. G. S. Hurst, T. E. Bortner, and R. E. Glick, *J. Chem. Phys.* **42**:713, 1965.
H3. J. B. Hasted, *Physics of Atomic Collisions*, Butterworth, London, 1964.
H4. J. B. Hasted, Charge Transfer and Collisional Detachment, in: Bates [B4].
H5. R. E. Huffman, Y. Tanaka, and J. C. Larrabee, *J. Chem. Phys.* **39**:910, 1963.
H6. J. J. Hopfield, *Phys. Rev.* **35**:1133, 1930; **36**:789, 1930.
H7. G. Herzberg and E. Teller, *Z. Physik. Chem.* **B21**:410, 1933.
H8. G. Herzberg, *Phys. Rev.* **69**:362, 1946.
H9. L. Herzberg and G. Herzberg, *Astrophys. J.* **105**:353, 1947.
J1. P. Jacquinot and J. Brochard, *Compt. Rend. Acad. Sci.* **216**:581, 1943.
K1. A. Kuppermann and L. M. Raff, *J. Chem. Phys.* **37**:2497, 1962.
K2. A. Kuppermann and L. M. Raff, *Discussions Faraday Soc.* **35**:30, 1963.
K3. C. E. Kuyatt, S. R. Mielczarek, and J. A. Simpson, *Phys. Rev. Letters* **12**:293, 1964.
K4. P. Kebarle and E. W. Godbole, *J. Chem. Phys.* **36**:302, 1962.
K5. H. von Koch, *Arkiv Fysik* **28**:559, 1965.
K6. H. von Koch, *Arkiv Fysik* **28**:529, 1965.
K7. S. E. Kupriyanov and A. A. Perov, *Zh. Tekhn. Fiz.* **33**:823, 1963.
K8. S. E. Kupriyanov, *Kinetika i Kataliz* **3**:61, 1962.
K9. J. P. Keene, *Phil. Mag.* **40**:369, 1949.
L1. E. N. Lassettre and S. A. Francis, *J. Chem. Phys.* **40**:1208, 1964.
L2. E. N. Lassettre and E. A. Jones, *J. Chem. Phys.* **40**:1218, 1964.
L3. E. N. Lassettre and E. A. Jones, *J. Chem. Phys.* **40**:1222, 1964.
L4. E. N. Lassettre, A. S. Berman, S. M. Silverman, and M. E. Krasnow, *J. Chem. Phys.* **40**:1232, 1964.
L5. E. N. Lassettre, M. E. Krasnow, and S. M. Silverman, *J. Chem. Phys.* **40**:1242, 1964.
L6. E. N. Lassettre and M. E. Krasnow, *J. Chem. Phys.* **40**:1248, 1964.
L7. E. N. Lassettre and S. M. Silverman, *J. Chem. Phys.* **40**:1256, 1964.
L8. E. N. Lassettre, S. M. Silverman, and M. E. Krasnow, *J. Chem. Phys.* **40**:1261, 1964.
L9. E. N. Lassettre, V. D. Meyer, and M. S. Longmire, *J. Chem. Phys.* **41**:2952, 1964.
L10. E. N. Lassettre, *J. Chem. Phys.* **42**:2971, 1965.
L11. E. N. Lassettre, V. D. Meyer, and M. S. Longmire, *J. Chem. Phys.* **42**:807, 1965.
L12. E. N. Lassettre, F. M. Glaser, V. D. Meyer, and A. Skerbele, *J. Chem. Phys.* **42**: 3429, 1965.
L13. W. Lichten, *J. Chem. Phys.* **37**:2152, 1962.
L14. W. Lichten and S. Schultz, *Phys. Rev.* **116**:1132, 1959.
L15. Z. Z. Latypov and S. E. Kupriyanov, *Russ. J. Phys. Chem. (English Transl.)* **39**:836, 1965 (1966).
L16. E. Lindholm, I. Szabo, and P. Wilmenius, *Arkiv Fysik* **25**:417, 1963.

L17. J. C. Lorquet, *Mol. Phys.* **9**:101, 1965.

L18. J. C. Lorquet and G. G. Hall, *Mol. Phys.* **9**:29, 1965.

L19. J. C. Lorquet, *Mol. Phys.* **10**:489, 1966; **10**:493, 1966.

L20. J. C. Leclerc and J. C. Lorquet, *J. Phys. Chem.* **71**:787, 1967.

L21. E. Lindholm, *Arkiv Fysik* **8**:257, 1954.

L22. E. Lindholm, *Z. Naturforsch.* **9a**:535, 1954.

L23. W. Lichten, *J. Chem. Phys.* **26**:306, 1957.

L24. H. C. Longuet-Higgins, *Mol. Phys.* **6**:445, 1963.

L25. A. Lorquet-Julien, *Bull. Soc. Roy. Liège* **30**:170, 1961.

L26. A. Lorquet-Julien, *Bull. Acad. Roy. Belg. Cl. Sci.* **48**:1128, 1962.

L27. G. R. Lester, *Advances in Mass Spectrometry I*, Pergamon, London, 1959.

M1. V. D. Meyer, A. Skerbele, and E. N. Lassettre, *J. Chem. Phys.* **43**:805, 1965.

M2. V. D. Meyer, A. Skerbele, and E. N. Lassettre, *J. Chem. Phys.* **43**:3969, 1965.

M3. V. D. Meyer and E. N. Lassettre, *4th Intern. Conf. Phys. Electron. Atomic Collisions* Quebec, 1965, p. 397.

M4. N. F. Mott and H. S. W. Massey, *The Theory of Atomic Collisions*, 2nd ed., Oxford Univ. Press, London, 1949.

M5. H. S. W. Massey and E. H. S. Burhop, *Electronic and Ionic Impact Phenomena*, Oxford Univ. Press, London, 1952.

M6. H. W. S. Massey, The Theory of Atomic Collisions, in: *Handbuch der Physik*, Vol. 36, Springer Verlag, Berlin, 1956.

M7. H. S. W. Massey, *Negative Ions*, 2nd ed., Cambridge Univ. Press, London, 1950.

M8. M. R. C. McDowell, *Atomic Collision Processes*, North-Holland, Amsterdam, 1964.

M9. W. B. Maier, II, *J. Chem. Phys.* **45**:1790, 1965.

M10. J. Momigny, H. Wankenne, and J. Urbain, *Bull. Acad. Roy. Belg. Cl. Sci.* **51**:371, 1965.

M11. C. E. Melton, *J. Chem. Phys.* **30**:847, 1959.

M12. W. Müller-Duysing, Ph. D. Thesis, Hamburg University, 1963 (reported by Abbe [A1]).

M13. V. D. Meyer and E. N. Lassettre, *J. Chem. Phys.* **44**:2535, 1966.

M14. J. Momigny, Thèse d'agrégation Enseignement Supérieur, Univ. Liège, 1966; *Mém. Soc. Roy. Sci. Liège*, 5e série, Tome XIII, fasc. 1, 1966.

M15. J. D. Morrison, *12th Conseil Chim. Solvay, Bruxelles, 1963*.

M16. V. D. Meyer and E. N. Lassettre, *J. Chem. Phys.* **42**:3436, 1965.

M17. R. S. Mulliken, *J. Chem. Phys.* **33**:1596, 1960.

M18. C. E. Melton, *J. Chem. Phys.* **37**:562, 1962.

M19. J. E. Monahan and H. E. Stanton, *J. Chem. Phys.* **37**:2654, 1962.

M20. J. C. McLennan and G. M. Shrum, *Proc. Roy. Soc.* **A108**:501, 1925.

M21. J. D. Morrison, *Rev. Pure Appl. Chem.* **22**:1955; *J. Chem. Phys.* **31**:1335, 1959.

M22. E. W. McDaniel, *Collision Phenomena in Ionized Gases*, Wiley, New York, 1964.

N1. C. W. Nutt, P. A. Millward, and K. N. Mehendale, *13th ASTM Conf. Mass Spectrometry, St. Louis, 1965*.

N2. R. N. Nicholls and A. L. Stewart, Allowed Transitions, in: Bates [B4].

P1. R. L. Platzman, *J. Phys. Radium* **21**:853, 1960.

P2. E. Petterson and E. Lindholm, *Arkiv Fysik* **24**:49, 1963.

P3. W. C. Price and W. T. Tutte, *Proc. Roy. Soc. (London)* **A174**:207, 1940.

Q1. Québec Conf. Book of Summaries, *4 th Intern. Conf. Phys. Electr. Atomic Collisions*, Quebec, 1965.

R1. M. E. Rudd and D. V. Lang, see [Q1], p. 153.

R2. H. M. Rosenstock and M. Krauss, in: F. W. McLafferty, *Mass Spectrometry of Organic Molecules*, Academic Press, New York, 1963.

R3. J. Ross, *Molecular Beams*, Wiley (Interscience), New York, 1966.

S1. S. M. Silverman and E. N. Lassettre, *J. Chem. Phys.* **40**:1265, 1964.

S2. A. M. Skerbele and E. N. Lassettre, *J. Chem. Phys.* **40**:1271, 1964.

S3. A. M. Skerbele and E. N. Lassettre, *J. Chem. Phys.* **42**:395, 1965.

S4. T. E. Sharp and H. M. Rosenstock, *J. Chem. Phys.* **41**:3453, 1964.

S5. B. L. Schram, Ph. D. Thesis, Univ. Amsterdam, 1966.

S6. B. L. Schram, M. J. Vander Wiel, F. J. de Heer, and H. R. Moustafa, *J. Chem. Phys.* **44**:49, 1966.

S7. G. J. Schulz, *Phys. Rev.* **125**:229, 1962.

S8. J. A. Simpson, S. R. Mielczarek, and J. Cooper, *J. Opt. Soc. Am.* **54**:269, 1964.

S9. J. A. Simpson and S. R. Mielczarek, *J. Chem. Phys.* **39**:1606, 1963.

S10. G. J. Schulz and J. Y. Dowell, *Phys. Rev.* **128**:174, 1962.

S11. G. J. Schulz, Gen. Conf. Plenary Lecture, *7th Intern. Conf. Ionization Phenomena Gases, Belgrade, 1965.*

S12. A. M. Skerbele, E. N. Lassettre, and V. D. Meyer, see [Q1], p. 400.

S13. S. M. Silverman and E. N. Lassettre, *J. Chem. Phys.* **44**:2219, 1966.

S14. R. I. Schoen, *J. Chem. Phys.* **37**:2032, 1962.

S15. R. H. Schuler and F. A. Stuber, *J. Chem. Phys.* **40**:2035, 1964.

S16. H. Sjögrèn, *Arkiv Fysik* **29**:565, 1965.

S17. M. J. Seaton, Theory of Excitation and Ionization by Electron Impact, in: D. R. Bates [B4].

S18. S. M. Silverman and E. N. Lassettre, *J. Chem. Phys.* **42**:3420,1965.

S19. G. J. Schulz, *Phys. Rev.* **116**:1141, 1959.

S20. G. J. Schulz, *Phys. Rev.* **135**:A988, 1964.

S21. I. Szabo, *Arkiv Fysik* (personal commun.), to be published.

S22. B. Steiner, C.F. Giese, and M. G. Inghram, *J. Chem. Phys.* **34**:189, 1961.

S23. T. J. Sluyters and J. Kistemaker, *Physica* **25**:1376, 1959.

S24. J. Schutten, F. J. de Heer, H. R. Moustafa, A. J. H. Boerboom, and J. Kistemaker, *J. Chem. Phys.* **44**:3924, 1966.

S25. A. Skerbele and E. N. Lassettre, *J. Chem. Phys.* **44**:4066, 1966.

T1. Y. Tanaka, A. Jursa, and F. LeBlanc, *J. Chem. Phys.* **32**: 1199, 1960.

T2. R. Thompson, *Mass Spectrometry*, Inst. of Petroleum, London, 1952, p. 53.

T3. R. Thompson, *Applied Mass Spectrometry*, Inst. of Petroleum, London, 1954, p. 154.

T4. D. W. Turner and M. I. Al-Joboury, *J. Chem. Phys.* **37**:3007, 1963; *J. Chem. Soc.* p. 4434, 1964.

V1. M. Vestal, *J. Chem. Phys.* **43**:1356, 1965.

V2. D. W. Vance and T. L. Bailey, *J. Chem. Phys.* **44**:486, 1966.

W1. H. F. Winters, *J. Chem. Phys.* **43**:426, 1965.

W2. S. Wexler, *J. Chem. Phys.* **41**:2781, 1964.

W3. G. Wannier, *Phys. Rev.* **90**:817, 1953.

W4. T. Watanabe, *J. Phys. Soc. Japan* **16**:510, 1961.

W5. R. L. Wolmer, *Phys. Rev.* **45**:689, 1934.

W6. K. Watanabe, E. C. Y. Inn, and M. Zelikoff, *J. Chem. Phys.* **21**:1026, 1953.

W7. K. Watanabe and M. Zelikoff, *J. Opt. Soc. Am.* **43**:56, 1953.

W8. P. G. Wilkinson and R. S. Mulliken, *Astrophys. J.* **126**:10, 1957.

# QUANTUM CHEMICAL ASPECTS
# OF FRAGMENTATION MECHANISMS
# IN MASS SPECTROMETRY

## G. R. Lester

*Dyestuffs Division*
*Imperial Chemical Industries Limited*
*Blackley, Manchester, England*

## INTRODUCTION

The main purpose of this article will be to try to place in perspective a range of quantum chemical concepts and techniques that appear to be relevant to a proper understanding of fragmentation mechanisms. It will be necessarily condensed as we propose to consider a diversity of topics so as to give a general picture of an approach to mass spectrometry that might, not too inappropriately, be designated "applied quantum chemistry." A full discussion clearly would not be possible within the present limitations of space, but it is hoped that a few illustrative examples will clarify the general principles that underlie practical applications.

Although mass spectrometry only recently has become a respectable branch of chemical physics, worthy of the attention of the serious research worker as well as the analyst, it is probably true that no other physical technique makes quite so broad demands on a whole range of theoretical concepts. Thus, not only are all the familiar aspects of spectroscopy in general implicated—energy levels, eigenfunctions, selection rules and so on—but, in addition, the whole theory of chemical kinetics becomes involved in a somewhat exacting form, requiring a detailed understanding of the processes of activation and energy transfer. It is the challenge presented by these wide-ranging demands of theoretical interpretation that provides much of the subject's special interest.

It is, of course, possible to approach the subject of mass spectrometry from the standpoint of some particular theoretical model and to study intensively certain well-defined aspects thus presented. While recognizing the extremely valuable contributions that have arisen from this type of approach, we feel that there is evidence of a growing tendency for the specialized aspects of the subject thus presented to become too closely identified with its theoretical basis in the wider sense. There are obviously many other facets, particularly those concerned with the general wave mechanical properties of positive ions and free radicals, that have an equal right to be regarded as an essential part of the theoretical foundations. We do not accede to the view that only certain special aspects deserve a rigorous foundation, the remainder being introduced largely on the basis of chemical intuition or empiricism.

Several main themes may be discerned in our discussion, such as the unusual importance of purely electrostatic internal forces of interaction in positive ions and the significance of configuration interaction both between molecular orbitals or configurations of the same symmetry species and between different species ($\pi$–$\sigma$ interactions). These are discussed with reference to particular examples, mainly tolunitriles and derivatives of anthraquinone. Theoretical evidence is presented for the incidence of intersections of potential energy surfaces, and an attempt is made to gain further insight into those structural features that appear conducive to multiple intersections.

Extensive application of simplified perturbational treatments is made, although it is emphasized that ionization frequently disturbs the system profoundly by creating very irregular electron distributions. While it is clearly hazardous to use the conventional polarizability coefficients of molecular orbital theory in such extreme situations, it is shown that this may sometimes be justified. We make some reference to the very powerful and general method of Green's function, because it appears that this is destined to provide the proper theoretical basis for the whole range of phenomena inside the ion-chamber of a mass spectrometer. It is clearly just as perfectly adapted to the dynamics of molecular ions as the corresponding Laplace transform method is to a whole range of diffusion phenomena in classical physics.

## GREEN'S FUNCTIONS FOR ELECTRON IMPACT AND ION FRAGMENTATION PROCESSES

To strike the right note from the outset, we propose to begin with an abstract mathematical approach, not that anyone has so far been wholly successful in manipulating the abstractions into one of the much-frowned-upon "models" that alone seem capable of providing anything useful in the long run. But Hall and Levine [1] recently have pointed the way to a more rigorous mathematical foundation, using the properties of Green's function and Green's operator.

The first stage in the production of a mass spectrum by electron impact concerns the process of excitation and ionization. It is not invariably true that this process can be distinguished from the subsequent activation and fragmentation, in which case the usual approach involving a time delay while electronic energy is transformed into vibrational energy is not really valid. But in any case the overall subsequent behavior is, in principle, determined by the Green's function for the system.

In principle we are concerned with solutions of the time-dependent Schrödinger equation

$$ i\hbar \frac{\partial \psi}{\partial t} = H\psi \tag{1} $$

where, in general, $H$ is a time-dependent Hamiltonian. As a general approach for linear differential equations, we seek a solution in the form of an integral:

$$ \psi^+ (x_2 t_2) = \int K(x_2 t_2 ; x_1 t_1) \, \psi(x_1 t_1) \, dx_1 \tag{2} $$

Here $K(x_2 t_2 ; x_1 t_1)$ is the kernel, or more specifically, the Green's function, for the partial differential equation with initial states determined by the wave function $\psi(x_1 t_1)$ ($x$ implies all three space variables $x$, $y$, $z$ and additional variables for a multiparticle system). Clearly, a knowledge of the initial state function implies that the entire future time dependence of the system is fully determined, since the wave equation is first-order only in the time variable and therefore does not demand any additional prior knowledge concerning the time derivatives.

In accordance with the usual Green's function approach, we first turn attention to the partial differential equation with a localized inhomogeneous component, represented by the Dirac $\delta$-function:

$$ (i\hbar \frac{\partial}{\partial t_2} - H_2) \, K(x_2 t_2 ; x_1 t_1) = i\hbar \, \delta(t_2 - t_1) \, \delta(x_2 - x_1) \tag{3} $$

Provided that the Green's function is identically zero for negative values of $t_2 - t_1$, we can, with sufficient accuracy, derive the initial behavior of $K$ as $t_2 \to t_1$, by solving the equation

$$ i\hbar \frac{\partial}{\partial t_2} K(x_2 t_2 ; x_1 t_1) = i\hbar \, \delta(t_2 - t_1) \, \delta(x_2 - x_1) \tag{4} $$

whence

$$K(x_2 \, t_2; x_1 \, 0) - K(x_2 \, 0; x_1 \, 0) = \delta(x_2 - x_1) \tag{5}$$

for

$$\int_{-\infty}^{t_2} \delta(t_2 - t_1) \, dt_2 = 1$$

and we have supposed that $K(x_2 \, 0; x_1 \, 0) \equiv 0$. Hence

$$\psi^+_{(t_2 \to t_1)} (x_2 \, t_2) = \int K(x_2 \, t_2; x_1 \, t_1) \, \psi(x_1 \, t_1) \, dx_1 \equiv \psi(x_2 \, t_2) \tag{6}$$

Thus, the functions $\psi^+$ and $\psi$ are identical and the behavior of the system is consistent with the initial conditions. Moreover, for times $t_2 > t_1$, the inhomogeneous equation reduces to the normal homogeneous form

$$\left( i\hbar \frac{\partial}{\partial t_2} - H_2 \right) K(x_2 \, t_2; x_1 \, t_1) = 0$$

whence, by differentiation under the integral sign,

$$i\hbar \frac{\partial \psi^+}{\partial t_2} - H_2 \, \psi^+ = \int \left( i\hbar \frac{\partial}{\partial t_2} - H_2 \right) K(x_2 \, t_2; x_1 \, t_1) \, \psi(x_1 \, t_1) \, dx_1 = 0 \tag{7}$$

By the well-known Fourier integral representation of the $\delta$ function [2],

$$\delta(t_2 - t_1) = \frac{1}{2\pi} \int_{-\infty}^{\infty} e^{-i\omega(t_2 - t_1)} \, d\omega \tag{8}$$

so that one can try to determine the time dependence for a sinusoidal disturbance and thereby reduce the investigation of the actual time dependence to the evaluation of an integral in the complex plane. By suitable indentations in the contour it is possible to avoid singularities of the integrand and to evaluate the integral by Cauchy's theorem.

It has to be realized that although we have here an elegant formal mathematical scheme for describing the dynamics of the whole process of electron impact and unimolecular dissociation, when we revert to a "basis," i.e., a set of eigenfunctions to represent the system, we actually need to suppose that we have substantially complete knowledge of the stationary states, which is a very considerable assumption indeed when it is recollected that the greater part of theoretical chemistry is currently concerned with attempts to investigate the first few such stationary states for quite simple molecules. Obviously then the main value of the Green's function approach is to produce a mathematical scaffolding which enables one to see more clearly the inherent limitations of model theories, such as the quasi-equilibrium theory of mass spectra. But any attempt to build a detailed numerical theory around the scaffolding thus provided must inevitably encounter difficulties due to the very limited knowledge presently available concerning the eigenfunctions for the molecular systems in equilibrium.

An important advantage of the Green's function procedure is that it lends itself very naturally to an iterative treatment, where the Hamiltonian operator may be split into a zero-order component with rather simple properties together with perturbational components due, for example, to the Coulomb interaction between the impact electron and the molecule or to the effect of the detailed shape of the activation energy barrier in the unimolecular fragmentation.

It will thus be seen that the theoretical approach, even at the deepest possible level, is concerned with perturbation theory and, indeed, it is impossible to envisage any conceptual scheme that does not invoke the idea of perturbations in some shape or form. Accordingly, we adopt this theme as the "leitmotif" of our whole discussion and, with acknowledgments to M. J. S. Dewar [3], we would opine that the whole theory (of organic mass spectrometry) can be regarded as "a classical exercise in perturbation theory."

But having thus set out with a preamble on abstract mathematical foundations, we shall in the sequel consider some admittedly oversimplified theories relating to the eigenfunctions, largely divorced from the abstract scheme itself. In other words, we shall have recourse to the more familiar and well-trodden ground of conventional theoretical chemistry.

## HAMMETT $\sigma$-VALUES AND ELECTRON DISTRIBUTIONS: APPLICATIONS TO IONIC DISSOCIATION

A well-known approach of the physical organic chemist to the interpretation of reaction mechanisms is that of the Hammett $\sigma$-values [4]. There is a close connection between these and other rather more theoretically significant electronic parameters, such as the Coulomb and resonance integrals of molecular orbital theory [5]. Both may be regarded as providing a more or less quantitative measure of electron density changes in an organic molecule and these frequently provide a good general indication of the location of the reactive centers. Some such assumption is clearly demanded in any attempt to unravel the detailed intricacies of fragmentation patterns for large organic ions, and it was McLafferty [6] who first drew attention to the value of this type of approach, as a possible first stage beyond the pure "rule of thumb" treatments.

### Table I.  Mass Spectrum of Benzonitrile

| $m/e$ | Relative abundance ($p^+ = 100$) |
|-------|----------------------------------|
| 39    | 7    |
| 50    | 18   |
| 51    | 10   |
| 52    | 6    |
| 75    | 8    |
| 76    | 33   |
| 77    | 6    |
| 103   | 100  |
| 104   | 8    |

## Applications to Tolunitriles

Let us begin by referring to several tables of mass spectra for benzonitrile and its derivatives [7]. We list in Tables I and II only the larger peaks (exceeding 5% of the base peak) and show rounded values since we cannot hope to understand the fine details with our admittedly primitive theoretical tools.

Perhaps the most striking feature is the very close correspondence between the ion abundances, all those below mass 89 being virtually identical in the three isomers. It also appears that the $(p-1)^+$ ion in the ortho compound is rather less stable so that 8% more (relative to $p^+$) breaks down to form $(p\text{-}HCN)^+$, $(p\text{-}H_2CN)^+$.

### Table II.  Mass Spectra of Benzonitrile Derivatives

| $m/e$ | $o$-Tolunitrile | $m$-Tolunitrile | $p$-Tolunitrile |
|-------|-----------------|-----------------|-----------------|
| 27    | 6   | 6   | 6   |
| 38    | 7   | 7   | 6   |
| 39    | 18  | 19  | 17  |
| 50    | 7   | 7   | 7   |
| 51    | 8   | 8   | 8   |
| 62    | 6   | 6   | 6   |
| 63    | 14  | 13  | 13  |
| 64    | 7   | 7   | 7   |
| 89    | 22  | 20  | 19  |
| 90    | 33  | 29  | 27  |
| 116   | 46  | 54  | 54  |
| 117   | 100 | 100 | 100 |
| 118   | 9   | 8   | 9   |

If one assumed that fragmentation occurred primarily from the parent ion in its initial configuration, it might reasonably be supposed that a methyl substituent exerts but a weak inductive perturbational effect on the parent system with some small measure of electron repulsion $(-I)$; consequently its effect is to a large extent localized on the adjacent ring carbon. From the point of view of the Hammett $\sigma$-value we would say that the negative value of the constant for this group implies that the ionization potential of the ring system is reduced and thus the reaction in which a neutral nitrile fragment is eliminated is facilitated.

If $k_0$ is the reaction rate for the parent system and $k$ the appropriate value when one hydrogen is replaced by a substituent group, the Hammett equation has the well-known form

$$\ln\left(\frac{k}{k_0}\right) = \sigma\rho \tag{9}$$

where $\sigma$, the Hammett reaction constant, is fixed for a particular type of system and $\sigma$ is the substituent constant varying with the nature of the substituent group.

Several commonly occurring values of substituent constants are as follows [5]: A para-methyl substituent is assigned the value $-0.17$; amino and hydroxy groups which can donate electrons by the electromeric effect are assigned numerically larger values of the same sign, $\sim -0.66$ and $-0.38$, respectively; but electron-withdrawing groups which leave the reactive center depleted of electrons have a positive value ($+1.27$ for the nitro group).

We next notice that the main variable features of the mass spectra concern the two ions $(p-1)^+$ and $(p-27)^+$. It is natural to make the assumption that these correspond to the benzyl ion derivative and its fragmented form, an odd electron species consisting of the benzyl ion which has lost a single hydrogen atom

$$\overset{+}{H_2C}\!\!-\!\!\left\langle\bigcirc\right\rangle\!\!-\!\!C\!\equiv\!N \;\rightarrow\; \overset{+}{H_2C}\!\!-\!\!\left\langle\bigcirc\right\rangle\!. \;+\; \cdot C\!\equiv\!N \tag{10}$$

Evidence from metastable ions, to be discussed, shows that the hydrogen remains closely associated with the ions and is eliminated as part of the saturated species HCN.

The reaction (10) should be much more dependent on the orientation of the methylene group because it is not simply a matter of a localized inductive effect but of a more powerful disturbance due to an electrometric and positively charged substituent propagating its effect through the entire ring system. There is good evidence from this that the benzyl ion moiety does not rearrange, prior to the splitting off of the nitrile group, into the tropylium ion form [8]. If it did so rearrange rapidly enough to overtake the fragmentation process, we would not anticipate any orientation effect at all. Statements often made that rearrangement occurs simultaneously with fragmentation are certainly inaccurate and misleading. While it is true that the orientation effect is not considerable yet it is clearly more consistent with the existence of a benzyl ion configuration.

The picture thus presented is that those fragment ions of mass lower than 89 originate from the benzyl cation, whereas the three main higher-mass species, which are sensitive to substituent orientation, implicate the benzyl ion derivate. Although the formation of the tropylium ion form seems not to occur so long as the nitrile group remains attached to the ring, it is not precluded that this does occur subsequently and prior to the further fragmentation.

## Evidence from Metastables

It is very illuminating to consider these aspects of the fragmentation mechanisms in the light of the evidence from metastables. The most important metastables, which occur largely independently of substituent orientation in the tolunitriles, can be assigned as in Table III, which is based on measurements using the MS9 double focusing mass spectrometer.

From our point of view it is significant that process C appears to be something of the order of ten times more probable than D, as judged by the peak amplitudes, although no attempt was made to measure these with any great precision.

**Table III.  Metastable Ions in the Mass Spectra of Tolunitriles**

|   | Process | | | Metastable $m/e$ value |
|---|---|---|---|---|
| A | $(p\text{-HCN})^+$ | $\rightarrow (p\text{-HCN—H})^+ +$ H | | 88.0 |
|   | $(90^+)$ | $(89^+)$ | $(1)$ | |
| B | $p_i^+$ | $\rightarrow (p\text{-HCN})_i^+ +$ HCN | | 70.2 (isotopic |
|   | $(118)$ | $(91)$ | $(27)$ | metastable) |
| C | $p^+$ | $\rightarrow (p\text{-HCN})^+ +$ HCN | | 69.2 |
|   | $(117)$ | $(90)$ | $(27)$ | |
| D | $(p\text{-H})^+$ | $\rightarrow (p\text{-HCN—H})^+ +$ HCN | | 68.3 |
|   | $(116)$ | $(89)$ | $(27)$ | |
| E | $(p\text{-H})^+$ | $\rightarrow (p\text{-H—CH}_3\text{NH}_2)^+ + \text{CH}_3\text{NH}_2$ | | 62.3 |
|   | $(116)$ | $(85)$ | $(31)$ | |
| F | $(p\text{-H}_2\text{CN})^+$ | $\rightarrow (p\text{-H}_2\text{CN-C}_2\text{H}_2)^+ + \text{C}_2\text{H}_2$ | | 44.6 |
|   | $(89)$ | $(67)$ | $(26)$ | |

It is clearly possible to envisage three or more idealized structures for the activated state:

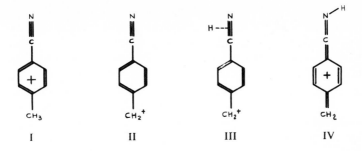

| | | | |
|---|---|---|---|
| I | II | III | IV |

Either I or III is consistent with the metastable process C, wherein the precursor ion has the same mass as the parent. If we are to understand the powerful orientation effect of the substituent, it is plausible that the transition species resembles III rather than I, which would involve only an inductive effect. Structure II with its detached hydrogen completely outside the reaction zone evidently plays some part in view of the metastable transition D, but it is clearly much less important. The intensity associated with C is well emphasized by the appearance of an isotopic metastable, which is a relatively uncommon feature.

In the activated state II or III it may be supposed that the unit positive charge is not localized but distributed in the nonbonding orbital (N.B.M.O.) of the isoconjugate hydrocarbon [9].

## Some Criteria for the Use of the σ-Values

We thus have a case in the tolunitrile ion where considerable direct forces of electrostatic interaction must be transmitted through space, but the charges themselves are in the first place distributed by a resonance effect within the ring system. The forces acting between different parts of the system, as between the nitrile groups and the ring system to which it is attached, may be calculated from a knowledge of the location of the various components of electrical charge and the purely electrostatic forces between them. This is, indeed, known to be true generally, if we evaluate the forces on the nuclei alone, in view of the Hellman–Feynman theorem [10] and stems from the fact that the only source of energy changes within a molecular system is electrostatic; no explicit reference to exchange or resonance forces is therefore required. Other features, such as electron spin, do not directly determine the energy (except in the refinement of spin–orbit and spin-spin interaction)—they merely predispose the charge distributions to take up particular locations.

We shall refer to I as the parent ion $p^+$, to II as $(p-1)^+$, and to the tautomeric parent ion III or IV as $p_T{}^+$. The general assortment of minor fragment ion components we denote collectively as $p_A{}^+$. Having regard to the obvious features of Table II, particularly that the lesser fragments below mass 89 are relatively insensitive to orientation of the ring substituent, we regard these as directly derived from $p^+$, i.e.,

$$p^+ \rightarrow p_A{}^+$$

This is also consistent with the consideration that the relative intensities on the basis of $p^+ = 100$ are substantially constant and with the plausible assumption that orientation effects should be the smallest possible for the parent ion, wherein none of the internal energy has been used up in an earlier fragmentation.

A simplified kinetic scheme is therefore as follows:

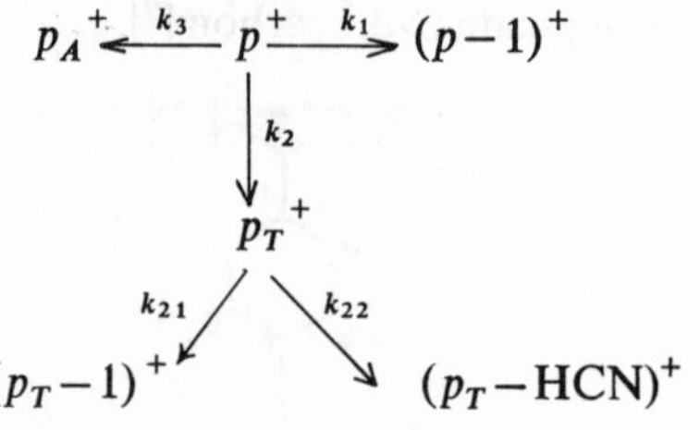

$$p_A{}^+ \overset{k_3}{\longleftarrow} p^+ \overset{k_1}{\longrightarrow} (p-1)^+$$
$$\downarrow k_2$$
$$p_T{}^+$$
$$(p_T-1)^+ \overset{k_{21}}{\swarrow} \qquad \overset{k_{22}}{\searrow} (p_T-\text{HCN})^+$$

From the material conservation in the ion source and the stationary state assumption, one derives

$$k_2\, p^+ - k_{21}\, p_T{}^+ - k_{22}\, p_T{}^+ = 0$$

The concentration of the mass 90 fragment is given by

$$\frac{d\,[p_T-\text{HCN}]^+}{dt} = k_{22}\, p_T{}^+$$

whence

$$[p_T\text{–HCN}]^+ = k_{22}\, p_T^{\ +}\, \tau$$

where the residence time in the ion source is $\tau$.

Now the observed parent ion intensity is the sum of the intensities of the original ion species and its tautomeric form, i.e.,

$$p_0^{\ +} = p^+ + p_T^{\ +}$$

and the relative abundance of mass 90 is

$$\frac{[p_T\text{–HCN}]^+}{p^+ + p_T^{\ +}}$$

Writing

$$p^+ + p_T^{\ +} = p^+\left[1 + \frac{k_2}{k_{21} + k_{22}}\right]$$

and

$$[p_T\text{–HCN}]^+ = \frac{k_{22}\, k_2\, \tau}{k_{21} + k_{22}} \cdot p^+$$

we then have

$$R.A.(90) = \frac{k_{22}\, k_2 \tau}{(k_{21} + k_{22} + k_2)}$$

We may with confidence suppose that $k_{21} \ll k_{22}$, on the grounds that $(p-H)^+$ does not appear in the metastable processes, so is presumably formed by a higher energy path. Moreover, we anticipate that

$$k_2 \gg k_{22}$$

because the first rate constant refers to a purely tautomeric rearrangement in a highly activated parent and does not involve any change in the total numbers of either $\sigma$ or $\pi$ bonds (in structure IV). On the other hand, $k_{22}$ refers to a fragmentation path where the total number of $\sigma$ bonds is reduced (by one); thus

$$R.A.(90) \sim k_{22}\, \tau$$

The measured abundances of $[p_T - \text{HCN}]^+$ referred to the parent as 100 can therefore legitimately be regarded as direct measures of a particular rate constant, and we can have some confidence that electronic features known to influence such rates will directly correlate with the particular ion intensity. In general, where several commensurate rates are involved and where there is no obvious reason to regard some of them as orders of magnitude smaller than others, it may be difficult to disentangle the relative contributions and to use any single ion intensity as a criterion of mechanistic rate effects. On the other hand, it seems possible that several fragment ion intensities might collectively enable one to determine the rate constants in favorable cases.

The most clear-cut application of the Hammett $\sigma$-value is to those cases where localized electrical charges are produced in the system, such as must be the case when a strongly electronegative group is attached, without direct conjugation to the parent system. Until recently it has been supposed that the long range effects were then transmitted by a bond polarization relayed from one atom to the next, probably attenuating exponentially. Recent work [3] suggests that the main effect is actually a purely electrostatic interaction in this case as well. The magnitude of the interaction at a reactive center $r$ may be supposed linearly related to the electron affinity of the substituent, or

$$\sigma\rho = \ln(k/k_0) = a_{rs}\delta_s \tag{11}$$

where $\delta_s$ is the Coulomb integral of the $s$th substituent in units of the resonance integral ($\beta$).

If there exists a direct chain of conjugation as in the case of an electromeric substituent, one ought to use a modified constant $\sigma^+$ [11, 12] which allows for the atom–atom polarizability $\pi_{rs}$ as a further factor.

Thus, we might suppose that

$$\sigma^+ \rho = \ln(k/k_0) = a_{rs}^+ \pi_{rs} \delta_s \tag{12}$$

as the simplest simultaneous dependence on both $\pi_{rs}$ and $\delta_s$, where $r$ is the reactive atom and $s$ the substituent.

This will be the main effect but clearly electrostatic interaction will occur in this case as well. However, what appears abundantly clear is that a rather different Hammett $\sigma$-factor is required for substituents in aromatic systems, such as benzonitrile, than for simple carboxylic acids, where the original $\sigma$ was introduced to measure the effect of a particular substituent on a side-chain ionization. Recent investigation has been much concerned with the question of whether the original Hammett $\sigma$ or Brown's $\sigma^+$ ought to be used in mass spectral fragmentation processes [13].

It may be worth mentioning that the considerable degree of success in using Hammett $\sigma$-constants for mass spectral mechanisms is strongly suggestive of the participation of some parameter corresponding to a temperature and measuring the degree of activation of the system in a similar way to that of the ordinary thermodynamic temperature in chemical kinetics [14, 15], for the logarithmic dependence used in the definition of the Hammett $\sigma$-value would appear to owe its origin to the ubiquitous Arrhenius law of chemical kinetics.

Thus,

$$k = A \exp(-\varepsilon/RT) \tag{13a}$$

$$k_0 = A \exp(-\varepsilon_0/RT) \tag{13b}$$

and

$$\ln(k/k_0) = \frac{\varepsilon_0 - \varepsilon}{RT} \tag{13c}$$

and the right-hand side is clearly a constant for a particular substituent measured by the electrostatic perturbation of the activation energy.

According to the simplest version of the quasi-equilibrium theory of mass spectra [16],

$$k = v\left(\frac{E-\varepsilon}{E}\right)^{n-1} \tag{14}$$

where $v$ is the frequency factor, $\varepsilon$ is the activation energy, and $n$ is the number of degrees of freedom.

Consequently,

$$\ln(k/k_0) = (n-1)\ln\left(\frac{E-\varepsilon}{E-\varepsilon_0}\right) \tag{15}$$

which is not of the Hammett form unless $\varepsilon \ll E$. But in this case,

$$\left(\frac{E-\varepsilon}{E}\right)^{n-1} = e^{(n-1)\ln[(E-\varepsilon)/E]} \approx e^{-(n-1)\varepsilon/E]} \tag{16}$$

which implies that the fixed quantity $E/(n-1)$ is actually taking the place of $RT$.

Thus, it appears reasonable to concude that a likely explanation for the success of the linear energy relation implied by the Hammett equation is that some parameter closely analogous to a temperature seems applicable to ionic fragmentation mechanisms.

## The Role of the Odd Electron Molecular Orbital Aspects

A further theoretical feature which has an important bearing on the extended application of the $\sigma^+$ constants to the fragmentation mechanisms concerns the approximate equality of polarizabilities for ions and free radicals. This can best be explained by reference to a particular example. We again refer to the case of a substituted benzonitrile,

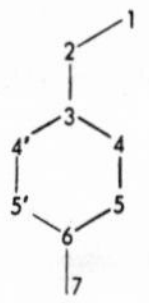

and consider the effect of a change of electron affinity of the substituent, numbered 7, in structure IV. We take all Coulomb and resonance integrals equal, because the perturbation method allows effects due to these to be determined readily.

It is convenient to choose as a basis set of orbitals the following combinations of the $p_z$ atomic orbitals:

$$\phi_1; \quad \phi_2; \quad \phi_3; \quad \tfrac{1}{2}(\phi_4+\phi_5+\phi_4'+\phi_5'); \quad \tfrac{1}{2}(\phi_4-\phi_5+\phi_4'-\phi_5');$$

$$\phi_6; \quad \phi_7; \quad \tfrac{1}{2}(\phi_4+\phi_5-\phi_4'-\phi_5'); \quad \tfrac{1}{2}(\phi_4-\phi_5-\phi_4'-\phi_5')$$

The last two are noncombining with the others because they change sign on reflection in a plane of symmetry of the benzene ring. We may now write down a secular determinant $\Delta(Z)$, excluding the noncombining antisymmetric pair. Let us arbitrarily shift the energy zero to, say, $0.3\,\beta$ so that, in the complex plane, all occupied energy levels will lie to the left of the imaginary axis. Or, if we decide to use $\beta$ as an energy unit, all the occupied levels will lie to the right of the imaginary axis. Then

$$\Delta(Z) = \begin{vmatrix} 0.3-Z & 1 & 0 & 0 & 0 & 0 & 0 \\ 1 & 0.3-Z & 1 & 0 & 0 & 0 & 0 \\ 0 & 1 & 0.3-Z & 1 & 1 & 0 & 0 \\ 0 & 0 & 1 & 1.3-Z & 0 & 1 & 0 \\ 0 & 0 & 1 & 0 & -0.7-Z & -1 & 0 \\ 0 & 0 & 0 & 1 & -1 & 0.3-Z & 1 \\ 0 & 0 & 0 & 0 & 0 & 1 & 0.3-Z \end{vmatrix}$$

$$(17)$$

Because the system is an alternant hydrocarbon, roots of $\Delta(Z) = 0$ must occur in pairs except for the one which is formally nonbonding (energy $Z_0$, the same as the carbon atomic orbitals themselves).

Thus,

$$\Delta(Z) = -(Z-Z_0-Z_1)\,(Z-Z_0+Z_1)\,(Z-Z_0-Z_2)\,(Z-Z_0+Z_2)$$

$$(Z-Z_0-Z_3)\,(Z-Z_0+Z_3)\,(Z-Z_0) \qquad (18)$$

Now suppose we wish to determine how the electron distribution in the nitrile group varies with the properties of the ring substituent.

For example, we may wish to evaluate $\Pi_{71}$, which is given [17] by

$$\frac{1}{\pi}\int_{-\infty}^{\infty}\frac{\Delta_{71}^2(iy)\,dy}{\Delta^2(iy)} \qquad (19)$$

Here $\Delta_{71}$ is the cofactor of the element in row 7 and column 1. It is readily seen that this has the value 2, so that

$$\pi_{71} = 4/\pi \int_{-\infty}^{\infty}\frac{dy}{\Delta^2(iy)} \qquad (20)$$

We shall now reverse the procedure by which these results for the polarizabilities were originally obtained and use the Cauchy theorem [18] in the form

$$\oint\frac{dz}{\Delta^2(Z)} = 2\pi i\sum_{\text{residues}} = i\int_{-\infty}^{\infty}\frac{dy}{\Delta^2(iy)}+\int_{(R)}\frac{dZ}{\Delta^2(Z)} \qquad (21)$$

The integral around the semicircle of large radius clearly vanishes in the limit.

Now the interesting property of the integrand is that it possesses poles of order unity at $Z_1, Z_2, Z_3$ within the contour, but the pole at $Z = Z_0$ is of the second order and its residue therefore vanishes identically. This is a direct result of the pairing property of bonding and antibonding levels, a feature which is, however, not applicable to the single nonbonding level. By our choice of $Z_0 = 0.3$, we ensure that this lies inside the contour.

To show that the pole at $Z = Z_0$ is of order two, we write, in the usual way, $Z - Z_0 = Z'$ and then

$$\Delta^2(Z) = [(Z-Z_0)^2 - Z_1{}^2]^2 [(Z-Z_0)^2 - Z_2{}^2]^2 [(Z-Z_0)^2 - Z_3{}^2]^2 [Z-Z_0]^2 \tag{22}$$

$$= Z_1{}^4 \left(1 - \frac{Z'^2}{Z_1{}^2}\right)^2 Z_2{}^4 \left(1 - \frac{Z'^2}{Z_2{}^2}\right)^2 Z_3{}^4 \left(1 - \frac{Z'^2}{Z_3{}^2}\right)^2 Z'^2 \tag{22a}$$

and

$$\Delta^{-2}(Z) = (Z_1 Z_2 Z_3)^{-4} \left[1 + 2 Z'^2 \left(\frac{1}{Z_1{}^2} + \frac{1}{Z_2{}^2} + \frac{1}{Z_3{}^2}\right) + \ldots\right] Z'^2 \tag{22b}$$

This has a pole of order two.

It is readily shown in the same way that the poles of $\Delta^{-2}(Z)$ at the remaining zeros are of order unity and therefore make finite contributions to the integral along the imaginary axis.

This shows that it is really immaterial whether the root $Z = Z_0$ lies inside the contour or otherwise. If it lies inside the contour, we have the case of the anion; if outside, that of the cation. Since a compound such as p-chlorobenzonitrile is isoconjugate with the anion, it must show polarizability characteristics similar to those of the tolunitrile ion minus a hydrogen. Moreover, the ground state positive ion of benzonitrile with an electromeric substituent must contain a single electron in its least bonding occupied $\pi$-orbital. From the preceding considerations, we conclude that this orbital has no effect on the polarizability and this must remain true whether singly or doubly occupied. Thus, effects on reactivity in the neutral and ionized states will be comparable.

Actual expansion of the secular determinant in its real and imaginary components, namely,

$$\Delta(iy) = A + iB \tag{23}$$

shows that

$$A = 2.10 \, y^6 + 11.06 \, y^4 + 13.19 \, y^2 + 1.96$$

$$B = y^7 + 6.11 \, y^5 + 10.08 \, y^3 + 3.73 \, y$$

and

$$\pi_{71} = 4/\pi \int_{-\infty}^{\infty} \frac{A^2 - B^2}{\{A^2 + B^2\}^2} \, dy \tag{24}$$

The following values are obtained by numerical integration of this and selected expressions:

| $\pi_{11}$ | $\pi_{71}$ | $\pi_{72}$ | $\pi_{7,12}$ | $p_{12}$ |
|------------|------------|------------|--------------|----------|
| 0.649      | $-0.140$   | $-0.019$   | 0.062        | 0.882    |

The charge densities due to polarizability will be of a lower order than those directly due to the charge distribution in the N.B.M.O., which leads to strong electrostatic interactions, particularly for an ortho substituent. The permanent effect of the N.B.M.O. must be carefully distinguished from its small or vanishing polarizability effect.

## Application to Acetophenone and Related Compounds

We have thus seen how one might attempt to rationalize the use of the Hammett $\sigma$-constant in an extended application to electron-impact induced fragmentations.

In the first reported studies of McLafferty [19], the effect of a wide range of substituents on benzoyl compounds isoconjugate with benzonitrile was discussed. Attention was focused on the primary processes:

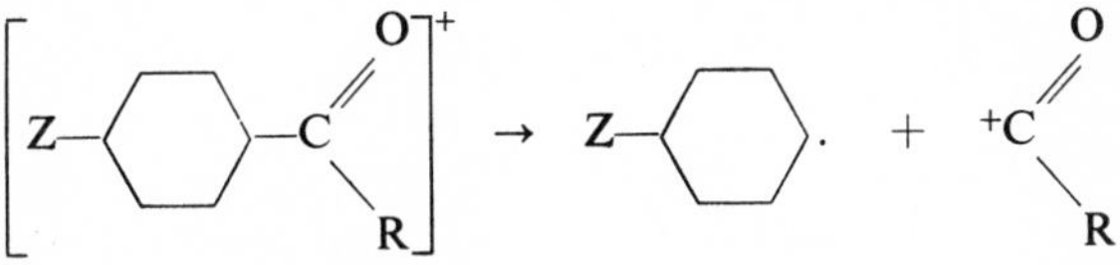

$$(25\text{-I})$$

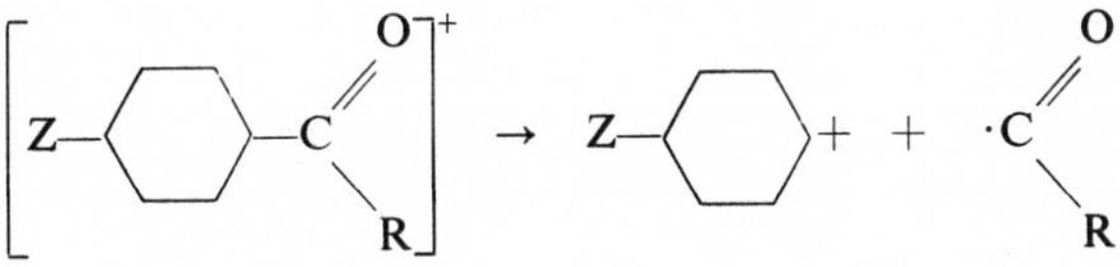

$$(25\text{-II})$$

One important feature is the presence of a lone pair which readily splits up on ionization. On the other hand, in the benzonitriles the lone pair is essentially accommodated in the digonal hybrid $2s+2p$ rather than in the more readily ionizable pure $2p$. The ratio of the ion abundances was taken as a measure of the rate of reaction $(k)$ and compared with $(k_0)$ for the case where both $R$ and $Z$ were hydrogen atoms.

Mass spectral data were used [19] to compile Table IV, which gives the relative rates for processes 25-I and 25-II.

The data for reaction I, when plotted logarithmically against the unmodified Hammett $\sigma$-values, fell astonishingly well on straight lines.

## Table IV.  $k/k_0$ for Benzoyl Compounds

| O | Z | R | | | |
|---|---|---|---|---|---|
| | | $-CH_3$ | | $-C_6H_5$ | |
| | | I | II | I | II |
| 1.27 | $p$-NO$_2$ | 3.02 | 0.03 | 4.37 | — |
| 0.710 | $m$-NO$_2$ | 3.47 | 0.07 | 5.25 | — |
| 0.391 | $m$-Br | 2.46 | 0.64 | 2.82 | 0.6 |
| 0.373 | $m$-Cl | — | 0.74 | 2.04 | 0.71 |
| 0.232 | $p$-Br | 1.29 | 0.72 | 1.62 | 0.80 |
| 0.226 | $p$-Cl | 1.23 | 0.74 | 1.38 | 0.94 |
| −0.002 | $m$-OH | 0.89 | 0.43 | — | — |
| −0.069 | $m$-CH$_3$ | 0.83 | — | 0.89 | 0.78 |
| −0.170 | $p$-CH$_3$ | 0.74 | 1.05 | 0.62 | 1.04 |
| −0.197 | $p$-tert. Bu | 4.90 | 0.20 | — | 0.04 |
| −0.268 | $p$-OCH$_3$ | 0.60 | 0.17 | 0.35 | — |
| −0.357 | $p$-OH | 0.47 | 0.46 | 0.35 | 0.44 |
| −0.660 | $p$-NH$_2$ | 0.22 | 0.36 | 0.14 | — |

Those for reaction II, which resembles more closely the tolunitrile fragmentation, do not follow any equally simple dependence because they depend on the stability of the $\left[ Z - \left\langle \hexagon \right\rangle \cdot \right]^+$ residue. It has been said by Jaffé [5] that, on the reasonable view that the reaction rates in organic chemistry depend on susceptibility to the electron density at the site of the reaction, the σ-constants may be regarded as providing a more or less quantitative measure of such electron density changes. Consequently, any substituent that is electron-repelling either on account of an inductive or electromeric effect will tend to leave the part of the system to which it is attached with a resultant positive charge and so will promote a reaction in which this fragment is the positive component. This is clearly in accordance with the well-known rule of Stevenson [20]. We would therefore expect that substituents with negative σ-values, implying electron repulsion, will reduce the rate of reaction I and, conversely, will enhance the rate of II. This is broadly in accordance with Table IV for reactions of type I but less clearly so for type II, because of the complicating features already mentioned.

Quite recently McLafferty [13] has discussed the relative merits of σ and σ⁺ as substituent constants for compounds of the same series. On the basis of this work, it seems impossible to make a definitive choice between the two sets of constants; if at all, the evidence favors slightly the original σ constants of Hammett, whereas a better correlation of ionization and appearance potential data seems possible with the $\sigma^+$ values. Since the original $\sigma$'s were essentially electrostatic or inductive in origin, perhaps this is evidence for the primary significance of this type of mechanism in many fragmentation processes involving ionic species.

## BOND DISSOCIATION ENERGIES, BOND ORDERS, AND ELECTROSTATIC FORCES WITHIN THE TOLUNITRILE ION

We shall now attempt to relate some of the foregoing results to various criteria concerning the "driving force" for release of HCN. These are as follows:

1. Electron population and distribution within the weak linkage joining the nitrile radical to the benzyl ion.
2. Variable bond-dissociation energy and bond order of the relatively weak link referred to in (1).
3. Electrostatic repulsion between positively charged atoms in the $(p-1)^{+}$ ion.
4. $\pi$–$\sigma$ interactions.
5. The shape of the potential energy surface.

Bykov[22] has drawn attention to the importance of bond electron density as the physical variable with the most immediate claim to real significance; he regards other criteria, such as bond order, as to some extent devoid of reality and less likely to be directly correlated with bond reactivity than the more immediately intuitive electron populations. We have evidence that the "equivalent orbitals" in alkanes and other systems form the most directly useful "basis" for the discussion of unimolecular dissociation processes in positive ions. It is unfortunate that there has been less inclination to discuss correspondingly the bonds and their electron deficiencies in conjugated organic molecules, since it is the usual practice to derive electron distributions over atoms rather than over the bonds. This is the objection that Bykov has stressed.

Within the molecular orbital theory we no doubt should have to employ as a basis the "localized" bond orbitals

$$\frac{1}{\sqrt{2}}(\psi_1 + \psi_2), \frac{1}{\sqrt{2}}(\psi_2 + \psi_3), \text{ etc.}$$

instead of the $p_z$ atomic orbitals

$$\psi_1, \psi_2, \ldots$$

if we wished to emphasize the discussion of bond properties, such as electron populations. This could only be done at the expense of an even more serious overlap between adjacent orbitals than for the conventional atomic ones. Thus,

$$\int \frac{1}{\sqrt{2}} (\psi_1 + \psi_2) \frac{1}{\sqrt{2}} (\psi_2 + \psi_3) \, d\tau = \tfrac{1}{2} [2S_{12} + S_{22}] = 0.75$$

if we put the ordinary overlap $S_{12}$ as 0.25 and $S_{22}$ as 1.00.

Thus, our choice of a modified basis has resulted in an increase in the overlap of 3:1. Moreover a rather trivial change of basis of this kind does not in itself really lead to anything new, as all the well-known results may readily be reinterpreted within the new framework. But notwithstanding this, there seems little doubt that there is some real deficiency in the conventional molecular orbital approach when we try to understand the reactivity of ions and that some approach where we invoke the basic idea of electrostatic forces between electron populations in bonds and external electric charges may be invaluable.

On the other hand, it seems likely that the greater part of Bykov's objection is removed if we explicitly include overlap between the $p_z$ orbitals and normalize the molecular orbitals accordingly. Thus, in the simplest diatomic case, we ought to replace

$$\frac{1}{\sqrt{2}} (\psi_1 + \psi_2)$$

by

$$\frac{1}{\sqrt{2(1+S)}} (\psi_1 + \psi_2)$$

since $\int \psi_1 \psi_2 \, d\tau = S$, the orbital overlap. If the electron density around each atom is then determined, this would appear to be $(1+S)^{-1}$ which leaves $[2 - 2(1+S)^{-1}]$ within the bond itself. But, by definition, the bond order $p = 2a_1 a_2$, where $a_1 = a_2 = [2(1+S)]^{-\frac{1}{2}}$ and the bond electron density is thus given by $pS$. This may be readily generalized and shows that the bond order itself is a suitable measure of the amount of electronic charge situated within the bonding region.

However, from the point of view of explaining the processes of dissociation we have not really advanced very far, because all that has been achieved is that the electronic charge has now been more correctly apportioned between atoms and bond regions; this cannot affect the general nature of its dependence on the substituent orientation.

## Bond Dissociation Energies

As in ordinary chemical kinetics we may discuss differences in the mass spectra in terms of $\pi$-electronic energy components, regarding the $\sigma$-electrons as sensibly unchanged from one isomeric form to another. It has to be recognized, however, that perturbations that can change an ordinary chemical reaction rate by an order of magnitude may have little effect on the mass spectra, in view of the much higher internal energy. Indeed, if we use an effective temperature criterion for the extent of vibrational activation of the ion, it could well be in the region of 5000°K [15], if due to a 50 eV electron beam. This should serve to warn us that a few percent change in intensity of a product ion may not necessarily imply that the variable activation energy is due to a perturbation vanishing to the second order. It is, in fact, not difficult to show that second-order polarizabilities can acquire unexpected importance in some ion fragmentations; thus, we must not necessarily expect that the conventional first-order theories involving atom–atom polarizabilities, atom–bond polarizabilities, and so on, will correctly describe the activation of ions. They may be no less useful if supplemented by at least the second-order components. But having recognized the possibilities of such sources of error, it will still be justifiable to make use of the simplest first-order theories to make an initial foray into the jungle of molecular interactions.

We shall use Dewar's N.B.M.O. method [9] to evaluate some first-order bond dissociation energies. To do this, we consider isoconjugate hydrocarbon radicals and the usual first-order differences in $\pi$-electron energy. Since the additional electron in the radical is accommodated in an N.B.M.O., its effect may be ignored in all the energy balances that follow (in accordance with the section in this article on the role of the odd electron).

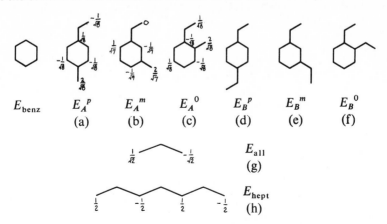

V. N.B.M.O. coefficients and $\pi$-electron energies

The N.B.M.O. coefficients in the odd A.H.'s, V ($a$–$c$, $g$, $h$), are as indicated and the meta-substituted compound is clearly cross-conjugated since not all the "starred" coefficients are different from zero.

It follows immediately that

$$E_B^P = E_A^P + (4/\sqrt{8})\,\beta \tag{26a}$$

$$E_B^m = E_A^m + (4/\sqrt{7})\,\beta \tag{26b}$$

$$E_B^0 = E_A^0 + (4/\sqrt{8})\,\beta \tag{26c}$$

Moreover the A.H.'s V($d$–$f$) can be divided into two odd A.H.'s (allyl and heptatrienate radicals) in the ways indicated below:

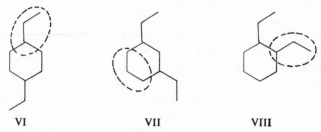

VI                            VII                            VIII

Thus we have

$$E_B^P = E_{all} + E_{hept} + \sqrt{2}\,\beta \tag{27a}$$

$$E_B^m = E_{all} + E_{hept} + \sqrt{2}\,\beta \tag{27b}$$

$$E_B^0 = E_{all} + E_{hept} + \sqrt{2}\,\beta \tag{27c}$$

The dissociation energies of the tolunitriles in the isoconjugate form are therefore given by

$$E_A - E_{benz} - E_{eth}$$

With use of the preceding results, these have the form

$$E_{all} + E_{hept} - E_{benz} - E_{eth} \qquad \text{(para)} \tag{28a}$$

$$E_{all} + E_{hept} - E_{benz} - E_{eth} + (\sqrt{2} - 4/\sqrt{7})\,\beta \qquad \text{(meta)} \tag{28b}$$

$$E_{all} + E_{hept} - E_{benz} - E_{eth} \qquad \text{(ortho)} \tag{28c}$$

The first-order calculations are therefore at variance with the result that the apparent rates of the processes involving release of HCN increase in the order para < meta < ortho. The preceding calculations would lead one to expect meta < para = ortho.

## Bond Orders

Since the overall dissociation energies in the preceding simple perturbational calculations fail to give a proper interpretation of the fragmentation
behavior, we turn next to the order of the bond linking the nitrile group to
the ring. This is subject to two important effects of the substituents: (a) the
purely orientational effect for a homopolar substituent as in the case of the
isoconjugate free radical; (b) the additional electromeric effect of change of
electron affinity of the substituent resulting from the concentration of positive
charge at this position in the N.B.M.O.

(a) We make the assumption that the main reason for the change in the
bond order is that the substituent interacts primarily with the least bonding
occupied orbital and the first antibonding orbital of the parent system (IX).
The expedient of the isoconjugate hydrocarbon is used throughout.

IX

The form of the relevant "frontier" electron orbital is as follows [23]:

$$0.5942\,\phi_1 + 0.3941\,\phi_2 - 0.3342\,\phi_3 - 0.3007(\phi_4 + \phi_4{}^1)$$
$$+ 0.1305(\phi_5 + \phi_5{}^1) + 0.3941\,\phi_6$$

and the antibonding one has the same coefficients but with alternating
changes of sign.

The bond order $p_{23}$ is reduced in every case owing to the electron
"spillage" into the substituent, and the estimates for this effect are as follows:

$$0.0622\ \text{(para)}\qquad 0.0093\ \text{(meta)}\qquad 0.0433\ \text{(ortho)}$$

(b) It is well known that the bond-atom polarizabilities in even A.H.'s
vanish identically so that whatever effect on the value of $p_{23}$ arises from
changes in electron affinity in other parts of the ion must depend crucially
on the additional atom. In a multiatomic system, it is unlikely that one
additional orbital can vitally change the reactivities.

We should therefore expect the bond-atom polarizabilities to be quite
small, and indeed they vanish altogether to the first order in the meta
compound. Thus, from this point of view, the meta substituent does not
really belong to the conjugated system at all and the latter still behaves in all

essentials as an even A.H. with vanishing bond-atom polarizabilities. The reason for this is that the system is formally cross-conjugated and may be regarded as involving a first-order interaction between an allyl radical and a hexatrienate radical (X and XI).

$$-\frac{1}{\sqrt{2}} \qquad \qquad -\frac{1}{\sqrt{2}}$$

$$\frac{1}{\sqrt{2}} \qquad \qquad \frac{1}{\sqrt{2}}$$

$$\frac{1}{\sqrt{3}} \quad \frac{1}{\sqrt{3}} \qquad \frac{1}{\sqrt{15}} \quad -\frac{2}{\sqrt{15}}$$

$$-\frac{1}{\sqrt{3}} \qquad O \qquad -\frac{1}{\sqrt{15}} \quad \frac{3}{\sqrt{15}}$$

$$X \qquad\qquad\qquad XI$$

The presence of a positively charged substituent will split the degeneracy between the two N.B.M.O. forms for the branched-chain hexatrienate radical. Admixture of the various forms cannot make any first-order changes in the bond orders because of the alternating zeros in the N.B.M.O. coefficients. Thus, it cannot make any difference whether the degeneracy is split or not.

By similar arguments it may be shown that the bond-atom polarizabilities for the other two isomers do not vanish and are of similar orders of magnitude. Again, therefore, we do not succeed in understanding the effects of substituents on the cleavage process.

## Electrostatic Interactions

The most promising interpretation, in view of the inconclusive nature of the alternatives so far discussed, would appear to be based on purely electrostatic considerations. We feel this to be inherently plausible because the high concentration of electronic charge on the substituent can clearly exert an increasing electrostatic force on the reaction zone in the order para < meta < ortho. It can hardly be mere coincidence that this is also the order of increasing reaction rate.

We have shown in the previous section that the first-order atom-bond polarizabilities vanish in the meta-substituted compound. Thus, if direct electrostatic effects are primarily exerted on the atoms, they can only influence the bonds through a higher-order term in the atom–bond polarizability. We shall now show that such higher-order effects are not likely to be very significant.

From simple geometry, the distances between the substituent and the relevant atoms are as shown in Table V.

### Table V.  Interatomic Distances (Measured in Bond Lengths)

|        | $x_{2S}$     | $x_{3S}$    |
|--------|--------------|-------------|
| Ortho  | 2            | $\sqrt{3}$  |
| Meta   | $\sqrt{12}$  | $\sqrt{7}$  |
| Para   | 4            | 3           |

Now the share of the positive charge carried by the substituent is $a_s^2$, where $a_S$ is the N.B.M.O. coefficient, so that the ionization potential in the region of a particular atom $j$ is raised by $(a_s^2/x_{js})\,(e^2/R_0)$. (1 au of energy $= 27.2$ eV $= 34.8\,\beta$ and $R_0 \simeq 1.40$ Å $= 2.65$ au.) If we regard the Coulomb integral of the particular atom as directly measured by the ionization potential, then the change in $\alpha_j$ expressed as $\delta_j\,\beta$ is given by

$$\delta_j \approx \frac{13\,a_S^2}{x_{js}} \tag{29}$$

We have seen that the first-order bond-atom polarizabilities are small or negligible. Calculation of higher-order effects is generally rather complicated so that we shall restrict attention to the actual bond 2,3 in isolation and determine the general nature of higher-order polarizabilities for this hypothetical localized bond.

The secular equation is given by

$$\begin{vmatrix} \delta_2 - x & 1 \\ 1 & \delta_3 - x \end{vmatrix} = 0 \tag{30}$$

The bond order is clearly equal to

$$\frac{2\,(x - \delta_3)}{1 + (\delta_3 - x)^2} \tag{31}$$

reducing to the expected value of unity when the Coulomb integrals are equal.

Now

$$(x - \delta_2)\,(x - \delta_3) = 1$$

so that

$$x = \tfrac{1}{2}(\delta_2 + \delta_3) + \sqrt{1 + \left(\frac{\delta_2 - \delta_3}{2}\right)^2} \tag{32}$$

Hence

$$p_{23} = \frac{2[\delta + \sqrt{1 + \delta^2}]}{1 + [\delta + \sqrt{1 + \delta^2}]^2} \tag{33}$$

where

$$\delta = \tfrac{1}{2}(\delta_2 - \delta_3)$$

To $0(\delta)$ this is of course exactly equal to unity in accordance with the known result that the first-order polarizability vanishes. But we have seen that $a_S = \tfrac{1}{2}$ and so

$$\delta = 1.6\left(\frac{1}{x_{3S}} - \frac{1}{x_{2S}}\right) = 0.123$$

whence $p_{23} = 0.993$. The second-order change in bond order is thus less than 1%. It appears therefore that second-order polarizabilities are almost certainly too small to be significant in the present application at least.

## $\pi$–$\sigma$ Interactions and Electrostatic Energy

It has been shown [24] that $\pi$–$\sigma$ interactions play a significant part in organic chemistry. Although the $\sigma$-orbitals have the wrong symmetry to overlap with the $\pi$-orbitals, yet it is still possible for interaction to occur. This is a consequence of the fact that many of the molecular integrals involved in solving the wave equation are of the two-electron type and so the product of a pair of antisymmetric $\pi$-orbitals can have the same symmetry as that of a pair of $\sigma$-orbitals.

In our electrostatic model we are now going to assume that $\pi$–$\sigma$ interaction can occur between the nonbonding atomic orbital of the nitrogen atom (N.B.A.O.) and the nonbonding molecular orbital of the $\pi$-electron system (N.B.M.O.). Since the Hamiltonian is modified during the act of electron impact [25] by an effective electrostatic charge distribution associated with the distortion in the impacting electron beam, it is reasonable that $\pi$–$\sigma$ interaction might achieve a greater degree of importance than in the case of the isolated molecule, and it has to be remembered that the N.B.M.O. and N.B.A.O. can be much closer in energy than the $\pi$- and $\sigma$-molecular orbitals of ethylene, on which the original $\pi$–$\sigma$ interaction calculations were made.

We shall therefore suppose that the least bonding orbital from which the electron is ionized can be written as

$$a\psi_{\text{N.B.M.O.}} + \sqrt{1-a^2}\,\psi_{\text{N.B.A.O.}}$$

The distribution of positive charge in the meta compound is then as shown below in XII:

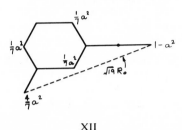

XII

The electrostatic repulsion energy is $a^2(1-a^2)\,(4/7\,\sqrt{19})\,(e^2/R_0)$. In the absence of $\pi$–$\sigma$ interaction, this is, of course, zero, in view of $a$ then being exactly equal to unity.

We similarly obtain the electrostatic energies for the other two isomers, which are as follows:

| Compound | Repulsion energy |
|---|---|
| para | $a^2(1-7/8\,a^2)\,\frac{1}{10}\,(e^2/R_0)$ |
| ortho | $a^2(1-7/8\,a^2)\,\dfrac{1}{2\sqrt{7}}(e^2/R_0)$ |

Within the limitations of this simple electrostatic model, we can, therefore, put some restrictions on the required amount of $\pi$–$\sigma$ interaction, for in order to explain the mass spectra we have to place the electrostatic energies in the order

$$\tfrac{1}{10}\,a^2(1-7/8\,a^2) < \frac{4}{7\sqrt{19}}\,a^2(1-a^2) < \frac{1}{2\sqrt{7}}\,a^2(1-7/8\,a^2)$$

These inequalities imply that

$$a^2 < \frac{320-56\sqrt{19}}{320-49\sqrt{19}} = 0.72$$

A lower limit on $a^2$ may be placed if we can estimate in some way the least amount of energy required to produce a measurable effect on the mass spectra. If we tentatively suppose this to be in the order of $\frac{1}{2}$ eV and put $e^2/R_0 = 10.3$ eV, this requires that $a^2 > 0.434$, whence $0.434 < a^2 < 0.774$. This would imply a rather similar incidence of the N.B.M.O. and N.B.A.O. in the act of ionization.

## The Shape of the Potential Energy Curve

The rather oversimplified N.B.M.O. treatment of the electron distribution which we have been considering may be used to derive an explicit expression for the electrostatic repulsion energy term in the dissociating ion. We shall consider only the ortho isomer, the necessary changes for the para compound being sufficiently obvious. Also, we do not allow for $\pi$–$\sigma$ interaction, the necessary changes in the energy being of a trivial kind and readily incorporated.

Let us suppose that, in the course of the dissociation, the (2,3) bond length has increased by a factor $x$ from its initial value $R_0$. Thus $R = xR_0$. The N.B.M.O. has the form (XIII) in the partly dissociated configuration

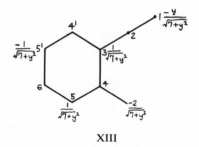

XIII

For the interatomic distance we have

$$R_{rs} = R_0 \sqrt{3+(1+x)^2}$$

The main component of the electrostatic repulsion energy is

$$\frac{4\,e^2\,y^2}{(7+y^2)^2\,R_{rs}} = \frac{e^2}{R_0}\,\frac{4\,y^2}{(7+y^2)^2\,\sqrt{3+(1+x)^2}} \tag{34}$$

It is usually assumed that

$$\frac{\beta(xR_0)}{\beta(R_0)} = \frac{S(xR_0)}{S(R_0)} \quad (=y) \tag{35}$$

where $S$ is the overlap integral between the pair of $p_z$ orbitals [26].

The overlap integral may be readily evaluated [27] and it is known that

$$S(R) = \frac{\alpha 5}{24} \left[ \tfrac{1}{5} A_0(\alpha) - \tfrac{6}{5} A_2(\alpha) + A_4(\alpha) \right] \tag{36}$$

where

$$A_n(\alpha) = \int_1^\infty \xi^n e^{-\alpha \xi} \, d\xi \tag{36a}$$

and

$$\alpha = \mu R$$

Numerically, the Slater orbital parameter for a carbon $2p_s$ orbital is usually taken to be 1.59. Thus

$$y = \frac{S(xR_0)}{S(R_0)} e^{-\mu R_0(x-1)} \frac{[15 + 15\mu R_0 x + 6\mu^2 R_0^2 x^2 + \mu^3 R_0^3 x^3]}{[15 + 15\mu R_0 + 6\mu^2 R_0^2 + \mu^3 R_0^3]} \tag{37}$$

Equation (37) combined with equation (34) provides a simple explicit functional form for the electrostatic energy as a function of $x$, which we take to be the parameter defining the shape of the activated state.

Other contributions to the form of the potential energy may be equally important so that the above expression cannot be taken as properly defining the form of the surface. In some cases it might nevertheless provide a useful closed-form expression of a simplified kind.

## SPECIFIC FRAGMENTATION PROCESSES

While it is true that electron densities and Hammett $\sigma$–values (which are related to these) can in many cases provide a useful guide to fragmentation mechanisms, there are more subtle features which are less amenable to this type of approach. We have in mind particularly the case of specific processes, of which the release of carbon monoxide in two stages from anthraquinone is a well substantiated example [28]. A plausible mechanistic route to biphenylene was suggested in this work and partly supported by measurements on metastables; it has often been cited as a particularly well-defined example of a specific elimination process so that we shall not trouble to repeat here the detailed mechanistic arguments.

But what is perhaps not so well-known is the important fact that substituents can profoundly modify the specificity of this elimination process, as though the intersection of energy surfaces can be induced by appropriately placed substituents in the ring system. Remarkably enough, 1,4 substitution was found to restrict the release of CO a great deal more effectively than 1,5 substitution, an effect that would be impossible to interpret from the standpoint of the Hammett $\sigma$-values. Quite clearly, the particular irreducible representations for which the $p_z$ orbitals of the substituents form a basis will determine the nature of the perturbation of the parent compound. In other words, we have to do not so much with a simple additive effect but rather with a cooperative effect associated with a particular symmetry of the substituents considered together (i.e., a synergistic effect).

Phenomena of this kind are by no means unknown in dyestuffs chemistry, and it was largely the knowledge that 1,5 derivatives are sometimes more catalytically active than 1,4 in oxidation phenomena (such as in the "tendering" of cotton fabrics) that led us to explore possible differences in their mass spectra. The more important fragmentation peaks are listed in Table VI [29].

The essential features of the molecular orbital calculation which enable one to assess the effect of substituents may be described in the simplest terms for a single substituent, as in the case of a monosubstituted ethylene.

XIV

**Table VI.   Relative Abundances of Ions Formed by Anthraquinone and Its Diamino Derivatives**

|  | $O$ ... $O$ | $O$, $NH_2$ ... $NH_2$, $O$ | $O$, $NH_2$ ... $O$, $NH_2$ |
|---|---|---|---|
| $p^+$ | 100 | 100 | 100 |
| $p\text{-}H^+$ | 14 | 6 | 12 |
| $p\text{-}CO^+$ | 77 | 12 | 3 |
| $p\text{-}CHO^+$ | 5 | 4 | 3 |
| $p\text{-}2(CO^+)$ | 51 | 6 | 5 |
| $p\text{-}2(CO)\text{—}H^+$ | 25 | 6 | 5 |
| $p\text{-}C_4H_8N_2^+$ |  | 5 | 4 |
| $p^{++}$ | 2 | 10 | 8 |
| $C_6H_5^+$ <br> $C_{12}H_{10}^{++}$ | 7 | 5 | 7 |

Then, if the Hamiltonian operator $H = H_0 + H^1$, the secular determinant for the parent system (in this case ethylene) is already diagonalized if we choose the basis orbitals to be

$$\frac{\phi_1 + \phi_2}{\sqrt{2}}, \frac{\phi_1 - \phi_2}{\sqrt{2}}$$

For the expanded system with an extra conjugated atom, the secular equation is seen to be

$$\begin{vmatrix} 1-x & 0 & \gamma/\sqrt{2} \\ 0 & -1-x & -\gamma/\sqrt{2} \\ \gamma/\sqrt{2} & -\gamma/\sqrt{2} & \delta-x \end{vmatrix} = 0 \tag{38}$$

The Coulomb integral for the substituent is $\delta$, the resonance integral for the C–Y bond is $\gamma$, and these as well as all other energies are in units of the resonance integral $\beta$ for a C–C linkage.

Expanding the partially diagonalized determinant with respect to the last row and column, we see that

$$\frac{x-\delta}{\gamma^2} = \sum_{r=1}^{n} \frac{a_r^2}{x-\delta_r} \tag{39}$$

This result is readily generalized and shows that the energy levels for the system with one or more substituent groups can be found by plotting the function

$$\sum_{r=1}^{n} \frac{a_r^2}{x-\delta_r}$$

summed over all the molecular orbitals of the parent system, and finding the intersections with a straight line that intercepts the axes at the points $(\delta, 0)$ and $(0, -\delta/\gamma^2)$, respectively.

The form of this function for 1,4- and 1,5-disubstituted derivatives of anthraquinone is shown in Figs. 1 and 2, respectively. It will be noticed that the different branches of the function for the 1,5 isomer remain quite separate and distinct, whereas those for the 1,4 isomer show multiple intersections. This is all reminiscent of the requirements for the statistical theory of mass spectra, namely, that the potential energy surfaces should intersect extensively in order that energy may be readily interchanged between electrons and nuclei. But we must not jump to the conclusion that our simple and rather naïve Hückel model has actually established that potential energy surfaces really do show similar behavior to this rather specialized function, which

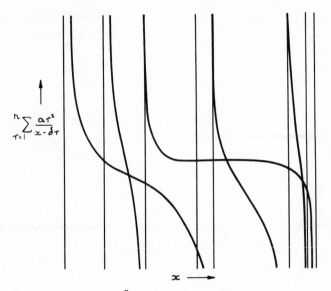

Fig. 1.   The function $\sum_{r=1}^{n} \dfrac{a_r^2}{x-\delta_r}$ for 1,4-dihydroxyanthraquinone.

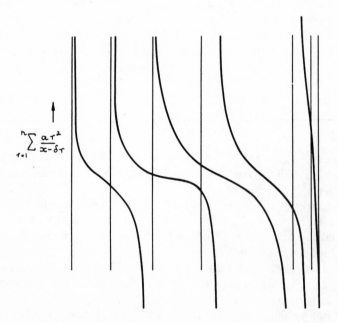

Fig. 2.   The function $\sum_{r=1}^{n} \dfrac{a_r^2}{x-\delta_r}$ for 1,5-dihydroxyanthraquinone.

is not in any sense a direct representation of a potential energy curve. But it seems not unlikely that, quite fortuitously, we have here provided a simple functional criterion that does point the way to the existence of the intersections that actually take place in reality over a multidimensional energy surface. For the amino groups must surely be set in vibration by the electron impact process and the intersecting line that determines the energy levels may be conceived as thereby caused to "sweep across" the prescribed pattern of energies that characterizes the parent ring system. This means that each time the line passes through one of the crossing points of this function it becomes possible for an electron to move on to another branch of the energy surface. Thus, we begin to see how the symmetry of the group orbitals for the substituents might influence the processes of energy transfer.

When the branches of the curve are well-separated, statistical distribution of energy cannot be attained and an adiabatic process over a single energy surface characterized by a specific fragmentation is thus predominant. The ideal case is that of the parent compound where the branches of the curve degenerate into parallel straight lines at right angles to the energy axis. Because there is no conjugative substituent, the intersections do not change their positions.

Although we have not given detailed consideration to the analogous case of $\sigma$-bonds, it seems likely that a corresponding function may be set up for nonconjugative substituents and that possibilities of crossing over of potential energy surfaces might be explored in an essentially similar way. In our treatment of branched-chain alkanes [14], it did, in fact, appear that extensive interaction between energy surfaces was occurring and that, accordingly, an average effect of positive charge distributed over a whole subset of excited states was being experienced. The resulting charge distributions were shown to be uniform as in the parent neutral hydrocarbon, and the fragmentation therefore correlated with second-order changes in bond order.

A phenomenon closely related to the effect on reaction specificity of substituents concerns the color of quinones. As the size of the conjugated system increases, there occurs a hypsochromic shift but this ultimately becomes bathochromic. Thus, while the pronounced yellow color of benzoquinone becomes progressively weaker in naphthoquinone and anthraquinone, naphthacene quinone reverses the trend [30], an effect which has been attributed to a crossing over of the first and second antibonding levels. The latter moves progressively to lower energies and eventually becomes the first excited level, following which further extension of the size of the ring system implies a bathochromic effect. We may regard this as a strong indication that the suggested interchange of energy levels does, in fact, occur.

It is also important to notice that, while the most readily excited or ionized electron is, in aliphatic ketones, one of the unshared oxygen electrons, crossing over of the $\sigma$ and $\pi$ energy levels as well as $\pi$, $\pi$ can eventually occur. It follows from the upward trend in the energies of the least bonding occupied orbital in quinodimethanes [30] that some point must be reached where this level overtakes the energy of the nonbonding oxygen orbital in the isoconjugate quinones. Moreover, the introduction of electromeric $(-E)$ groups, such as amino, hydroxy, and methoxy, reduces the ionization potential of the $\pi$-electron system by repelling electrons into the aromatic ring.

A further factor is that of hydrogen bonding which destabilizes the positive ion relative to the parent molecule, because the proton in the substituent group can form a strong electrostatic linkage with a quinone oxygen atom but not with the oxygen cation formed when a nonbonding electron has been eliminated. Thus, we have a variety of effects leading to an interchange of the energy levels in these compounds and permitting a redistribution of electronic energy by switching over from one energy surface to another. But this depends crucially on the nature and orientation of the substituents.

Beynon [29] has shown that 1,4,5,8-tetrahydroxyanthraquinone is of unusually high stability, as though the carbonyl oxygens were effectively screened by the four hydroxyl groups. Our view of the mechanism of ionization is that the $\sigma$ and $\pi$ levels have changed places and that the loss of a $\pi$ electron implies little or no loss in stability, because the repulsive effect of four $-E$ groups has contributed to make the highest occupied orbital a formally antibonding one.

Unlike a nonbonding electron which, contrary to common belief, can have an important effect on stability and molecular shape (*cf*. the effect on bond angles in $NH_3$), the loss of an antibonding $\pi$-electron does not impair stability and the consequent electron deficiency is spread over many atoms. In contradistinction the loss of a localized unshared electron can lead to rearrangement processes in which the single nonbonding electron forms an additional electron pair as in the specific release of CO [28].

It is clearly important to try to disentangle effects caused by hydrogen bonding from those due to properties of the potential energy surfaces for the aromatic-ring systems. While it is easy to speak glibly of hydrogen bonds stabilizing a ring system, such as 1,4,5,8-tetrahydroxyanthraquinone, the previous discussion will have served to emphasize that the situation is not entirely clear-cut and that the ordering and intersecting of $\sigma$ and $\pi$ energy surfaces is almost certainly no less significant. An extensive and quite comprehensive mass spectral study of polyhydroxyquinones in these laboratories a few years ago [29] clearly demonstrated that something more than hydrogen bonding was involved in the subtle differences between closely related systems. The most striking case of all is that already discussed of 1,4- and 1,5-disubstituted anthraquinones wherein important differences occur both in the case of amino and hydroxy substituents. If it were simply a case of hydrogen bonding suppressing the specific elimination of CO, we should expect a quite similar suppression effect in the two isomers, where the proximity of protons to carbonyl oxygens is, insofar as electrostatic forces are involved, identical. In view of the consensus of opinion [31] that hydrogen bonding is primarily an electrostatic effect, we would not expect the consistently large difference between CO elimination in 1,4 and 1,5 isomers shown in Table VII.

The most reasonable conclusion would seem to be that we have here the involvement of a symmetry property, wherein the effect of disubstitution is not a simply additive phenomenon. There is a clear evidence of synergism associated with the relative positions of the substituents, and we have seen that this is in line with the crossing of energy surfaces in one but not in the other. We do not propose to analyze the very interesting data on the hydroxy-anthraquinones in great detail, but a comparison of the R.A. of the $(p\text{-CO})^+$ ion from the following compounds

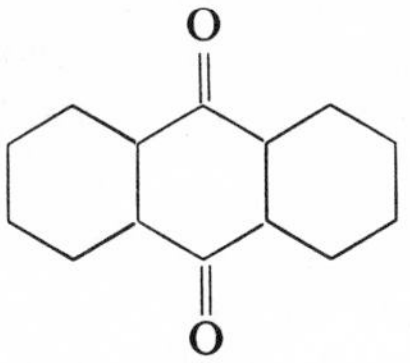

76.6

(a)

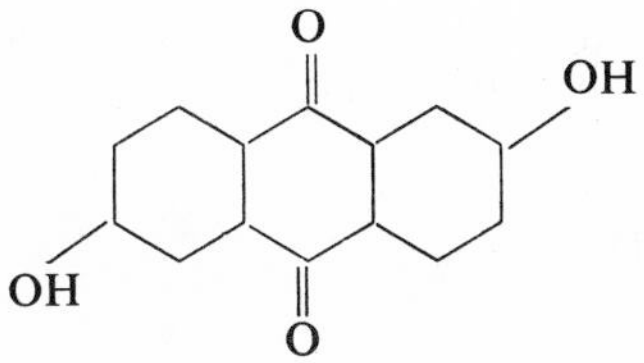

29.5

(b)

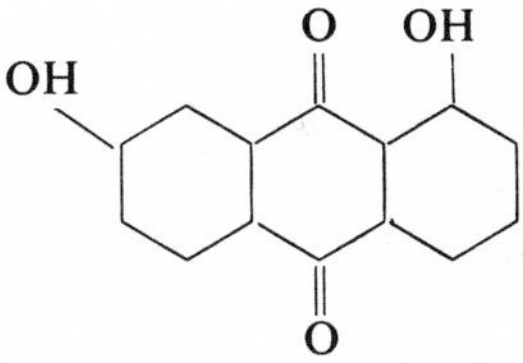

25.1

(c)

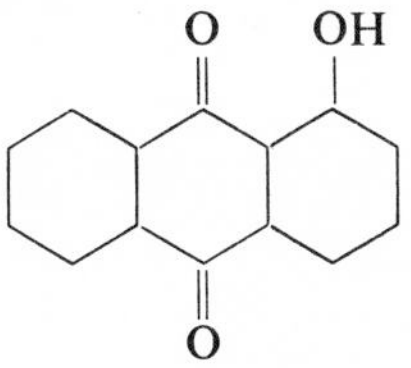

10.4

(d)

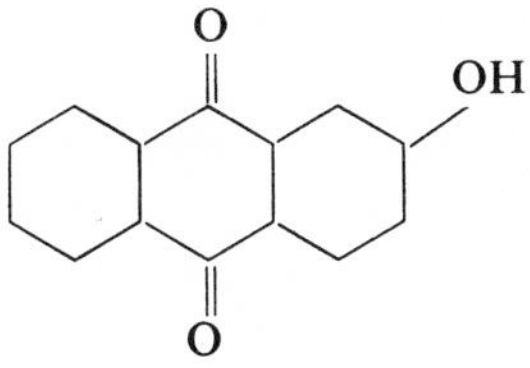

27.4

(e)

XV

### Table VII.   Relative Abundance ($p^+ = 100$) of ($p-28$)$^+$ in Disubstituted Anthraquinone

| Isomer | Substituent | |
|--------|-------------|--------|
|        | Amino | Hydroxy |
| 1,4 | 3.31 | 2.62 |
| 1,5 | 11.95 | 10.55 |

indicates clearly that proximity of the carbonyl oxygen and the substituent is not an indispensable feature of increased stability.

One must also not lose sight of the fact that the amount of ($p$-28)$^+$ formed may not correlate with the stability of the parent ion, for it is conceivable that additional routes to alternative specific elimination processes might reduce the amount of ($p$-28)$^+$ observed. But that a genuine, not merely an apparent, suppression of fragmentation occurs when substituents are present is clearly shown by a comparison of the total fragmentation intensities relative to $p^+ = 100$. These are given in Table VIII for monohydroxy compounds.

Related compounds occurring naturally as, e.g., mould metabolites, have been investigated by Reed [32]. For example, in the case of $\varepsilon$-rhodomycinone, which may be considered as a typical example,

XVI

the parent ion, though of high abundance, is not the base peak of the spectrum. As might be expected, the main "driving force" for fragmentation arises from aromatization of the ring system on the right, successive elimi-

### Table VIII.   Total Fragment Ion Intensities ($p^+ \equiv 100$)

| | |
|--------|--------|
| Anthraquinone | $\sim$ 387 |
| 1-Hydroxyanthraquinone | $\sim$ 194 |
| 2-Hydroxyanthraquinone | $\sim$ 286 |

nation of two molecules of water and one of methanol permitting, in turn, the formation of (1) a double bond, (2) an allyl radical, and (3) a complete aromatic ring.

The energy regained from process (1) is clearly $2\beta$, where $\beta$ is the resonance integral and the additional energy due to the conjugation of three consecutive atoms (allyl radical) is $2(\sqrt{2}-1)\beta$. Finally, immediately before elimination of methanol, there exists a transitory species equivalent to Wheland's transition state [33] in aromatic substitution mechanisms. This consists of a naphthacene derivative wherein atom localization is involved (XVII).

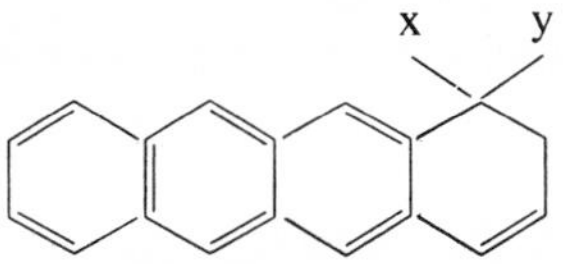

XVII

The localization energy may be estimated from the N.B.M.O. of the odd A.H. consisting of naphthacene less one carbon.

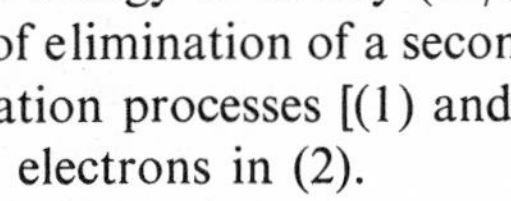

$$a = \frac{1}{\sqrt{50}}$$

XVIII

The atom localization energy is clearly $(10/\sqrt{50})\beta$. We may conjecture that the intermediate step of elimination of a second water molecule is slower than the other two elimination processes [(1) and (3)], in view of the rather smaller driving force of $\pi$ electrons in (2).

In the mass spectrum of $\varepsilon$-rhodomycinone, the relevant ion abundances are as shown in Table IX.

**Table IX.   Relative Intensities for $\varepsilon$-Rhodomycinone Ions**

| $m/e$ | Ion | Relative abundance |
|-------|-----|--------------------|
| 428 | $p^+$ | 96 |
| 410 | $(p\text{-}H_2O)^+$ | 9 |
| 392 | $(p\text{-}2H_2O)^+$ | 41 |
| 360 | $(p\text{-}2H_2O\text{-}CH_3OH)^+$ | 100 |

## EQUIVALENT ORBITALS

Before we can begin to apply the machinery of perturbation theory to any system, saturated or unsaturated, we require a suitable basis set of orbitals. One such set with which we have been much concerned, comprises the $p_z$ atomic orbitals, and in terms of these we can discuss many of the low-energy phenomena of greatest importance to the organic chemist, such as color, biochemical activity, orientation effects of substituents, and so on. On the other hand, in ion-fragmentation mechanisms, the higher-energy processes involving $\sigma$-electrons are often directly implicated. A suitable basis set for discussing these is provided by one or more of the subsets of so-called equivalent orbitals [34], which represent the localized bonds between similar pairs of atoms. Such subsets would comprise C–C, C–H, C–O $\sigma$-bonds in anthraquinone.

An important feature of these equivalent orbitals [35] is that self-consistency is preserved when the ion is formed, with the accompanying variable electron density along a chain of bonds. This is a very useful attribute indeed, because it enables one to ignore one of the major difficulties when using the L.C.A.O. theory, namely, that self-consistency is lost as soon as variable electron densities on similar atoms are encountered. Thus, even in a hydrocarbon such as fulvene, with a five-membered ring, the simple Hückel treatment of molecular orbitals becomes inconsistent and more complex iterative schemes, notably Streitwieser's $\omega$-technique [36], have to be applied to make the calculations more realistic. There is a good reason why the equivalent orbitals should be largely free from this disadvantage, namely, that they behave essentially as a filled shell, wherein ionization implicates the highest energy orbital of the set (the degeneracy in the set is, of course, removed by the interactions between adjacent members). There is consequently no scope for rearrangement of the remaining electrons when a single one is ionized, unless excitation to an independent antibonding set can be set up. This is energetically improbable, whereas in the case of $\pi$-electrons the bonding and antibonding molecular orbitals are all components of a single $\pi$-electron shell. This does not mean that the Coulomb and resonance integrals do not change at all—they must obviously depend significantly on the electron densities—but that useful results can be obtained if we care to disregard such changes and especially where we are only concerned with the undisturbed nuclear geometry. Once the particular bond has begun to stretch appreciably the separation between the bonding and antibonding sets of orbitals is not preserved and it no longer remains acceptable to treat them as quite independent.

The recent detailed study of alkanes (*loc. cit.*) has confirmed the validity of the simple model system used by Lester [14], namely, that the in-phase contributions from the CH equivalent orbitals make only the slightest difference and that, substantially, the most readily ionizable electron is accommodated in a delocalized orbital formed from a linear combination of CC equivalent orbitals. In this early version, which was purposely over-simplified, we showed that the electron deficiency in the $r$th bond from the end of the chain could be very simply expressed as

$$\frac{2}{n+1} \sin^2 \frac{r\pi}{n+1} \tag{40}$$

We note that

$$\frac{2}{n+1} \sum_{r=1}^{n} \sin^2 \frac{r\pi}{n+1} = 1 \tag{41}$$

in conformity with the ionization of a single electron.

This result showed that the closer the bond concerned to the center of the chain the greater the electron deficiency in the ground state of the ion and, if bond charge alone were a criterion of fragmentation, we would conclude that the parent ion should break at the center. This apparent discrepancy was also emphasized by Coggeshall [37].

In our treatment we emphasized that bond dissociation energies and electron densities both have a part to play and that sometimes one, sometimes the other, seems more important. Perturbation theory can again tell us something about the bond dissociation energy. In an analogous way to that extensively developed by Dewar [9] for conjugated systems, we can conclude that first-order perturbations occur when the fragment orbitals have the same energy. Consequently, breaking a molecule ion into two equal parts maximizes the perturbational splitting ($\Delta$). One half of this ($\Delta/2$) is the (variable) part of the energy difference for the least bonding orbitals in the parent ion and the fragment ion. This shows that the overall dissociation energy is maximal for a central fragmentation. It is perhaps not surprising, therefore, that the actual mode of preferred fragmentation represents a compromise between central and terminal bond rupture, whence it commonly arises that the bond undergoing rupture most readily turns out to be the third or fourth from the end.

There are two additional features, or rather different aspects of a common feature, that may explain why the particular compromise appears to settle frequently on a choice of the third or fourth bond. This is really a matter of molecular geometry in that both bond rotations and actual distortion of the bond angles can occur. In the first place, the chain can readily take the form of a ring if it contains more than a few carbons. That this does in fact occur has been convincingly demonstrated by Beynon *et al.* [38] using $^{13}C$ isotope substitution. For short chains, such change of geometry is resisted by limitations on the bond angles, and recourse to the alternative change of hybridization of a single carbon atom or limited change in topology (i.e., rearrangement) is adopted. Since it is known that a methyl group can hyperconjugate with a methylene radical in the planar form, this leads to a further product stability criterion and, although the details have yet to be fully worked out, gives grounds for believing that there is here provided a basis for an eventual rational understanding of alkane ion fragmentation mechanisms.

A very schematic rationalization of the dependence of the activation energy on both bond dissociation energy and bond order may be put forward as shown in Fig. 3.

Let us suppose that the fragmentation process is substantially complete when the length of the bond has been extended to $l$ and that the potential energy curve may be regarded as formed by two rectilinear sections on each side of the activated state. Then we have

$$y_1 = E_1 + x \tan \alpha_1$$

$$y_2 = E_2 + (l-x) \tan \alpha_2 \tag{42}$$

and these intersect where

$$x(\tan \alpha_1 + \tan \alpha_2) = E_2 - E_1 + l \tan \alpha_2 \tag{43}$$

$$y = \text{constant} + \frac{(E_2 - E_1 + l \tan \alpha_2)}{(1 + \tan \alpha_2 / \tan \alpha_1)}$$

As the point of cleavage varies along the chain, $E_1$ and $\alpha_2$ may be assumed constant, but $E_2$ and $\alpha_1$ are variable, the first depending on the bond dissociation energy and the second on the bond order, i.e., the electron density. If there is no reverse activation and no release of kinetic energy

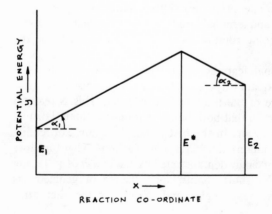

Fig. 3. Potential energy *versus* reaction coordinate.

during the fragmentation we have $\alpha_2 = 0$, and the energy of activation then varies only with $E_2$. But if $\alpha_2$ differs from zero, the activation energy will be a function of both $E_2$ and $\alpha_1$, and with the assumption that the most important fragmentation occurs where the activation energy is the least possible we conclude that neither minimization of energy nor of bond order alone will be a valid criterion. A compromise will do doubt be reached where the combination $E_2/(1 + \tan \alpha_2/\tan \alpha_1)$ is minimized. This viewpoint depends of course on the assumption that at least some release of kinetic energy accompanies the process, a feature symptomatic of some change of hybridization.

It should perhaps be mentioned that we have here almost certainly an example of a violation of a chemical "noncrossing rule" mentioned by Brown [39]. As the point of cleavage changes, the bond orders and dissociation energies show an inverse relationship, which implies that the energy curves intersect in the intervening region between the initial and activated configurations.

Fueki [40] has recently evaluated the energy levels of alkanes and alkyl halides using the extended method of equivalent orbitals, wherein CH as well as CC equivalent orbitals are explicitly introduced. This, of course, leads to secular determinants of a much higher order than in the case of the united atom model of Franklin [41] in which groups such as $CH_3$, $CH_2$, $CH$ are considered as pseudo-atoms of equivalent valency, i.e., as F, O, N. Fueki evaluated the roots of the high-order secular equations using an electronic computer and concluded that in the $n$-alkane ions $C_nH_{2n+2}$ there were two groups of $n$ levels with an energy gap of some 3 V separating them. The reason for this becomes apparent if suitable combinations of the CH equivalent orbitals are chosen, in much the same way that one discusses hyperconjugation [42]. There is, however, one important distinction, namely, that in the case of hyperconjugation one considers linear combinations of atomic orbitals, but in the present case equivalent orbitals are combined. Thus, in the case of an $n$-alkane we can denote C–C equivalent orbitals by $\chi$ and the C–H equivalent orbitals by $\omega$, and then take the linear combinations

$$\frac{1}{\sqrt{3}} (\omega_1 + \omega_2 + \omega_3) \tag{a}$$

$$\frac{1}{\sqrt{6}} (2\omega_1 - \omega_2 - \omega_3) \tag{b}$$

$$\frac{1}{\sqrt{2}} (\omega_2 - \omega_3) \tag{c}$$

This corresponds exactly to the procedure adopted in previous sections where we discussed benzonitrile and derivatives of anthraquinone.

Obviously, only the first of these has the appropriate symmetry to interact with an adjacent $\chi$ orbital. Combinations (b) and (c) belong to independent sets and play a part equivalent to the $p_x$ and $p_y$ orbitals in acetylene. But they do not overlap appreciably with similar group orbitals on the adjacent atoms and so their energy levels remain unperturbed. Since there are clearly $n$ group orbitals of the form (b) and $n$ further group orbitals (c), we have a $2n$-fold degeneracy. On the other hand, the $(n-1)$ orbitals $\chi$ can interact with the $n$ orbitals of the symmetric type (a). Thus, altogether, we have $n+n-1+1 = 2n$ energy levels, and the most stable group will consist of delocalized combinations of the $(n-1)$ $\chi$ orbitals with a relatively small admixture of the symmetrized $\omega$-orbitals. Presumably, in order to understand Fueki's results, we must suppose that the $2n$-fold degenerate level lies closer in energy to the more stable set, which seems quite reasonable as the overall effect of the interaction is to push the remaining levels apart, thus making the combination (a) less bonding.

Hatada and Hirota [43] have used the equivalent orbital approach in the simpler group orbital form to investigate the fragmentation behavior of aliphatic ketones, and they have invoked the hypothesis that the electron deficiencies in the parent ion correspond to ionization of the most readily removed electron. This corresponds to the least bonding level of the low-energy set in the preceding discussion. A methyl group is taken as a group orbital, equivalent to a single fluorine atom. No account was taken of the electron density in the carbonyl group as scission does not involve this. A very impressive agreement was found between the positive charge distribution and the scission probability.

The case of methyl tertiary butyl ketone (Fig. 4) shows the general form of the results, and the degree of accordance between the theoretical prediction and experimental values is certainly impressive. Isotopic substitution of hydrogen atoms was used to determine the course of the fragmentations.

It seems clear that, in these cases at least, the fragmentation behavior is adequately described by the adiabatic case for a single ground state potential energy surface. The repeated intersections required by the statistical theory evidently do not occur to any degree.

## ORGANOMETALLIC COMPLEXES

There appears to be a growing interest in the field of organometallic complexes and (in several important respects) it appears to be well-suited to basic studies of ion fragmentation. The great stability of some of these complexes—notably phthalocyanines and metallocenes—means that we are

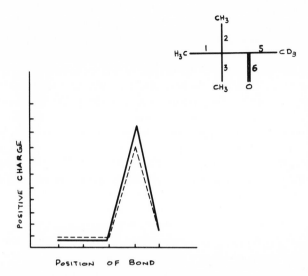

Fig. 4.   Charge distribution in the methyl tertiary butyl ketone ion.

not unduly worried by the bric-a-brac of minor ion fragments. Very clean mass spectra seem to be typical, sometimes little more being found than the parent ion itself, singly and multiply charged, and ions due to a simple splitting into two, three, or four major fragments[25].

From the standpoint of fundamental studies of ion impact, it is, again, extremely valuable to have available large complicated systems which, in view of many elements of symmetry, behave much more like simple oligo-atomic systems. Since theoretical studies of ion impact based on Born's approximation have hardly yet even encompassed many-electron atoms, the most promising extension to the molecular field would naturally be to cases where the nuclear framework has extensive elements of symmetry. This is often encountered with transition metal complexes because the $d$ or $f$ orbitals, which undergo perturbation to produce bonding in the complexes, themselves belong primarily to a compact group.

It is a little unfortunate and sometimes confusing that ligand field theory is used by different authors to mean rather different things. In its restricted use, it refers to a highly developed mathematical theory [44] wherein only the transition metal is treated quantum mechanically and the ligands are regarded as providing a formally rigid electrostatic environment with a particular symmetry. In this form it develops the equivalent of the whole mathematical apparatus of Condon and Shortley [45] for atoms and ions, but for the case of finite symmetry groups. In the truest sense it is therefore the first and most obvious extension of the wave mechanics of atoms to polyatomic systems. Conceptually, it is based on the same theoretical model as its forerunner, "crystal field theory", but in a refined and highly developed mathematical form. A more flexible use of the term "ligand field theory" refers to a molecular orbital treatment of the complete system, in which strong orbital overlap occurs between ligands and the central atom. On account of the almost insurmountable difficulties, developments in this extended sense have been mainly limited to qualitative and schematic considerations, depending very largely on recourse to symmetry properties.

There is some evidence [25] that the first electron to be ionized in complexes such as the phthalocyanines is one of the metal electrons. From the ligand field viewpoint we have a system of $d$-electrons that become split in energy by the (substantially) electrostatic perturbations due to the ligands. It is this initially perturbed atom that provides the main "target" for the electron beam and we need to modify our discussion of electron impact to take account of the circumstance that the system has now a lower symmetry than that of a centrosymmetric atomic system.

There is, as we have already indicated, no real justification apart from that of mathematical tractability, for regarding the effects of the ligands as substantially electrostatic perturbations on the $d$-electron configuration. As a largely empirical expedient, it is, in fact, common practice [46] to "adjust" the Racah parameters of the theory to force some measure of agreement for covalent bonding. It seems likely that some such expedient might also be introduced to represent the effect of the electron beam itself, for again, according to Feynman [10] the forces acting on the nuclei can (in an ultimate sense) be reduced to electrostatic interactions with suitably placed electron distributions. Thus, we might proceed by making some empirical adjustment of the Racah parameters and then treating the electrostatic effect of the electron beam as essentially another (pseudo) ligand. It would then be of considerable interest to see whether this particular parameter could be simply related to the energy of the electron beam or whether there were some degree of coupling between the ligand fields themselves and pseudo-ligand field of the electron beam. We might hope to find some evidence of an additivity principle, though it is equally possible that cross-interactions of the type which we have discussed for disubstituted anthraquinones will occur. As in the latter case, it will clearly matter a great deal on how far long-range electronic effects are propagated throughout the entire system.

The entire subject of electron impact and unimolecular dissociation is still largely undeveloped as far as polyatomic molecular systems are concerned and recourse must therefore be made to "model" theories, however artificial. All model theories, to be useful, must depend upon a rather sweeping assumption concerning one's choice of the more important features of the model, and discrepancies must be accommodated as well as possible by detailed refinements as a result of an extended experience. This is precisely the way that the currently most widely accepted model theory—the quasi-equilibrium theory [16]—has developed. Even some of the most basic assumptions of that theory, such as the manifold possibilities for the crossing of energy surfaces, have needed to be treated with reserve in the latter developments. We feel, therefore, that it is not necessarily a disadvantage if an over-simplified model is adopted at the outset; it is at least preferable to the adoption of an unduly elaborate scheme which must perforce render abortive all attempts at its detailed exploration.

In certain respects the spectra of metallocenes are similar to those of aromatic compounds, in conformity with the ordinary chemical evidence for their pronounced aromaticity. Thus [47], the parent ion is normally the base peak and multiple ionization is commonly encountered. On the other hand, a methyl substituent in the five-membered rings does not seem to lose a hydrogen as in the case of toluene. There is probably a fairly obvious reason for this, namely, that the benzyl radical contains a nonbonding molecular orbital whereas the least bonding occupied orbital of fulvene is bonding to the extent of $0.618 \beta$ [23]. Thus, it requires about 11 kcal/mole additional energy to remove an electron from fulvene, formed when a hydrogen atom is removed from the methyl pentadiene component. It should also be noted that the least bonding orbital in fulvene has the following electron distribution (XIX) in the Hückel approximation, wherein the electron deficiency is entirely within the five-membered ring.

XIX

It is not exactly known to what extent ferrocene should be formulated as $Fe^{2+} (C_5H_5)_2{}^{2-}$, with the iron in the second oxidation state, rather than as $Fe(C_5H_5)_2$. But it seems almost certain that the removal of an electron from the five-membered ring itself, which is thus implied by the assumed process of ionization, would seriously reduce the overall stability of the system and is thus energetically improbable. In fact, if one attempted to represent the system as a ligand-field complex (a concept not too easy to justify in a case where covalent bonding is so prominent a feature) the stability would depend very considerably on the splitting of the $d$-shell energy level of the metal by the negative charges on the rings and a serious depletion of the net charge such as the one contemplated would cause the complex to become unstable.

The importance of the excess electron density in the pentadienate rings has been well shown by Clancy and Spilners [48] who have examined the effects of ring substitution at low impact energies (8 V) where electron density variations might be expected to exert a significant effect on rates of fragmentation processes. While their observations of ion intensities were not intended to be strictly comparable in a quantitative sense, there seemed little doubt that strongly acid substituent groups markedly impaired stability, presumably by reducing or reversing the residual charge on the five-membered rings. On the other hand, silyl, siloxy, and other electron-repelling groups appeared, in general, to increase the stability as judged by parent ion intensity data. If we adopt Moffitt's interpretation [49] of the strong bonding as primarily involving a single molecular orbital of the ring, that is, on symmetry grounds, well adapted to overlap with one of the $d$-orbitals of the metal, then it is apparent that strong bonding demands that the energies of these two overlapping orbitals must be closely similar. Suppose that their actual values are $E_1$, $E_2$ and that $\beta$ measures the resonance integral for the covalent linkage (we use the simplest one-electron argument). Then, in combination, their energy $E$ is given by

$$\begin{vmatrix} E_1 - E & \beta \\ \beta & E_2 - E \end{vmatrix} = 0$$

or

$$E = \tfrac{1}{2}(E_1 + E_2) - \sqrt{\left(\frac{E_2 - E_1}{2}\right)^2 + \beta^2} \tag{44}$$

The dissociation energy of the bond $(D) = 2(E_1 - E)$ where we suppose that $E_2 > E_1$ so that the lowest energy state of the products is that where the metal has donated an electron to the radical.

Thus,

$$D = 2\sqrt{\left(\frac{E_2 - E_1}{2}\right)^2 + \beta^2} - (E_2 - E_1) \tag{45}$$

If $E_2 - E_1 = 0$,

$$D = 2\beta$$

whereas if $E_2 - E_1 = \beta$

$$D = \beta(\sqrt{5} - 1) = 1.236\,\beta$$

and clearly the dissociation energy falls away rapidly as the difference in the energies grows larger.

It seems likely that the $\pi$-electrons in aromatic systems and the non-bonding $d$-orbitals in metallocenes fulfill a similar function of what may be loosely described as "shock absorption". In each case they provide the most facile mechanism for dissipating the kinetic energy of the impact electron without inducing any gross disruption of the nuclear skeleton such as would no doubt arise from the loss of a $\sigma$-electron.

As in a previous discussion [25] we can regard the process of electron impact as involving a distortion in the electron beam, the effect of which can be simulated electrostatically by one or more point charges appropriately placed in the environment of the molecule. Because of the equivalence between the impact and ionized electron we can visualize the process as follows (XX):

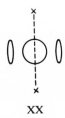

XX

While the system remains in a quasi-stationary state within the electron beam, it is as though two immovable point charges, rather equivalent to a hypothetical pair of ligands, extend the number of nuclei in the impact-activated state. This is not, of course, the same as the transition state in the conventional sense after the parent ion leaves the environment of the ionizing beam. The latter involves the same number of nuclei in a modified geometrical configuration; our hypothetical state is one with the initial geometry but expanded by two negatively charged nuclei.

It has been shown [50] that an octahedral arrangement of ligands produces only a second-order contraction of the $d$-shell. There is an obvious reason for this, namely, that the "cage" produced by the ligands is very nearly equivalent to a smeared-out charge having spherical symmetry which, in view of Gauss' theorem, implies constancy of the potential within it. Only the stray charge from the $d$-electrons which leaks outside the cage will be subject to a higher potential and therefore the resultant effect will be for the $d$-shell to contract to avoid this energetically unfavorable region. No form of hybridization can effect this type of overall contraction of the charge cloud; it is only achievable if the radial factor of the atomic orbitals is modified. The process may be compared with a hydrostatic compression in the theory of elastic deformation. On the other hand, a change of shape in which the atomic orbital is pushed in laterally at the expense of expansion in other directions is realizable by hybridization—in other words, this concerns angular rather than radial factors. In the case of electron impact, some of the lateral stress can be thus relieved by a process of hybridization in which the $4s$ orbital takes part; this reduces the amplitude of a $3d$ orbital where it protrudes toward the point charges. But in so doing the charge cloud bulges out too far in the perpendicular direction and thus suffers repulsion from the pentadiene rings. Thus, hybridization alone cannot provide a mechanism for comfortably absorbing all the energy due to impact; a further component must be involved which is concerned with lateral contraction of the $d$-shell. To pursue the metaphor, we may say that the "shock-absorber" efficiency of the $d$-electrons can be visualized as partly dependent on a hydrostatic compression and partly on a shear-stress component.

It is possible to go further and to invoke the concept of a splitting energy within the $d$-shell due to the twin charges. To emphasize the analogy with ordinary ligand field splitting, we shall designate this as $\Delta$, and use a rather simple-minded model.

On any reasonable model, the kinetic energy of the system can be written as $T = A/r^2$, where $r$ is the effective radius of the region which the electrons occupy (e.g., this is obviously true for a free electron in an environment of dimension $r$).

XXI

For the potential we may write

$$V = -B/r + 2C/(L-r)$$

where $C/(L-r)$ represents the ligand-field splitting energy $\Delta$.

On minimizing the total energy $E = T + V$, it follows that

$$r_0 = 2A/B \qquad \frac{\delta r}{r_0} = \frac{-2r_0^2 \Delta^2}{BC} \tag{46}$$

It may appear extraordinary that a process which is responsible for increasing the internal energy can do so by actually contracting the valence shell during the process of ionization. But there is no real anomaly, since the ion in the free state will expand its valence shell again to accommodate the excess energy in the compressed orbitals. The latter have no meaning in the free ion, but are a feature of the perturbed state in its particular temporary environment within the electron beam. They are expressible in the ordinary way as linear combinations of atomic orbitals for the isolated system.

## IONIZATION PROBABILITY IN AROMATIC HYDROCARBONS

Further evidence that the wole set of $\pi$-electrons in conjugated ring systems is involved in the act of ionization can be inferred from some recent work of Deverse and King [51]. They find that the ionization probability increases linearly with the number of atoms (i.e., $N$, the number of $\pi$-electrons). One interpretation might be that each atom is functioning as an independent system, so that if $p$ is the chance that it undergoes ionization and $1-p$ the chance that it does not, it follows that the probability of the whole molecule being ionized is $1-(1-p)^N$. Since $p$ is always very small compared to unity, we may conclude that the ionization probability is $Np$, thus increasing linearly with $N$.

In wave-mechanical terms, we would write

$$\psi^{(r)} = \sqrt{1-p}\,\psi_0^{(r)} + \sqrt{p}\,\psi_I^{(r)}$$

where $\psi_0^{(r)}$, $\psi_I^{(r)}$, represent all contributions to the neutral and ionized forms of the $r$th atom. Provided that the atoms are independent systems, a simple product form represents the wave function for the molecule. Thus,

$$\Psi = \prod \psi^{(1)}\psi^{(2)} \dots \psi^{(N)}$$

and as before, the weight of the ionized form is $1-(1-p)^N$.

But one might consider two other possibilities: (1) the ionization probability depends linearly on the energy of the most loosely bound $\pi$-electron, and (2) the ionization probabilities depend linearly on the energies of *all* $\pi$-electrons. Thus,

$$P = A(E - \varepsilon_{N/2}) \tag{47a}$$

$$P = \sum_{S=1}^{N/2} A(E - \varepsilon_S) \tag{47b}$$

where $A$ measures the (constant) transition probability.

If we may use the polygon approximation to the $\pi$-orbital energies [25] we have

$$\frac{1}{2\beta} \sum_{s=1}^{N/2} \varepsilon_s = 1 + 2\cos\frac{2\pi}{N} + 2\cos\frac{4\pi}{N} + \cdots + 2\cos \pi/N\left(\frac{N-2}{2}\right) \quad (48)$$

and this is readily evaluated to give cosec $\pi/N$. Thus

$$P = A(E - 2\beta \sin \pi/N) \quad (49a)$$

or

$$P = A(\tfrac{1}{2} NE - 2\beta \cosec \pi/N) \quad (49b)$$

If $N$ is not too small, $\sin \pi/N \approx \pi/N$, cosec $\pi/N \approx N/\pi$. So we may write

$$P = A(E - 2\beta \pi/N) \quad (50a)$$

$$P = \tfrac{1}{2} NA(E - 4\beta/\pi) \quad (50b)$$

While equation (50a) is asymptotic to a limiting value $AE$, equation (50b) increases in the required way as a linear function of $N$. Thus, another interpretation of the data would be that all the $\pi$-electrons are ionizable and that they each obey the usual dependence on energy for a two-electron process of ionization [52]. Deverse and King's determinations were expressed in arbitrary units referred to benzene as $P = 200$. In Fig. 5 we have chosen $A$ accordingly and plotted the measured values against

$$A \sum_{S=1}^{N/2} (E - \varepsilon_S)$$

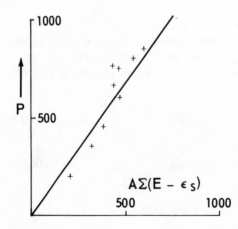

Fig. 5. Ionization probability of polyacenes as a function of the total $\pi$-electron energy.

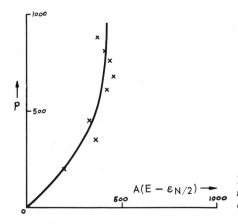

Fig. 6. Ionization probability of polyacenes as a function of frontier electron energy.

using values of $\varepsilon_S$ taken from Coulson and Daudel's Dictionary of Molecular Constants [23]. As we would have expected from our preceding arguments, a reasonably good straight-line plot passing through the origin is obtained. On the other hand, there is no agreement if we consider case (a), as will be apparent from Fig. 6.

Thus, we might tentatively conclude that the evidence from the ionization probabilities of polyacenes supports our view that a complete shell of electrons—$\pi$ electrons in aromatic systems and $d$-electrons in metallocenes—is involved as a whole unit in the initial ionization step.

## REFERENCES

1. G. G. Hall and R. D. Levine, *J. Chem. Phys.* **44**:1567, 1966.
2. P. M. Morse and H. Feshbach, *Methods of Theoretical Physics*, McGraw-Hill Book Co., Inc., New York, 1953, p. 577.
3. M. J. S. Dewar, *Advances in Chemical Physics*, Vol. VIII, Interscience Publishers, John Wiley & Sons Ltd., 1965, p. 65.
4. L. P. Hammett, *Physical Organic Chemistry*, McGraw-Hill Book Co., Inc., New York, 1940.
5. H. H. Jaffé, *Chem. Rev.* **53**:191, 1953.
6. F. W. McLafferty, in: J. D. Waldron (ed.), *Advances in Mass Spectrometry*, Pergamon Press, Oxford, England, 1959.
7. A. P. I. Catalogue of Mass Spectral Data.
8. R. N. Rylander, S. Meyerson, and H. M. Grubb, *J. Am. Chem. Soc.* **79**:842, 1957.
9. M. J. S. Dewar, *J. Am. Chem. Soc.* **74**:3341, 1952.
10. R. P. Feynman, *Phys. Rev.* **56**:340, 1939.
11. H. C. Brown, *J. Am. Chem. Soc.* **77**:3037, 1955.
12. H. C. Brown and Y. Okamoto, *J. Am. Chem. Soc.* **80**:4979, 1958.
13. M. M. Bursey and F. W. McLafferty, Paper presented at 150th Meeting A. C. S., Atlantic City, New Jersey, 1965.

14. G. R. Lester, in: J. D. Waldron (ed.), *Advances in Mass Spectrometry*, Pergamon Press, Oxford, England, 1959.
15. G. R. Lester, *Brit. J. Appl. Phys.* **14**:414, 1963.
16. H. M. Rosenstock and M. Krauss, in: F. W. McLafferty (ed.), *Mass Spectrometry of Organic Ions*, Academic Press, New York, 1963.
17. C. A. Coulson and H. C. Longuet-Higgins, *Proc. Roy. Soc.* **191**:39, 1947.
18. E. G. Phillips, *Functions of a Complex Variable*, Oliver and Boyd, Edinburgh, 1946.
19. F. W. McLafferty, *Anal. Chem.* **31**:477, 1959.
20. D. P. Stevenson, *Discussions Faraday Soc.* **10**:35, 1951.
21. A. Buchs, G. P. Rossetti, and B.P. Susz, *Helv. Chim. Acta* **47**:1563, 1964.
22. G. V. Bykov, *Electronic Charges of Bonds*, Pergamon Press, Oxford, England, 1964.
23. C. A. Coulson and R. A. Daudel (eds.), *Dictionary of Values of Molecular Constants*, Mathematical Institute (Oxford) and Centre de Chimie théorique de France (Paris), 1956.
24. S. L. Altmann, *Proc. Roy. Soc.* **A210**:327, 1952.
25. G. R. Lester, in: R. I. Reed (ed.), *Mass Spectrometry*, Academic Press, New York, 1966.
26. R. S. Mulliken, C. A. Rieke, and W. G. Brown, *J. Am. Chem. Soc.* **63**:41, 1941.
27. H. Preuss, *Integraltafeln zur Quantenchemie*, Springer-Verlag, Berlin, 1956.
28. J. H. Beynon, G. R. Lester, and A. E. Williams, *J. Phys. Chem.* **63**:1861, 1959.
29. J. H. Beynon and A. E. Williams, *Appl. Spectr.* **14**:156, 1960.
30. A. Pullman and B. Pullman, *Les Théories Électroniques de la Chimie Organique*, Masson et Cie, 1952, p. 511.
31. C. A. Coulson, in: D. Hadzi (ed.), *Symposium on Hydrogen Bonding*, Ljubljana, Pergamon Press, Oxford, England, 1959, p. 339.
32. R. I. Reed and W. K. Reid, *Tetrahedron* **19**:1817, 1963.
33. G. W. Wheland, *J. Am. Chem. Soc.* **64**:900, 1942.
34. J. E. Lennard-Jones and G. G. Hall, *Discussions Faraday Soc.* **10**:18, 1951.
35. J. C. Lorquet, *Mol. Phys.* **9**:101, 1965.
36. A. Streitwieser, Jr., *J. Am. Chem. Soc.* **82**:4123, 1960.
37. N. D. Coggeshall, *J. Chem. Phys.* **30**:595, 1959.
38. J. H. Beynon, R. A. Saunders, A. Topham, and A. E. Williams, *J. Phys. Chem.* **65**:114, 1961.
39. R. D. Brown, *Quart. Rev.* **6**:63, 1952.
40. K. Fueki, *J. Phys. Chem.* **68**:2656, 1964.
41. J. L. Franklin, *J. Chem. Phys.* **22**:1304, 1954.
42. C. A. Coulson, *Valence*, Oxford Univ. Press, Oxford, 1952, p. 360.
43. M. Hatada and K. Hirota, *Phys. Chem.* **44**:328, 1965.
44. J. S. Griffith, *The Theory of Transition-Metal Ions*, Cambridge University Press, Cambridge, 1961.
45. E. U. Condon and G. H. Shortley, *The Theory of Atomic Spectra*, Cambridge University Press, Cambridge, 1935.
46. F. A. Cotton and G. Wilkinson, *Advanced Inorganic Chemistry*, Interscience, New York, 1962, p. 595.
47. R. I. Reed and Fahzani M. Tabrizi, *Appl. Spectr.* **17**:124, 1963.
48. D. J. Clancy and I. J. Spilners, *Anal. Chem.* **34**:1839, 1962.
49. W. Moffitt, *J. Am. Chem. Soc.* **76**:3386, 1954.
50. D. P. Craig and E. A. Magnusson, *J. Chem. Soc.*, p. 4895, 1956.
51. F. T. Deverse and A. Bruce King, *J. Chem. Phys.* **41**:3833, 1964.
52. S. Geltman, *Phys. Rev.* **102**:171, 1956.

# IONIZATION AND DISSOCIATION PROCESSES

## Morton E. Wacks

*Department of Chemistry and*
*Department of Nuclear Engineering*
*University of Arizona*
*Tucson, Arizona*

A mass spectrometer is an instrument which separates ions into groups having the same mass-to-charge ratio. This permits qualitative and quantitative analysis of samples, the determination of precise atomic and molecular weights, and the elucidation of the structure of complex organic compounds. It is possible to obtain information of other types which remove the mass spectrometer from the category of an analytical instrument or detection device. This information concerns the process of formation of the ions in the mass spectrometer and provides a means for evaluating the energetics and identifying the fragmentation pathways in ionization–dissociation processes. Experimentally, complete understanding of the energetics of these processes requires the obtaining of data relating to (1) ionization as a function of the energy of the ionizing medium for positive and negative ions, (2) pathways for ion dissociation by study of metastable transitions, and (3) measurement of the excess energy associated with the ionization–dissociation processes. This chapter shall be concerned with these processes in idealized species with specific molecules or groups of molecules being used for illustrative purposes. The reader is referred to any one of the many good texts available (e.g., [1-6]) for detailed discussions of particular points covered.

## IONIZATION PROCESSES

The plot of the ion intensity as a function of the energy of the ionizing medium is called the ionization efficiency curve. This curve contains information on the energetics of ionization when it is for an ionization process; the plot of a secondary ion produced by a dissociative ionization is referred to as the appearance potential curve for that ion. The experimental aspects of obtaining these curves and their interpretations have been the subject of many papers (viz., M. Krauss and V. H. Dibeler, Chapter 3 in McLafferty [3]).

In brief, for ionization by electron bombardment, these curves are obtained by varying the electron accelerating potential and recording the ion current as a function of this voltage. However, due to the energy distribution in the ionizing medium, stray fields, and contact potentials in the ion-source region, the energy of the ionizing electrons is not an absolutely measurable quantity. Therefore, a method for calibration of the energy scale is needed, and the fields within the ion source have to be examined and controlled to prevent instrumental distortion of the curves. In addition, the energy spread in the ionizing medium must be reduced to a minimum in order to obtain the maximum information available from these curves.

## Monatomic Species

Ionization is usually produced in a mass spectrometer ion source by electron or photon bombardment. For electron-bombardment ionization, the electrons are emitted from a hot filament and consequently have a Maxwellian energy distribution. The shape of the ionization efficiency curve can readily be predicted from simplified theoretical considerations for idealized instrumental conditions and molecular species having well-defined energy levels. Assume that the ionizing medium is a beam of monoenergetic electrons and that the species being ionized is monatomic and has an excited electronic state of the ion 2 eV above the ionization energy. Under these conditions, the ion current remains zero as the electron energy is increased until the electron energy reaches the ionization energy; at that point, ion current appears (providing the mass spectrometer has 100% detection efficiency). The ion current then increases linearly with increasing energy of the ionizing electron. There are several alternate explanations of the behavior of the ionization efficiency curve as a function of energy above threshold which predict curve shapes ranging from the 1.1 power to a square-law dependency. However, it is accepted that the ionization efficiency curve increases in a linear manner with respect to the excess energy above ionization of the bombarding electron for ionization involving loss of one electron. Thus, the curve rises linearly until the energy of the ionizing electrons reaches 2 eV above the ionization potential; at this point, a new ionic state is made available and an increase in slope of the ionization efficiency curve (a break) is observed. The overall appearance then is that of a curve consisting of two straight lines intersecting as shown in Fig. 1.

The same idealized case for ionization by a beam of monoenergetic photons produces a step function. This occurs since the ionization efficiency curve, in the first approximation, is determined by the number of particles

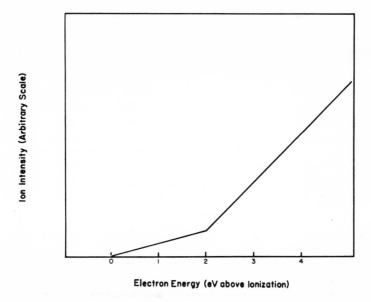

Fig. 1.  Idealized ionization efficiency curve (produced by monoenergetic electrons) for a species having an excited electronic state 2 eV above its ionization energy.

leaving the ionization intermediate. Thus, as the energy of the ionizing photon beam increases, a sudden onset in the ionization current occurs at the ionization energy. The ion current then remains constant until the second ionization occurs 2 eV higher. At this point, a second jump is observed in the ion current as shown in Fig. 2.

In the case of electron bombardment, the ratio of the slopes of the two portions of the ionization efficiency curve is the relative probability of ionization to the two electronic states of the ion. In the case of photoionization, the relative probabilities are given by the two step heights. This predicted behavior is dependent upon one additional assumption, i.e., that the ionization cross-section behavior with energy of the ionizing medium holds for the region being investigated and therefore the electronic transition probabilities are independent of each other.

In the actual rather than idealized situation, the ionizing medium has a finite energy distribution which alters the shape of the ionization efficiency curve especially for electron production from a heated filament. Assuming that there are no stray potentials to distort the energy distribution present in the electron beam thermally emitted, it can be assumed that the energy distribution is essentially Maxwellian. This assumption has been verified by

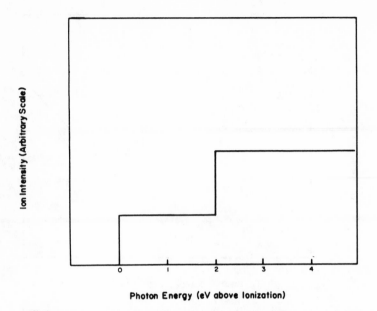

**Photon Energy (eV above Ionization)**

Fig. 2.   Idealized ionization efficiency curve (produced by monoenergetic photons) for a monatomic species having an excited electronic state 2 eV above ionization.

experimental measurement of this energy distribution [7, 8]. This distribution can be expressed by

$$dN_e(U) = \frac{4\pi m A}{h^3}\, U \exp\left(-\frac{\phi + U}{kT}\right) dU \qquad (1)$$

where $dN_e(U)$ is the number of electrons with energy between $U$ and $U + dU$ leaving the filament per second having total energy $E = U + V$, where $V$ is the accelerating voltage applied to the electron produced from a filament of absolute temperature $T$, area $A$, and work function $\phi$. If $P(E)$ is the probability that an electron of total energy $E$ produces a detectable ion, then the number of detectable ions produced per second is given by $N_i(V)$ as follows:

$$N_i(V) = \int_{U=0}^{\infty} P(E)\, dN_e(U) \qquad (2)$$

Following the development of Honig [8] and assuming $P(E)$ is proportional to the square of the electron energy in excess of the critical energy $V_c$ necessary for the production of ions, i.e.,

$$P(E) = 0 \qquad\qquad \text{for } E \leqslant V_c \qquad (3a)$$

and

$$P(E) = C_1 (E - V_c)^2 \qquad\qquad \text{for } E \geqslant V_c \qquad (3b)$$

then

$$N_i(V) = 2 C_2 kT^3 [(V_c - V) + 3 kT] \exp\left(-\frac{\phi + V_c - V}{kT}\right) \qquad (4)$$

However, for $V \geqslant V_c$,

$$N_i(V) = K [(V_c - V) + K'] \exp\left(-\frac{K'' - V}{kT}\right) \qquad (5)$$

Thus, as $V$ approaches $V_c$, the ion current increases approximately exponentially, as observed experimentally for the beginning portion of the ionization efficiency curve, and the theoretically predicted ionization efficiency curves are modified by the energy distribution in the ionizing medium. The resulting curve exhibits an exponential foot which tends to rise linearly at some energy above onset. The sharp break which is seen in Fig. 1 will be obscured by this energy distribution and thus useful information lost or made less exact by the actual physical experiment. This situation is complicated by stray fields, ion draw-out potentials, and contact potentials which change the energy and distort the Maxwellian distribution of the energy in the beam of ionizing electrons.

In the case of photoionization, the energy bandwidth present in the beam of photons produces a similar effect. There is a rounding off of the steps, which produces a decrease in information in that the exact location of onset is no longer obvious. However, in this case, the onset is usually taken as the point of steepest ascent on the rise of the ion current.

The ability to detect structure in ionization efficiency curves depends then upon the separation between energy levels giving rise to the observed structure as compared to the energy spread present in the ionizing medium as well as the relative transition probabilities as compared to the overall instrument sensitivity. In addition, the reliability of the results depends to a large extent upon the method used in the interpretation of the data. Since these curves exhibit an exponential onset, the actual point of onset of ion current is virtually impossible to determine and the absolute energy scale for the ionizing electrons is similarly indeterminate from experimental parameters due to the presence of contact potentials and stray fields in the ionization region. In the case of photoionization, however, the energy of the ionizing photons is accurately known from the physical geometry of the system.

## Interpretation of Experimental Ionization Efficiency Curves

The ionization efficiency curve produced in most conventional mass spectrometers, i.e., those not producing ionization with monoenergetic electrons or photons, consists of an exponential foot (reverse Boltzmann) extending upward into a more or less linear portion. The slope of this linear portion depends upon the electron beam current, ionization cross section, molecule density (gas pressure), source efficiency, and instrument discrimination. The interpretation of these curves requires a means of calibration of the electron energy scale and a decision on the method for determining the onset of ionization. There are several techniques for determining onset; however, all follow from the method of calibration [8-18]. Calibration usually consists of obtaining the ionization efficiency curves for a molecule having a known ionization energy and for the molecule of interest at the same time. Differences in cross section between the calibration gas and the unknown are adjusted for by normalizing the ion intensities with 50- or 70-eV electrons. This usually results in parallel curves between the calibration gas and the gas being measured, an arbitrary condition taken as meaning that similar regions of similar processes are being examined. Comparison of the two curves can be made by extrapolating the linear portions, by comparison of the intersection of the feet of the curve (linear plots) with the axis, or by using the exponential nature of the foot and a semilogarithmic plot. There have been many other suggested techniques (e.g., mathematical or electronic data extraction, comparison at a fixed percentage level of the 70-eV ionization, and use of the critical slope from Honig's interpretation). However, all have in common the comparison to a gas of known ionization energy under some predetermined normalization conditions. It has been found by comparison of the results obtained from the use of these previous techniques that the semilogarithmic approach gives reliably good agreement between molecules of known ionization energy when the curves are normalized at 50–70 eV. This technique is also quite easy to use and therefore has been apparently the most favored by experimentalists.

The separation between electronic states, even those as close as the $^2P_{\frac{3}{2}}$ and $^2P_{\frac{1}{2}}$ states in krypton and xenon, has been observed by careful interpretation of ionization efficiency curves obtained by conventional mass spectrometers. Techniques such as those of Morrison [19] involving derivative curves have been especially useful in this respect. However, the observation of vibrational levels, even when spaced relatively far apart as in diatomic species, requires special experimental techniques in addition to an almost intuitive interpretation of the data.

## Diatomic Molecules and the Franck–Condon Principle

The previous discussion concerns only the simplest possible idealized case, i.e., ionization of a molecule having only translational degrees of freedom, with electronic energy levels separated by an energy gap large in comparison to the energy spread in the ionizing medium. The next complication which would logically occur is that of introducing vibrational degrees of freedom. The energy separation of the vibrational levels in diatomic molecules is small compared to the separation between electronic states. As a consequence, vibrational energy levels are most difficult to observe unless ionization is produced by a "monoenergetic" ionizing medium.

Ionization of polyatomic molecules in the mass spectrometer is governed by the Franck–Condon principle, i.e., the time of the ionization interaction is short compared to the time of a vibration and therefore there is no change in the positions of the nuclei in the molecule during ionization. This describes the vertical or Franck–Condon ionization transition as compared with an adiabatic (0–0) transition in which ionization results in an ion in the same vibrational level as was the molecule. Energy level diagrams for the most probable types of ionization processes encountered are illustrated in Fig. 3.

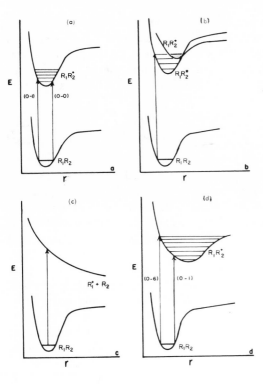

Fig. 3. Ionization processes: (a) adiabatic (0–0) and nonadiabatic (0–1) Franck–Condon transitions; (b) autoionization; (c) dissociative ionization; (d) Franck–Condon (vertical) transition with zero adiabatic probability.

Figure 3(a) illustrates the case of an adiabatic (0–0) and nonadiabatic (0–1) Franck–Condon (vertical) transitions. Figure 3(b) shows the process of autoionization where the molecule is excited to an electronic state $(R_1 R_2^*)$ above the ionization energy. The potential curve of this state crosses that of the ionized state $(R_1 R_2^+)$ and after one or more vibrations the excited molecule crosses over and autoionizes. Figure 3(c) illustrates the case of ionization to a dissociative state resulting in the direct formation of $R_1^+ + R_2$. Figure 3(d) presents a situation in which there is zero probability for the vertical ionization process to be adiabatic and, therefore, the experimentally determined ionization energy will be greater than the spectroscopic value.

Theoretically, the Franck–Condon transition probabilities can be calculated and those features of the ionization efficiency curves that are due to transitions to the various vibrational levels of the ion can be described to a good approximation by the square of the vibrational overlap integral (Franck–Condon factor). With use of the Born–Oppenheimer approximation, the probability of a transition is given by

$$P_{ev,e'v'} \sim \left| \int G_{e,e'}(R, r) \, \psi_{e,v}(R) \, \psi_{e'v'}(R) \, dT_R \right|^2 \tag{6}$$

where $\psi_{e,v}(R)$ and $\psi_{e',v'}(R)$ are the vibrational wave functions for the neutral molecule and ion, respectively [20]. For electron impact ionization near threshold, it is assumed that the electronic perturbation integral $|G_{e,e'}|^2$ varies linearly with the excess energy above threshold [21], while for photoionization a step function probability is assumed. If the variation of $G_{e,e'}$ with $R$ is small, then

$$P_{ev,e'v'} \sim |G_{e,e'}(R_e \, r)|^2 \cdot \left| \int \psi_{ev}(R) \, \psi_{e'v'}(R) \, dT_R \right|^2 \tag{7}$$

The overlap integral squared, Frank–Condon transition probability, can be calculated by the method of Nicholls [22, 23] assuming a Morse potential and using known spectroscopic data for the molecule and ion of interest.

These calculations have been made for several diatomic molecules [24–26]; however, the predicted ionization efficiency curves obtained have only recently been verified experimentally. The presence of autoionization levels and the use of ionizing media with poor energy monochromatization have made verification of the theoretical interpretation difficult. Recent results of ionization studies using photoelectric-produced electrons and examination of the energies of the ionized (ejected) electron as well as the use of highly sophisticated photoionization instrumentation have led to an increased acceptance of this simplified theoretical description of the ionization process in diatomic species.

In this method Morse potentials are assumed, each member of the two families of wave functions $[\psi_i', i = 0 \rightarrow v_{max}'; \psi_j'', j = 0 \rightarrow v_{max}'']$ is computed at 0.01-Å intervals, and the overlap integrals between all pairs are computed and squared. The computer input data are $\omega_e$, $\omega_e x_e$, $r_e$, $\mu_a$, and $v_{max}$ for the ground electronic state of the molecule and each of the electronic states of the ion for which the vibrational transition probabilities are being computed.

Franck–Condon factors for the Lyman and Werner absorption bands in $H_2$ were computed as a check on the applicability of this technique. These probabilities were computed for the following transitions:

$$H_2(X^1 \Sigma_g^+, v'' = 0) \rightarrow H_2(B^1 \Sigma_u^+, v' = 0 \rightarrow 25)$$

and

$$H_2(X^1 \Sigma_g^+, v'' = 0) \rightarrow H_2(C^1 \Pi_u, v' = 0 \rightarrow 13)$$

Tables I and II present all the vibrational transition probabilities $P_v$ that were computed for these excitation processes. More than 99% of the total probability was accounted for in both cases. From previous considerations of the general dependence of the Franck–Condon factors on the computer input data [25], it is obvious that the vibrational overlap integrals for the $C^1 \Pi_v$ state would also describe transitions to the $D^1 \Pi_u$ state of $H_2$ (Table III). Comparison of those results with the work of Kuyatt and co-workers [27] who studied the zero-angle elastic and inelastic scattering of monoenergetic electrons (33 eV) by $H_2$ is possible. In the experimental work, the incident electron beam had a Gaussian energy distribution with a half-width of about 0.09 eV. The energy losses in the electrons scattered in the forward direction indicated that the vibrational levels in the $B$, $C$, and $D$ states were being observed. By use of computed Franck–Condon factors and the experimental curve (Fig. 1, Reference 27) it is possible to estimate the relative electronic transition probabilities for these states.

A synthetic curve can be constructed by combining the vibrational transition probabilities, weighted by the appropriate relative electronic transition probability, and making the assumptions that (1) the natural line width and rotational interactions are small compared to the energy half-width in the incident electron beam and therefore the individual peak shapes can be approximated by a triangle, the height of which is the weighted Franck–Condon factor and its width at half this value is 0.1 eV; (2) the vibrational transition probabilities for the transitions

$$H_2(X^1 \Sigma_g^+, v'' = 0) \rightarrow H_2(D^1 \Pi_u, v' = 0 \rightarrow 10)$$

are the same as those computed for the transitions to the same vibrational levels of the $C^1 \Pi_u$ state (Table III) since the vibrational constants and equilibrium internuclear separations for the $C$ and $D$ states are essentially

Table I.   Franck–Condon Factors for the Transitions

$$H_2(X^1 \Sigma_g^+, v'' = 0) \rightarrow H_2(B^1 \Sigma_u^+, v' = 0 \rightarrow 25)^*$$

| $v'$ | $E$ (eV) | $P_v$ | $P_e P_v$ |
|---|---|---|---|
| 0 | 11.1835 | 0.00682 | 0.007 |
| 1 | 11.3470 | 0.03054 | 0.030 |
| 2 | 11.5058 | 0.07173 | 0.072 |
| 3 | 11.6604 | 0.11734 | 0.117 |
| 4 | 11.8108 | 0.14994 | 0.150 |
| 5 | 11.9571 | 0.15905 | 0.159 |
| 6 | 12.0994 | 0.14531 | 0.145 |
| 7 | 12.2377 | 0.11702 | 0.117 |
| 8 | 12.3720 | 0.08429 | 0.084 |
| 9 | 12.5026 | 0.05472 | 0.055 |
| 10 | 12.6293 | 0.03205 | 0.032 |
| 11 | 12.7523 | 0.01681 | 0.017 |
| 12 | 12.8716 | 0.00773 | 0.008 |
| 13 | 12.9874 | 0.00296 | 0.003 |
| 14 | 13.0810 | 0.00084 | 0.001 |
| 15 | 13.1694 | 0.00011 | 0.000 |
| 16 | 13.2525 | 0.00001 | 0.000 |
| 17 | 13.3303 | 0.00011 | 0.000 |
| 18 | 13.4027 | 0.00024 | 0.000 |
| 19 | 13.4698 | 0.00031 | 0.000 |
| 20 | 13.5316 | 0.00034 | 0.000 |
| 21 | 13.5880 | 0.00032 | 0.000 |
| 22 | 13.6391 | 0.00028 | 0.000 |
| 23 | 13.6848 | 0.00023 | 0.000 |
| 24 | 13.7253 | 0.00018 | 0.000 |
| 25 | 13.7603 | 0.00014 | 0.000 |

* Spectroscopic constants were taken from G. Herzberg and
L. L. Howe, *Can. J. Phys.* 37: 636, 1959. $T_e = 91,699.1_0 \text{cm}^{-1}$
$(1 \text{ cm}^{-1} = 1.23981 \times 10^{-4} \text{ eV}); \frac{1}{2} h\nu_0 (H_2 X^1 \Sigma_g^+) = 0.2688_1$ eV. Relative electronic transition probability $P_e$
inferred from Ref. 27 = 1.0.

the same; (3) the relative electronic transition probabilities for the $B$, $C$, and $D$ states are 1.0, 1.2, and 0.3, respectively.

The theoretical curve (Fig. 4) synthesized from the first 16 vibrational levels of Table I, the 14 levels of Table II, the first 10 levels of Table III, and the above assumptions closely reproduces the relative peak heights and widths of the experimental curve of Kuyatt and co-workers. The experimental curve intensity in the region of 13.5 eV and higher decreases more slowly than the theoretical curve. This is undoubtedly due to contributions from the $B'$, $B''$, and $D'$ states in this region. These are the states which give

### Table II.　Franck–Condon Factors for the Transitions

$$H_2(X^1 \Sigma_g^+, v'' = 0) \to H_2(C^1 \Pi_u, v' = 0 \to 13)^*$$

| $v'$ | $E$ (eV) | $P_v$ | $P_e P_v$ |
|---|---|---|---|
| 0 | 12.2839 | 0.12616 | 0.152 |
| 1 | 12.5702 | 0.20930 | 0.251 |
| 2 | 12.8398 | 0.20843 | 0.250 |
| 3 | 13.1001 | 0.16358 | 0.196 |
| 4 | 13.3379 | 0.11244 | 0.135 |
| 5 | 13.5587 | 0.07150 | 0.086 |
| 6 | 13.7635 | 0.04346 | 0.052 |
| 7 | 13.9515 | 0.02580 | 0.031 |
| 8 | 14.1236 | 0.01518 | 0.018 |
| 9 | 14.2768 | 0.00894 | 0.011 |
| 10 | 14.4111 | 0.00531 | 0.006 |
| 11 | 14.5244 | 0.00320 | 0.004 |
| 12 | 14.6135 | 0.00195 | 0.002 |
| 13 | 14.6732 | 0.00121 | 0.001 |

* Spectroscopic constants were taken from G. Herzberg, *The Spectra of Diatomic Molecules*, D. Van Nostrand Co., Inc., New York, 1950. Relative electronic transition probability $P_e$ inferred from Ref. 27 = 1.2. The $v' = 13$ is probably the highest existing vibrational level of the state (A. Monfils, *Bull. Classe Sci., Acad. Roy. Belg.* **47**: 587, 1961).

### Table III.　Frank–Condon Factors for the Transitions

$$H_2(X^1 \Sigma_g^+, v'' = 0) \to H_2(D^1 \Pi_u, v' = 0 \to 10)^*$$

| $v'$ | $E$ (eV) | $P_v$ | $P_e P_v$ |
|---|---|---|---|
| 0 | 13.9766 | 0.12616 | 0.038 |
| 1 | 14.2726 | 0.20930 | 0.063 |
| 2 | 14.5327 | 0.20843 | 0.062 |
| 3 | 14.7768 | 0.16358 | 0.049 |
| 4 | 15.0051 | 0.11244 | 0.034 |
| 5 | 15.2174 | 0.07150 | 0.021 |
| 6 | 15.4138 | 0.04346 | 0.013 |
| 7 | 15.5943 | 0.02580 | 0.008 |
| 8 | 15.7589 | 0.01518 | 0.004 |
| 9 | 15.9075 | 0.00894 | 0.003 |
| 10 | 16.0403 | 0.00531 | 0.001 |

* Spectroscopic constants were taken from A. Monfils, *Bull. Classe Sci., Acad. Roy. Belge* **47**: 816, 1961. Relative electronic transition probability $P_e$ inferred from Ref. 17 = 0.3.

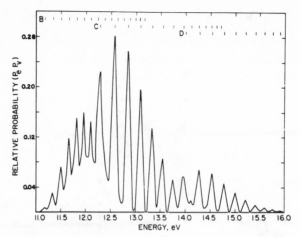

Fig. 4. Theoretical curve for the zero-angle inelastic scattering of 33-eV electrons by $H_2$.

rise to the autoionization observed in the ionization of $H_2$ by monoenergetic photons [26]. However, the structure observed in the experimental curve is not sufficiently detailed to account for the contribution from these states in the theoretically synthesized curve (Fig. 4). In addition, the assumption of a triangular peak shape (instead of the true Gaussian shape) results in deeper valleys between the peaks of the synthesized curve than were observed experimentally.

Since the weighted Frank–Condon factors computed with the assumption of a Morse potential reproduce the experimental observations, the Morse potential must provide a satisfactory mathematical description for the computation of the lower vibrational wave functions in the $B\,^1\Sigma_u^+$, $C\,^1\Pi_u$, and $D\,^1\Pi_u$ electronic states of $H_2$. The Born–Oppenheimer approximation is also valid for the excitation of these states by 33-eV electrons and the results of the inelastic scattering of monoenergetic electrons can be used to obtain relative electronic transition probabilities.

This technique has also been applied to the computation of Franck–Condon factors for the ionization of CO, NO, and $O_2$ [25]. The probabilities for the transitions

$$CO\,(X^1\,\Sigma^+,\,v'' = 0) \rightarrow CO^+\,(X, A, B)$$

$$NO\,(X^2\,\Pi,\,v'' = 0) \rightarrow NO^+\,(X, A)$$

and

$$O_2\,(X^3\,\Sigma_g^-,\,v'' = 0,1) \rightarrow O_2^+\,(X, a, A, b)$$

were computed using the data of Table IV. The synthesis of theoretical ionization efficiency curves for these transitions can be discussed in terms of the data of Tables V–XIII. In these tables, the spectroscopic constants have their usual meanings, $P$ is the calculated probabilitiy, $\Sigma P$ is the sum of the probabilities from $v' = 0$ to $v'$, and $\Delta E$ is the energy difference between

### Table IV.    Computer Input Data*

| State | | $\omega_e$ (cm$^{-1}$) | $\omega_e x_e$ (cm$^{-1}$) | $r_e$(Å) | $\mu_a$ |
|---|---|---|---|---|---|
| O$_2$ | $X^3\Sigma_g^-$ | 1580.361$_3$ | 12.0730 | 1.20739$_3$ | 8.00000 |
| O$_2^+$ | $X^2\Pi_g$ | 1876.4 | 16.53 | 1.1227 | 7.99986 |
| | $a^4\Pi_u$ | 1035.69 | 10.39 | 1.38126 | 7.99986 |
| | $A^2\Pi_u$ | 900 | 13.4 | 1.4089 | 7.99986 |
| | $b^4\Sigma_g^-$ | 1196.77 | 17.09 | 1.27953 | 7.99986 |
| NO | $X^2\Pi$ | 1904.03 | 13.97 | 1.1508 | 7.46881 |
| NO$^+$ | $X^1\Sigma^+$ | 2377.1 | 16.35 | 1.0619 | 7.46869 |
| | $A^1\Pi$ | 1608.9 | 23.3 | 1.1926 | 7.46869 |
| CO | $X^1\Sigma^+$ | 2170.21 | 13.461 | 1.12819 | 6.85841 |
| CO$^+$ | $X^2\Sigma^+$ | 2214.24 | 15.164 | 1.11506 | 6.85823 |
| | $A^2\Pi_i$ | 1562.06 | 13.532 | 1.24368 | 6.85823 |
| | $B^2\Sigma^+$ | 1734.18 | 27.927 | 1.16868 | 6.85823 |

* The data for O$_2$, O$_2^+$, CO, CO$^+$, and NO were obtained from G. Herzberg, *The Spectra of Diatomic Molecules*, D. Van Nostrand Company, Inc., Princeton, New Jersey, 1950. The data for NO$^+$ were taken from E. Miescher, *Helv. Phys. Acta* **29**:135, 1956.

### Table V.    Transition Probabilities

$$CO(^1\Sigma^+)_{v''=0} \rightarrow CO^+(^2\Sigma^+)_{v'=0\rightarrow 10} \text{ *}$$

| $v'$ | $\Delta E$ (eV)[†] | $P$ | $\Sigma P$ |
|---|---|---|---|
| 0 | 0.000 | 0.96355 | 0.96355 |
| 1 | 0.271 | 0.03634 | 0.99989 |
| 2 | 0.538 | 0.00011 | 1.00000 |
| 3 | 0.801 | 0.00000 | 1.00000 |
| 4 | 1.060 | 0.00000 | 1.00000 |
| 5 | 1.316 | 0.00000 | 1.00000 |
| 6 | 1.568 | 0.00000 | 1.00000 |
| 7 | 1.816 | 0.00000 | 1.00000 |
| 8 | 2.060 | 0.00000 | 1.00000 |
| 9 | 2.301 | 0.00000 | 1.00000 |
| 10 | 2.538 | 0.00000 | 1.00000 |

* Ionization potential = 14.013 eV.
[†] $1/2\, h\nu_0 = 0.137$ eV.

### Table VI.  Transition Probabilities

$$CO(^1\Sigma^+)_{v''=0} \rightarrow CO^+(^2\Pi_i)_{v'=0\rightarrow10}{}^*$$

| $v'$ | $\Delta E$ (eV)† | $P$ | $\Sigma P$ |
|------|--------|---------|---------|
| 0  | 0.000 | 0.07937 | 0.07937 |
| 1  | 0.190 | 0.17618 | 0.25555 |
| 2  | 0.377 | 0.21517 | 0.47072 |
| 3  | 0.561 | 0.19212 | 0.66284 |
| 4  | 0.741 | 0.14062 | 0.80346 |
| 5  | 0.918 | 0.08979 | 0.98320 |
| 6  | 1.091 | 0.05187 | 0.94507 |
| 7  | 1.261 | 0.02786 | 0.97293 |
| 8  | 1.428 | 0.01416 | 0.98709 |
| 9  | 1.591 | 0.00690 | 0.99399 |
| 10 | 1.752 | 0.00326 | 0.99725 |

\* $T_e = 2.570$ eV.
† $1/_2 h\nu_0 = 0.096$ eV.

### Table VII.  Transition Probabilities

$$CO(^1\Sigma^+)_{v''=0} \rightarrow CO^+(^2\Sigma^+)_{v'=0\rightarrow10}{}^*$$

| $v'$ | $\Delta E$ (eV)† | $P$ | $\Sigma P$ |
|------|--------|---------|---------|
| 0  | 0.000 | 0.68853 | 0.68853 |
| 1  | 0.208 | 0.24825 | 0.93678 |
| 2  | 0.409 | 0.05248 | 0.98926 |
| 3  | 0.603 | 0.00895 | 0.99821 |
| 4  | 0.790 | 0.00146 | 0.99967 |
| 5  | 0.971 | 0.00026 | 0.99993 |
| 6  | 1.144 | 0.00005 | 0.99998 |
| 7  | 1.311 | 0.00001 | 0.99999 |
| 8  | 1.470 | 0.00000 | 0.99999 |
| 9  | 1.619 | 0.00000 | 0.99999 |
| 10 | 1.769 | 0.00000 | 0.99999 |

\* $T_e = 5.687$ eV.
† $1/_2 h\nu_0 = 0.107$ eV.

## Table VIII. Transition Probabilities

$$NO(^2\Pi)_{v''=0} \rightarrow NO^+(^1\Sigma^+)_{v'=0\rightarrow10}\,^*$$

| $v'$ | $\Delta E$ (eV)[†] | $P$ | $\Sigma P$ |
|------|------|------|------|
| 0 | 0.000 | 0.15500 | 0.15500 |
| 1 | 0.290 | 0.32417 | 0.47917 |
| 2 | 0.577 | 0.29725 | 0.77642 |
| 3 | 0.860 | 0.15702 | 0.93344 |
| 4 | 1.138 | 0.05281 | 0.98625 |
| 5 | 1.411 | 0.01180 | 0.99805 |
| 6 | 1.683 | 0.00178 | 0.99983 |
| 7 | 1.949 | 0.00018 | 1.00001 |
| 8 | 2.211 | 0.00001 | 1.00002 |
| 9 | 2.469 | 0.00000 | 1.00002 |
| 10 | 2.723 | 0.00000 | 1.00002 |

* Ionization potential = 9.250 eV.
† $1/_2 h\nu_0 = 0.147$ eV.

## Table IX. Transition Probabilities

$$NO(^2\Pi)_{v''=0} \rightarrow NO^+(^1\Pi)_{v'=0\rightarrow10}\,^*$$

| $v'$ | $\Delta E$ (eV)[†] | $P$ | $\Sigma P$ |
|------|------|------|------|
| 0 | 0.000 | 0.68850 | 0.68850 |
| 1 | 0.194 | 0.24249 | 0.93099 |
| 2 | 0.381 | 0.05512 | 0.98611 |
| 3 | 0.564 | 0.01103 | 0.99714 |
| 4 | 0.740 | 0.00222 | 0.99936 |
| 5 | 0.910 | 0.00048 | 0.99984 |
| 6 | 1.075 | 0.00012 | 0.99996 |
| 7 | 1.234 | 0.00003 | 0.99999 |
| 8 | 1.387 | 0.00001 | 1.00000 |
| 9 | 1.535 | 0.00000 | 1.00000 |
| 10 | 1.676 | 0.00000 | 1.00000 |

* $T_e = 9.01$ eV.
† $1/_2 h\nu_0 = 0.099$ eV.

## Table X.   Transition Probabilities

$$O_2(^3\Sigma_g^-) \rightarrow O_2^+ (^2\Pi_g)^*$$

| $v'$ | $\Delta E$ (eV)[†] | $P_{v''-0}$ | $P_{v''-1}$ |
|---|---|---|---|
| 0 | 0.000 | 0.23545 | 0.29803 |
| 1 | 0.228 | 0.39021 | 0.04403 |
| 2 | 0.453 | 0.26277 | 0.09828 |
| 3 | 0.673 | 0.09197 | 0.02958 |
| 4 | 0.889 | 0.01771 | 0.19898 |
| 5 | 1.101 | 0.00182 | 0.05690 |
| 6 | 1.309 | 0.00008 | 0.00759 |
| 7 | 1.513 | 0.00000 | 0.00421 |
| 8 | 1.712 | 0.00000 | 0.00000 |
| 9 | 1.908 | 0.00000 | 0.00000 |
| 10 | 2.100 | 0.00000 | 0.00000 |

\* Ionization potential $= 12.065$ eV.
[†] $1/2 h\nu_0 = 0.116$ eV.

## Table XI.   Transition Probabilities

$$O_2(^3\Sigma_g^-) \rightarrow O_2^+ (^4\Pi_u)^*$$

| $v'$ | $\Delta E$ (eV)[†] | $P_{v''-0}$ | $P_{v''-1}$[‡] |
|---|---|---|---|
| 0 | 0.000 | 0.00988 | 0.05400 |
| 1 | 0.126 | 0.03667 | 0.12436 |
| 2 | 0.249 | 0.07410 | 0.14261 |
| 3 | 0.370 | 0.10839 | 0.10191 |
| 4 | 0.488 | 0.12872 | 0.04396 |
| 5 | 0.603 | 0.13202 | 0.00687 |
| 6 | 0.716 | 0.12152 | 0.00128 |
| 7 | 0.826 | 0.10301 | 0.01730 |
| 8 | 0.934 | 0.08192 | 0.03972 |
| 9 | 1.039 | 0.06197 | 0.05757 |
| 10 | 1.142 | 0.04506 | 0.06643 |
| 11 | 1.242 | 0.03176 | ... |
| 12 | 1.339 | 0.02185 | ... |
| 13 | 1.424 | 0.01475 | ... |
| 14 | 1.526 | 0.00981 | ... |
| 15 | 1.616 | 0.00646 | ... |

\* $T_e = 3.952$ eV.
[†] $1/2 h\nu_0 = 0.064$ eV.
[‡] $\cdots$ Not calculated.

## Table XII. Transition Probabilities

$$O_2(^3\Sigma_g^-) \rightarrow O_2^+(^2\Pi_u)^*$$

| $v'$ | $\Delta E$ (eV)[†] | $P_{v''-0}$ | $P_{v''-1}$[‡] |
|---|---|---|---|
| 0 | 0.000 | 0.00281 | 0.01925 |
| 1 | 0.108 | 0.01226 | 0.05959 |
| 2 | 0.213 | 0.02920 | 0.09696 |
| 3 | 0.315 | 0.05038 | 0.10886 |
| 4 | 0.413 | 0.07068 | 0.09258 |
| 5 | 0.508 | 0.08583 | 0.06105 |
| 6 | 0.599 | 0.09375 | 0.02989 |
| 7 | 0.688 | 0.09455 | 0.00887 |
| 8 | 0.773 | 0.08970 | 0.00040 |
| 9 | 0.854 | 0.08116 | 0.00196 |
| 10 | 0.932 | 0.07078 | 0.00926 |
| 11 | 1.008 | 0.06000 | — |
| 12 | 1.079 | 0.04976 | ... |
| 13 | 1.148 | 0.04059 | ... |
| 14 | 1.212 | 0.03270 | ... |
| 15 | 1.274 | 0.02612 | ... |
| 16 | 1.333 | 0.02074 | ... |
| 17 | 1.388 | 0.01641 | ... |
| 18 | 1.439 | 0.01296 | ... |
| 19 | 1.488 | 0.01024 | ... |
| 20 | 1.533 | 0.00809 | ... |

\* $T_e = 4.807$ eV.
† $1/_2 h\nu_0 = 0.055$ eV.
‡ ⋯ Not calculated.

## Table XIII. Transition Probabilities

$$O_2(^3\Sigma_g^-) \rightarrow O_2^+(^4\Sigma_g^-)^*$$

| $v'$ | $\Delta E$ (eV)[†] | $P_{v''-0}$ | $P_{v''-1}$ |
|---|---|---|---|
| 0 | 0.000 | 0.40574 | 0.37630 |
| 1 | 0.144 | 0.33613 | 0.00193 |
| 2 | 0.284 | 0.16424 | 0.16394 |
| 3 | 0.419 | 0.06294 | 0.20778 |
| 4 | 0.551 | 0.02123 | 0.13667 |
| 5 | 0.678 | 0.00671 | 0.06727 |
| 6 | 0.801 | 0.00207 | 0.02843 |
| 7 | 0.919 | 0.00064 | 0.01107 |
| 8 | 1.034 | 0.00020 | 0.00414 |
| 9 | 1.144 | 0.00006 | 0.00153 |
| 10 | 1.250 | 0.00002 | 0.00057 |

\* $T_e = 6.008$ eV.
† $1/_2 h\nu_0 = 0.074$ eV.

$v' = 0$ and $v'$. The evaluation of the Franck–Condon factors in all cases except $O_2(^3\Sigma_g^-, v'' = 1) \to O_2^+ \,(^4\Pi_u)$ was made to sufficiently high $v'_{max}$ to account for unit probability.

The general remarks of Nicholls [23] concerning the variations in the band systems as a function of $\Delta r_e$ can be expanded somewhat by examining the data in his papers and the data contained in Tables V–XIII. The dominant factor affecting the distribution of the Franck–Condon probabilities is seen in Fig. 5 to be $\Delta r_e$ rather than variations in the vibrational frequency. When $r_e$ for the electronic state of the ion is within 4% of that for the ground state of the molecule, ionization occurs to a very narrow band of vibrational levels of the ionic configuration involved. In this case the 0–0 transition is the most probable. Where $10\% \geqslant \Delta r_e \geqslant 5\%$, the transition becomes more diffuse but still localized to a group of $v'$ levels; however, the maximum transition probability occurs for the 1–0 or 2–0 transition with almost equal probability for transition to the first three or four vibrational levels of the ion. With $\Delta r_e > 10\%$, the transition probabilities become small to any particular

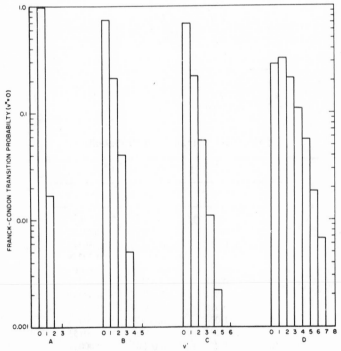

Fig. 5. Franck–Condon factors as a function of $\Delta r_e$ and $\Delta \omega_e$. A, $\Delta \omega_e = 15\%$ and $\Delta r_e < 1\%$; B, $\Delta \omega_e = 10\%$ and $\Delta r_e = 3\%$; C, $\Delta \omega_e = 15\%$ and $\Delta r_e = 3.5\%$; D, $\Delta \omega_e = 5\%$ and $\Delta r_e = 5\%$.

$v'$ and spread over many vibrational levels. Multiple maxima in the Franck–Condon transition probabilities occur when $\Delta r_e > 10\%$.

The computed values of the vibrational transition probabilities permit a closer look at several ionization experiments. It is necessary, however, to keep in mind the limitations placed on the use of these data by the occurrence of ionization from other types of transitions, e.g., autoionization. There are further limitations based on the method used for calculating these values, i.e., the assumption of a Morse model for the molecular potentials involved and the unknown trend of the transition moment with internuclear distance, as well as the assumptions concerning the threshold behavior of the ionization process as determined by the ionizing medium. The photoionization probability near threshold is taken as a step function, and in electron-impact ionization the energy dependence of the electronic transition is assumed to be linear in the excess energy of the ejected electron for the range of energies under observation. Without further data it is only possible to examine the onset of the ionization efficiency curves, since the total transition probability for ionization to each of the electronic states of the ions investigated is not known. Despite the above limitations, these computed values are of great utility in understanding ionization efficiency curves, in separating instrumental artifacts from physically significant structure in these curves, and for the interpretation of the more accurate experimental results now being obtained by mass spectrometric studies of photoionization [28].

Weissler and co-workers have reported the photoionization of CO, while the electron-impact ionization of CO, using the RPD method (retarding potential difference), has been reported by Fox and Hickam[30]. Morrison[31] has obtained the electron-impact differential ionization efficiency curve for CO. The energy spread of the electron beam used by Morrison to obtain the second-derivative curve obscured the vibrational energy levels. However, the peaks observed should, in this case, be a function of the energy distribution of the ionizing electron beam and the total transition probability to the electronic state of the ion which produce these peaks. The relative transition probabilities for

$$CO(X\,{}^1\Sigma^+) \to CO^+(X\,{}^2\Sigma^+)$$

and

$$CO(X\,{}^1\Sigma^+) \to CO^+(A\,{}^2\Pi_i)$$

from Morrison's experimental results are approximately 1.0 and 0.3, respectively.

Fox and Hickam used the RPD technique to simulate ionization by a monoenergetic electron beam. The total electronic transition probabilities obtained from their experimental results are 1.0 for ionization to the $X\ ^2\Sigma^+$ state and 0.2 to the $A\ ^2\Pi_i$ state, in agreement with those inferred from Morrison's data. With this information, the data of Tables V and VI, and the assumed threshold behavior, the ionization efficiency curves of CO for electron impact and photoionization (Figs. 6 and 7) were constructed.

The large difference in $r_e$ for the $CO(X\ ^1\Sigma^+)$ and $CO^+(A\ ^2\Pi_i)$ states results in the probability for this transition being distributed fairly equally over four vibrational states with appreciable contribution to several others. The most probable transition, however, is not the adiabatic ionization, and therefore the resulting energy difference between the two electronic states of the $CO^+$ ion, $^2\Sigma^+$ and $^2\Pi_i$, obtained from Fig. 6, appears greater than the spectroscopic difference (3.1 versus 2.52 eV). However, Fox and Hickam report a smaller difference, $2.4\pm0.1$ eV, obtained from the observed breaks in their experimental curves.

The photoionization of NO has been studied by Watanabe et al. [32, 33], Hurzeler et al. [34], and Nicholson [35], while Morrison [36] obtained the derivative curves of the electron-impact ionization of NO. Since no data

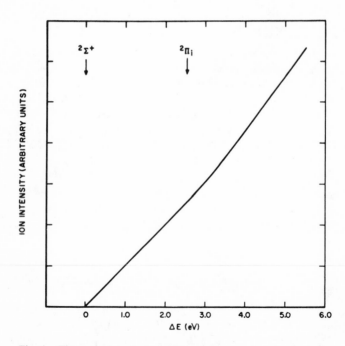

Fig. 6.   Theoretical ionization efficiency curve for the ionization of CO by monoenergetic electrons.

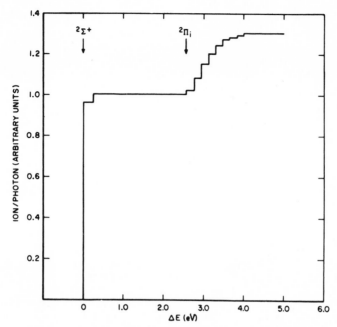

Fig. 7.   Theoretical photoionization efficiency curve for CO.

are available concerning the relative electronic transition probabilities for ionization, only the initial portion of the ionization efficiency curve for NO, i.e.,

$$NO(X\ ^2\Pi) \rightarrow NO^+(X\ ^1\Sigma^+)$$

is discussed. The experimental probabilities for transitions in this series to the first six vibrational levels are compared with the computed values in Table XIV. The major difference appears in transitions to the high vibrational states. The calculated values indicate essentially zero probability for ionization to the fifth or higher vibrational levels in the $^1\Sigma^+$ state of the $NO^+$ ion. In this region of the fourth vibrational level, all the experimental work indicates a further increase which continues for several additional vibrational levels. It has been thought that this difference in behavior in the case of photoionization was instrumentally produced from such sources as the decrease in ion intensity due to the decrease in transmission of the LiF windows in this energy region as well as the shape of the assumed correction curve for the sensitivity of the photon detector as a function of wavelength. However, this would not explain the odd double maxima at the fifth vibrational level in the derivative curve of Morrison for the photoionization of NO and the increase in his electron-impact second-differential ionization efficiency curve at about this same energy. It would seem more likely that another process must arise in the region of 10 to 11 eV where no known electronic states of the ion exist.

### Table XIV.   Ratio of Transition Probability

$$NO(X\ ^2\Pi) \rightarrow NO^+(X\ ^1\Sigma^+, v') \text{ to } NO^+(X\ ^1\Sigma^+, v' = 1)$$

| $v'$ | Calc. | Photoionization | | | Electron impact§ |
|---|---|---|---|---|---|
| | | * | † | ‡ | |
| 0 | 0.48 | $0.7_9$ | $0.7_3$ | $1.0_5$ | 0.5 |
| 1 | 1.00 | 1.00 | 1.00 | 1.00 | 1.0 |
| 2 | 0.92 | $1.0_5$ | $0.7_8$ | $0.9_3$ | 0.9 |
| 3 | 0.49 | $0.6_7$ | $0.4_9$ | $0.5_2$ | 0.8 |
| 4 | 0.16 | $0.4_3$ | $0.4_1$ | $0.5_3$ | 0.4 |
| 5 | 0.04 | ... | $0.2_9$ | $0.2_9$ | ... |

\* Watanabe *et al.* [32].
† Hurzeler *et al.* [34]. Direct photoionization with correction for efficiency of Inconel surface based on Watanabe *et al.* [33].
‡ Hurzeler *et al.* [34]. Derivative of corrected photoionization curve.
§ Morrison [36]. Second derivative of electron-impact ionization efficiency curve, 0.03-eV intervals.

Huber [37] reports an electronic state for the NO molecule with a minimum at about 10 eV leading to the α series of absorption bands corresponding to the transition $ns\sigma$, $^2\Sigma^+ \leftarrow X\ ^2\Pi$, the limiting term of this series being $NO^+(A\ ^3\Sigma^+)$. Tanaka [38] also reports an α series of Rydberg lines with slightly different wavelengths. Autoionization transitions from these α series to the ground state of $NO^+$ should be possible under the restrictions placed on these transitions by the Franck–Condon principle, i.e., that the position and velocity of the nuclei cannot alter appreciably at the instant of the transition. Autoionization transitions appear as more or less broadened and asymmetric peaked functions, depending upon the lifetimes of the states involved. The resultant photoionization efficiency curve therefore is composed of a series of steps due to the Franck–Condon vibrational level interaction with peaks due to the autoionization transitions superimposed upon these steps. The experimental work of Nicholson [35] confirms the contribution from these autoionization transitions for $n = 4, 5$ of Tanaka's α series of Rydberg lines as well as the $n = 2$ of Huber's α series. The reproducibility of the curve shapes, the accuracy of the energy separation of the vibrational levels, and the correlation of observed peaks with lines reported by both Huber and Tanaka indicate the strong reliability of Nicholson's experimental data. Figure 4 of his paper indicates other processes leading to ionization especially in the 11- to 12.5-eV region. In this region there is a group of peaks which appear to be rising in a stepwise manner with a spacing of 0.25 eV. This can be explained by an electronic state, probably of the ion, whose minimum lies about 11.15 eV and with vibrational spacing of 0.25 eV. This leads to a value of approximately 2000 cm$^{-1}$ for $\omega_e$ for this state. There appear to be at least four and possibly six vibrational levels represented, each having a reasonable transition probability. The dependence of the transition probabilities on $\Delta r_e$ indicates an $r_e$ of about 1.27 Å. The assumption of an excited antibonding state is not unreasonable in view of other previously reported electronic states of NO [39], e.g., the $B\,^2\Pi$ and $B'\,^2\Delta_i$ electronic states of the NO molecule.

The photoionization of oxygen has been reported by Weissler and co-workers [29], Watanabe and Marmo [40], and Nicholson [35]. Frost and McDowell [41] have obtained data on the electron-impact ionization of $O_2$ using the RPD technique of Fox et al. [21] to simulate ionization by a mono-energetic source of electrons. The photoionization data of Weissler consist of many peaks superimposed on some underlying structure. However, the vibrational structure is not evident. Watanabe and Marmo, in their study of the photoionization of $O_2$, found it difficult to observe vibrational structure in the ionization continuum due to the presence of strong pre-ionized bands. They found weak bands even in the regions between these strong bands, so that the minima do not necessarily represent points on the continuum. The observed ionization continuum, however, showed a progressive rise which appeared to be in steps corresponding to vibrational levels. The minimum cross sections in each of the levels $v = 0, 1, 2$ of the $X\,^2\Pi_g$ state of $\bar{O}_2{}^+$ are given by Watanabe as approximately $0.7 \times 10^{-18}$cm$^2$, $1.3 \times 10^{-18}$ cm$^2$, and $2 \times 10^{-18}$ cm$^2$, respectively. The ratio of the steps then is approximately $1:1.9:2.9$, while the relative calculated values are $1:1.6:1.1$.

The data of Frost and McDowell can be compared with the computed Franck–Condon factors if the total transition probability to each electronic state of $O_2{}^+$ is known. An ionization efficiency curve was synthesized by normalizing the final slope for each electronic state to the final slope for this state as presented by Frost and McDowell. In this way, the relative transition probabilities to the various electronic states are taken into account. The resulting curve [24] utilizing a 97.4% contribution from the $v'' = 0$ and 2.6% contribution from $v'' = 1$ for the $O_2\,X\,^3\Sigma_g{}^-$ ground state (population in levels based upon a 600°K ion source temperature) is shown in Fig. 8. It is seen that the vibrational transitions obscure the electronic transition thresholds evident in the experimental work. It would be necessary to introduce an additional unknown factor to explain the observation of these thresholds by the intersection of linear sections of the curve.

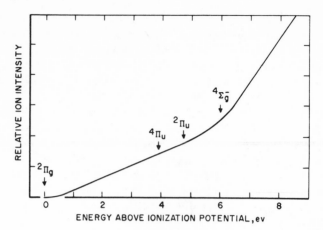

Fig. 8.   Theoretical ionization efficiency curve for $O_2 \rightarrow O_2^+$.

The experimental study by Nicholson [35] on the photoionization of Xe, $O_2$, and NO shows the importance of autoionization as a mechanism contributing to the observed ionization of the oxygen molecule. The reproducibility of his curve structure and the correspondence of observed peaks with the preionization bands reported by Price and Collins [42], Matsunaga and Watanabe [43], and Watanabe and Marmo [40] indicate that the observed ionization efficiency structure for oxygen consists of more than the vibrational transitions. Autoionization is shown to be an important process in many ionization studies and is probably the origin of the structure in the curves obtained by Weissler.

Since total electronic transition probabilities based upon theoretical considerations are lacking, the synthesis of ionization efficiency curves from the computed values of the Franck–Condon factors is incomplete. Experimentally, the vibrational structure in the ionization efficiency curves obtained by ionization with monoenergetic electrons or photons is obscured by autoionization phenomena as well as instrumental artifacts. More detailed knowledge of these autoionization transitions and the spectroscopic constants of the electronic states of the molecules and ions is needed to determine completely and theoretically the origin of the observed structure in these curves.

## IONIZATION–DISSOCIATION

Although there is very little information available concerning the relative transition probabilities to the various possible electronic states of a diatomic ion and on some occasions little information concerning the potential curves describing these states, meaningful interpretation of the experimental results and comparison between theory and experiment are possible. The mass spectra of polyatomic molecules are not as well suited to theoretical calculation due to the larger number of ions formed and, therefore, the greater number of states needed to describe the overall processes of ionization and dissociation. There are several good discussions of polyatomic mass spectra elsewhere [1, 3, 4] as well as the excellent discussions of Rosenstock and Krauss (Chapter 1 in McLafferty [3]) and Krauss and Dibeler (Chapter 3 in McLafferty [3]) on the quasi-equilibrium theory [44] and its application to large molecules. This theory assumes (1) that the molecular processes leading to the formation of a mass spectrum consist of a series of competing, consecutive unimolecular decomposition reactions of excited parent ions, and (2) that the rate constants for each of these reactions can be calculated by means of an appropriate form of absolute reaction rate theory. Thus, in the mass spectrometer ion source an assembly of isolated molecules is ionized by the ionizing medium. This process, followed by internal energy transfer processes, is assumed to lead very rapidly to a more or less uniform distribution of excited ions among all permitted accessible quantum states of the ions. The rate of decomposition of those ions in quantum states corresponding to an activated complex can be found by multiplying the concentration of these complexes by the average rate at which they cross the potential barrier. The extent of fragmentation is then determined by the time available for decomposition to occur.

Experimental elucidation of these ionization–dissociation processes requires, in addition to the ionization energy and appearance potential data, a knowledge of the ionic fragmentation pathways and the excess energy associated with these fragmentation processes. The pathways can be identified in some cases by comparison of the appearance potential curves and observation of ion peaks associated with metastable transitions. The metastable transition peak arises from an ion which dissociates after acceleration but prior to mass analysis. These ions are focused at an apparent $m/e$ of $m^*$, where $m^*$ is given by

$$m^* = \frac{m_f^{\,2}}{m_i} \tag{8}$$

where $m_i$ is the $m/e$ of the ion before dissociation and $m_f$ is the $m/e$ after dissociation. The $m/e$ of the ion peak corresponding to the metastable transition $m^*$ usually occurs at a nonintegral mass value with the metastable transition ion peak being quite broad compared to the normal ion peak. This permits identification of the dissociation pathway

$$m_i^+ \rightarrow m_f^+ + X \tag{9}$$

Combining the information obtained on the ionization process, dissociation pathways, and appearance potentials of secondary ions permits calculation of the heats of formation of ions, providing none of the fragments are formed with excess energy. In turn, then, bond strengths can be calculated from these heats of formation.

The appearance potential $A(R_1{}^+)$ of an ion $R_1{}^+$ is the heat of the reaction by which the ion is formed, providing no excess energy is involved. For the reaction

$$e^- + R_1 R_2 \rightarrow R_1{}^+ + R_2 + 2e \tag{10}$$

the following thermochemical relation is obtained

$$A(R_1{}^+) = \Delta H_{\text{reaction}} = \Delta H_f(R_1{}^+) + \Delta H_f(R_2) - \Delta H_f(R_1 R_2) \tag{11}$$

when the products are formed with no excess energy. Substitution of bond strengths and ionization potentials yields

$$A(R_1{}^+) = I(R_1) + D(R_1 - R_2) \tag{12}$$

Since

$$I(R_1) = \Delta H_f(R_1{}^+) - \Delta H_f(R_1) \tag{13}$$

and

$$D(R_1 - R_2) = \Delta H_f(R_1) + \Delta H_f(R_2) - \Delta H_f(R_1 - R_2) \tag{14}$$

heats of formation of radicals and ions, ionization energies of radicals, and bond strengths can be calculated from properly obtained and interpreted appearance potential data.

In general, appearance potential curves are more complex and have a longer foot and a less well-defined linear region than ionization efficiency curves. It is very difficult to decide on normalization of the appearance potential curve with that of the calibration gas due to these less well-behaved shapes. Consequently, good appearance potential values can be obtained only for the more intense secondary ions. These data for the less well-behaved ions can be obtained by careful evaluation of the appearance potential curve and become more reliable if some prior knowledge of the values is available. Interpretation of these data is complicated by the uncertainty of the identity of the neutral fragments and the excess energy, if present, involved in the process. Measurements of excess energy in ions have been made by several people [45-49]. In general ions formed with kinetic energy show somewhat broadened peaks, asymmetrically toward the lower mass side, and under certain conditions the excess energy is quite well defined and a satellite peak can occur.

The fused-ring aromatic hydrocarbons illustrate the type of information obtainable by examination of the mass spectra, metastable ion transitions, ionization efficiency curves, and appearance potential curves. The mass spectra of the fused-ring aromatic hydrocarbons [50−52] show quite clearly that the major portion of the observed ionization in these compounds is due to the parent ion, loss of H and $H_2$ from the parent ion, and the corresponding multiply charged ions. The only significant ion produced by cleavage of carbon–carbon bonds is that due to the loss of a $C_2$ fragment from the molecular ion. This loss is statistical [53] and the probability for this process can be described mathematically by the ratio of the number of ways in which a $C_2$ fragment can be lost to the total number of carbon–carbon bonds. Thus, the ionization–dissociation processes in these compounds are restricted quite severely. Multiply charged ions are very dominant in their mass spectra and the cleavage of carbon–carbon bonds is not very probable. This is a direct consequence of the resonance stabilization of these compounds. Previously calculated electron affinities [54] indicate that anthracene as well as some of the larger fused-ring polynuclear aromatic hydrocarbons might possibly form negative parent molecular ions. However, no negative ions are reported for these compounds.

### Table XV.  Molecular Ionization Energies (eV)

| Compound | | Electron impact | ASMO | Charge transfer | Group equivalents |
|---|---|---|---|---|---|
| Benzene | | 9.38 | 9.37 | — | (9.12) |
| Naphthalene | | 8.26 | (8.12) | (8.12) | 8.50 |
| Anthracene | | 7.55 | 7.25 | 7.23 | 7.57 |
| Phenanthrene | | 8.03 | 7.94 | 8.02 | 7.84 |
| Naphthacene | | 6.95 | 6.92 | 7.00 | 7.02 |
| Naphthaphene | | 7.53 | 7.11 | 7.60 | 7.18 |
| Chrysene | | 8.01 | 7.70 | 7.80 | 7.44 |
| Triphenylene | | 8.19 | 8.02 | 8.10 | 7.44 |
| Pyrene | | 7.72 | 7.06 | 7.55 | 7.70 |

The electron-impact molecular ionization energies for nine fused-ring aromatic compounds are found in Table XV as well as those obtained from molecular orbital calculations [54], from the empirical group equivalent technique of Franklin [55] as modified by Wacks and Dibeler [50], and from ionization energies inferred from charge transfer spectra [56, 57]. The experimental electron impact values have a reproducibility of better than ±0.25 eV based upon the results of Watanabe [58] for the photoionization of benzene and naphthalene.

The values obtained from charge transfer spectra agree quite well with the experimentally measured electron-impact values. It is also seen that the empirical technique of group equivalents gives reasonable results for these energies by the simple summation of the empirical heats of formation of the various groups necessary to construct the ions. However, lack of information as to the heats of formation of the molecules and the uncertainty of the structure of the ions result in it being impractical to give much value to the ionization energies calculated in this manner for the larger polynuclear aromatic hydrocarbons.

The appearance potentials of the doubly charged molecular ions of these nine compounds lie in the range of 21 to 27 V and are given in Table XVI. The predominance of these ions formed at relatively high electron-accelerating potentials in the mass spectra of these compounds in preference to the occurrence of dissociative ionization must be attributed to the large resonance stabilization energy of these compounds. The values given in Table XVI were reproducible to ±0.5 V (except triphenylene which was reproducible to ±1.0 V).

### Table XVI.   Doubly Charged Molecular Ionization Potential (V)

Compound

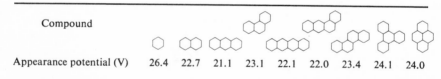

| Appearance potential (V) | 26.4 | 22.7 | 21.1 | 23.1 | 22.1 | 22.0 | 23.4 | 24.1 | 24.0 |
|---|---|---|---|---|---|---|---|---|---|

Additional information concerning the ionization–dissociation processes in the polynuclear aromatic hydrocarbons can be obtained by studying selectively deuterated compounds and by examining structural isomers. The latter approach can be illustrated by a detailed study of naphthalene and azulene [57]. The similarity of their mass spectra suggested that the dissociative processes in these two compounds follow similar paths and that the ions arise from a set of ionic intermediates common to both compounds. This assumption is also demonstrated by the occurrence of the same metastable ion transitions in both compounds at about the same relative intensity. These data are presented in Table XVII.

### Table XVII. Metastable Ion Transitions*
### in Naphthalene and Azulene

| $m^*$ | $N^\dagger$ | $A^\dagger$ | Transition | |
|---|---|---|---|---|
| | | | $m_0$ | $m$ |
| 126 | ... | ... | $C_{10}H_8^+$ | $\rightarrow C_{10}H_7^+ + H$ |
| 125 | ... | ... | $C_{10}H_7^+$ | $\rightarrow C_{10}H_6^+ + H$ |
| 81.3 | 7 | 7 | $C_{10}H_8^+$ | $\rightarrow C_8H_6^+ + C_2H_2$ |
| 56.7 | 5 | 4 | $C_8H_6^+$ | $\rightarrow C_6H_4^+ + C_2H_2$ |
| 46.6 | 2 | 2 | $C_{10}H_7^+$ | $\rightarrow C_6H_5^+ + C_4H_2$ |
| 40.7 | 4 | 5 | $C_{10}H_8^{++}$ | $\rightarrow C_8H_6^{++} + C_2H_2$ |

* The mass-to-charge ratio of the metastable ion $m^*$ is given by the relationship $m^* = m^2/m_0$, where $m$ is the $m/e$ for the final ion and $m_0$ is that for the initial ion in the metastable transition.
† $N$ is the relative abundance of the metastable ion in the mass spectrum of naphthalene with the parent-ion intensity equal to $10^4$. $A$ is similarly defined for azulene.

The ionization potentials, as well as the appearance potentials of some of the ions in the mass spectra of these compounds, are presented in Table XVIII. The data of this table indicate that the appearance potentials for a variety of ions in the mass spectrum of naphthalene are approximately 1.5 V higher than those for the same ions from azulene.

### Table XVIII. Appearance Potentials of Some Ions in the Mass Spectra of Azulene and Naphthalene (V)

| $m/e$ | Ion | Azulene $A(X_a^+)$ | Naphthalene $A(X_n^+)$ | $[A(X_n^+) - A(X_a^+)]$ |
|---|---|---|---|---|
| 128 | $C_{10}H_8^+$ | $7.7_2 \pm 0.05$ | $8.2_6 \pm 0.05$ | 0.5 |
| 127 | $C_{10}H_7^+$ | $14.0 \pm 0.10$ | $15.4 \pm 1.10$ | 1.4 |
| 126 | $C_{10}H_6^+$ | $14.7 \pm 0.10$ | $16.2 \pm 0.15$ | 1.5 |
| 102 | $C_8H_6^+$ | $13.6 \pm 0.10$ | $15.4 \pm 0.10$ | 1.8 |
| 101 | $C_8H_5^+$ | $16.3 \pm 0.15$ | $18.0_7 \pm 0.05$ | 1.8 |
| 78 | $C_6H_6^+$ | $13.8_6 \pm 0.05$ | $15.2_0 \pm 0.05$ | 1.3 |
| 77 | $C_6H_5^+$ | $16.9 \pm 0.10$ | $18.4_5 \pm 0.05$ | 1.5 |
| 76 | $C_6H_4^+$ | $16.7 \pm 0.15$ | $18.2 \pm 0.15$ | 1.5 |
| 75 | $C_6H_3^+$ | $19.2 \pm 0.15$ | $20.7_7 \pm 0.01$ | 1.5 |
| 52 | $C_4H_4^+$ | $17.8 \pm 0.10$ | $19.6 \pm 0.20$ | 1.7 |

The heats of formation of gaseous naphthalene [59] and azulene [60] are approximately $34.3 \pm 1.5$ and $72.5 \pm 2.5$ kcal/mole respectively. The difference in these heats of formation is $1.66 \pm 0.2$ eV. This is the same as the observed difference in the secondary ion appearance potentials (Table XVII) within the limits of experimental reproducibility. This difference can also be observed for ions which do not exhibit linear sections in their semilogarithmic ionization curves when the curves are compared at points of equal curvature. These observations when combined with the similarity of the mass spectra of azulene and naphthalene and the occurrence of the same metastable transitions having approximately the same ion intensities in both mass spectra indicate the occurrence of a set of ionic intermediates common to both azulene and naphthalene.

The secondary ions in the mass spectra of these compounds arise from these common ionic intermediates which are formed by isomerization of the ions of azulene and naphthalene.

Examination of the appearance potentials of the ions formed in the dissociation of azulene and naphthalene indicates another fragmentation pathway for the formation of $C_{10}H_6^+$ ions in addition to that determined by the metastable ion transition at $m/e = 125$. The appearance potentials of the $C_{10}H_6^+$ ions are about 0.7 V greater than those of the $C_{10}H_7^+$ ions in both compounds. Since the C–H bond strength in the ion is certainly greater than 0.7 V, this appearance potential could correspond to either of the following processes

$$C_{10}H_8^+ \rightarrow C_{10}H_6^+ + H + H \tag{15a}$$

$$C_{10}H_8^+ \rightarrow C_{10}H_6^+ + H_2 \tag{15b}$$

but not to the loss of a hydrogen atom from the $C_{10}H_7^+$ ion as indicated by the metastable ion transition at $m/e = 125$.

The formation of the $C_{10}H_7^+$ and $C_{10}H_6^+$ ions in these compounds is seen to require more than 6 eV of energy in excess of that necessary for ionization. This indicates that the Franck–Condon factors are such that population of the higher vibrational levels in the ground state of the molecular ion is not very probable. The primary fragment ions must therefore be formed from excited electronic states of the molecular ions. If the measured appearance potential for the $C_{10}H_6^+$ ions corresponds to process (15b) and the C–H bond in the excited molecular ion is not greatly different from the bond in $H_2$, then the $C_{10}H_7^+$ and the $C_{10}H_6^+$ ions arise from the same excited states of their respective molecular ions.

The $C_{10}H_6^+$ ions at onset do not arise from the $C_{10}H_7^+$ ions; however, the $C_{10}H_6^+$ ions from both compounds do have the same heat of formation. The $C_{10}H_7^+$ ions also have the same heat of formation independent of their

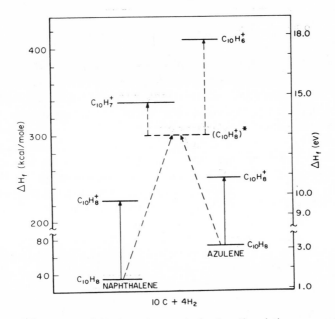

Fig. 9. Schematic representation of some ionization–dissociation processes in azulene and naphthalene. Dashed lines show the pathway indicated by the appearance potentials of the $C_{10}H_6^+$ and $C_{10}H_7^+$ ions and the assumption of the formation of an excited molecular ion $(C_{10}H_8^+)^*$ common to both compounds.

origin. Therefore, it is probable that the excited molecular ion from which these ions are formed is common to both azulene and naphthalene. This possibility is shown schematically in Fig. 9. Isomerization to a structure similar to a cyclodecapentadienyl radical ion with two hydrogens missing, i.e., removal of the ring-bridging carbon–carbon bond, or complete opening of the rings to a linear structure are possible rearrangements which would result in a structure accessible to the molecular ions of both compounds. The ring-bridging bond is predominantly of a $\sigma$ nature and therefore its cleavage requires ionization to one or more excited states with the resultant ion having sufficient additional vibrational energy to break the ring-bridging carbon–carbon bond which could occur simultaneously with or be followed by cleavage of the ring to form an open chain.

The ionization–dissociation processes in the fused-ring polynuclear aromatic hydrocarbons are severely restricted as a consequence of the large amount of resonance stabilization in these compounds. The majority of the ionization is due to ions formed without cleavage of a carbon–carbon bond, e.g., parent ions, loss of H or $H_2$ from the parent ion, and the corresponding multiply charged species. The only significant ion formed by breaking carbon–carbon bonds is that due to the loss of a $C_2$ fragment from the parent molecular ion.

The ionization–dissociation processes in azulene and napththalene indicate that these isomers behave as do other sets of isomers such as those studied byMeyerson and co-workers [61] and Momigny and co-workers [62], which break down under electron impact largely via common paths involving common ionic intermediates. The occurrence of a set of common ionic intermediates for azulene and naphthalene is qualitatively demonstrated by the similarity of their mass spectra and by the metastable transitions. Comparison of the difference of the appearance potentials for the same secondary ions in both compounds with the difference in the heats of formation for these molecules in the vapor state indicated that, for each of several fragment ions appearing in the spectra of naphthalene and azulene, the lowest ionized state through which the two isomers pass has energies equal within the limits of the experimental uncertainty. These common ionic intermediates appear to be states of the $C_{10}H_8^+$ ions.

## NEGATIVE IONS

Negative ions can be formed in the mass spectrometer by electron bombardment in two ways. The first manner in which this can occur is a capture process, which does not provide for removal of excess energy by a product species of the ionization process and thus is a resonance process. Therefore, electron-capture formation of negative ions will only occur if the energy of the electron is within a relatively narrow energy range. This holds for dissociative electron capture as well, since the range of kinetic energies occurring in a dissociation is finite, although the peak width may be increased over that for a simple electron capture process. The second manner in which negative ions can be formed is a pair-production process. Ionization is accompanied by the ejection of an electron which can carry away excess energy and therefore is not a resonance process in this case. The ionization efficiency curve for a negative ion formed by a dissociative electron attachment process ($O^-$ from CO) [63] will exhibit both types of behavior (Fig. 10). Here the ionization efficiency curve consists of a resonance peak resulting from the pair-production process.

In general, the width of the resonance capture peak is primarily associated with the energy inhomogeneity of the beam of ionizing electrons and may also be associated with the nature of the transition involved in the formation of the ions. In an investigation [64] of the negative ion formation in $SF_6$ using essentially monoenergetic electrons, it was found that the resonance capture peak for the formation of $SF_6$ has a half-width of 0.1 eV

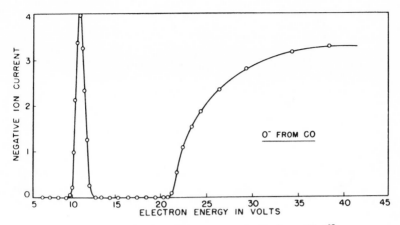

Fig. 10. Ionization efficiency curve for O⁻ from CO [63].

which corresponded exactly to the energy half-width of the ionizing electrons. This indicates that the capture cross section for this process has a finite value over an energy range of less than 0.1 eV. The half-width for the dissociative capture formation of $SF_5^-$ from $SF_6$ was 0.3 eV under the same conditions and measurable quantities of ions were formed at electron energies 1 eV higher than the peak maximum. This is not unexpected since the dissociation process provides for removal of energy from the excited parent negative ion and therefore production of $SF_5^-$ can occur over a larger range of electron energies than that for $SF_6^-$.

As in positive ion formation the production of negative ions can be discussed in terms of Franck–Condon transitions and potential surface crossings. The Franck–Condon region defines the accessible energy states of the ions and only electrons having energies in this range will be captured. Figures 11 and 12 show the potential energy curves for the formation of negative ions by resonance capture and pair production

For the electron-capture process, the appearance potential $A$ is related to the energetics of formation by

$$A - E_k = A_0 = D(A-B) - E_a(B) + \Sigma E_e \qquad (16)$$

where $E_k$ is the excess kinetic energy of the ion, $E_a(B)$ is the electron affinity of $B$, $E_e$ is the excitation energy (vibrational and electronic) above ground state for the fragments, and $D(A\text{-}B)$ is the $AB$ bond strength. Similarly for the pair-production formation of negative ions

$$A - E_k = A_0 = D(A-B) - E_a(B) + I(A) + \Sigma E_e \qquad (17)$$

where $I(A)$ is the ionization potential of $A$. Thus, the appearance potential

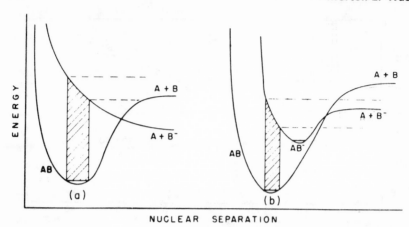

NUCLEAR   SEPARATION

Fig. 11.   Potential energy curves for resonance-capture negative ion formation [1].

of a negative ion permits calculation of the electron affinity of the corresponding neutral particle, providing the decomposition products are unexcited or a satisfactory correction can be made for the energy of excitation. Negative ions usually do not possess stable excited electronic states, while atoms and positive ions have many such states; thus, many appearance potentials of

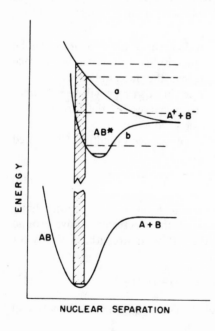

NUCLEAR   SEPARATION

Fig. 12.   Potential energy curves for pair-production processes [1].

negative ions can be accounted for only by assuming that the neutral or positive fragment is formed in a excited state. Excited negative ions are not stable and decompose or require collisional deactivation to become stable; thus, many molecular negative ions are not observed in the mass spectrometer where pressures are too low for stabilization by such a process.

## CONCLUSION

The fine structure in electron and photon ionization efficiency curves of simple molecules can be discussed in terms of the Franck–Condon probabilities for transition between vibronic states while the major features are a result of transitions between electronic states. The electron-impact ionization efficiency curve of a diatomic molecule, obtained with the energy spread in the ionizing beam small compared to the separation between vibrational levels, consists of straight-line segments of slightly increasing slopes (the change in slope being proportional to the vibrational transition probability) superimposed on larger slope changes corresponding to ionization transitions to electronic states of the ion. Similarly, for photoionization the single-step ionization efficiency curve of the monatomic species becomes a staircase function in the case of a diatomic molecule with the relative change in the heights of the steps being proportional to the vibrational transition probabilities. This simplified picture is complicated by the presence of auto-ionization transitions which appear as more or less broadened and asymmetric peaked functions depending upon the lifetimes of the states involved. In some molecules, e.g., hydrogen, autoionization phenomena are quite prevalent and almost completely obscure the vibrational transitions.

Rotational features, multiple ionization, dissociative ionization, and the closeness of energy levels in addition to instrumental variables make the interpretation of the ionization efficiency and appearance potential data extremely difficult for large molecules. In these cases, the best that can be hoped for is a reasonable value for the ionization energy (providing that the adiabatic transition can be observed) and a consistent set of appearance potential data for processes involving little if any excess energy. Under these conditions, interpretation of the energetics of the ionization–dissociation processes may result in data compatible with thermochemically obtained values.

## REFERENCES

1. F. H. Field and J. L. Franklin, *Electron Impact Phenomena*, Academic Press, New York, 1957.

2. K. Biemann, *Mass Spectrometry*, McGraw-Hill Book Company, Inc., New York, 1963.
3. F. W. McLafferty (ed.), *Mass Spectrometry of Organic Ions*, Academic Press, New York, 1963.
4. J. H. Beynon, *Mass Spectrometry*, Elsevier Publishing Company, Amsterdam, 1964 (first reprint).
5. R. W. Kiser, *Introduction to Mass Spectrometry and Its Applications*, Prentice-Hall, Inc., Englewood Cliffs, New Jersey, 1965.
6. R. I. Reed (ed.), *Mass Spectrometry*, Academic Press, London, 1965.
7. W. B. Nottingham, *Phys. Rev.* **55**:203, 1939.
8. R. E. Honig, *J. Chem. Phys.* **16**:105, 1948.
9. R. H. Vought, *Phys. Rev.* **71**:93, 1947.
10. T. Mariner and W. Bleakney, *Phys. Rev.* **72**:807, 1947.
11. M. B. Koffel and R. A. Lad, *J. Chem. Phys.* **16**:420, 1948.
12. J. J. Mitchell and F. F. Coleman, *J. Chem. Phys.* **17**:44, 1949.
13. J. W. Warren, *Nature* **165**:810, 1950.
14. F. P. Lossing, A. W. Tickner, and W. A. Bryce, *J. Chem. Phys.* **19**:1254, 1951.
15. J. D. Morrison and A. J. C. Nicholson, *J. Chem. Phys.* **20**:1021, 1952.
16. V. H. Dibeler and R. M. Reese, *J. Res. Natl. Bur. Std.* **54**:127, 1955.
17. A. J. C. Nicholson, *J. Chem. Phys.* **29**:1312, 1958.
18. R. W. Kiser and E. J. Gallegos, *J. Phys. Chem.* **66**:947, 1962.
19. J. D. Morrison, *J. Chem. Phys.* **21**:1767, 1953.
20. A. S. Collidge, H. M. James, and R. D. Present, *J. Chem. Phys.* **4**:193, 1936.
21. D. R. Bates, A. Fundaminsky, J. W. Leech, and H. S. W. Massey, *Trans. Roy. Soc. (London)* **A243**:93, 1950; S. Geltman, *Phys. Rev.* **102**:171, 1956; R. E. Fox, W. M. Hickam, and T. Kjeldaas, Jr., *Phys. Rev.* **89**:555, 1953; G. H. Wannier, *Phys. Rev.* **100**:1180, 1956.
22. R. W. Nicholls, *J. Res. Natl. Bur. Std.* **66A**:227, 1962.
23. R. W. Nicholls, *J. Res. Natl. Bur. Std.* **65A**:451, 1961.
24. M. E. Wacks and M. Krauss, *J. Chem. Phys.* **35**:1902, 1961.
25. M. E. Wacks, *J. Chem. Phys.* **41**:930, 1964.
26. M. E. Wacks, *J. Res. Natl. Bur. Std.* **68A**:631, 1964.
27. C. E. Kuyatt, S. R. Mielczarek, and J. A. Simpson, *Phys. Rev. Letters* **12**:293, 1964.
28. V. H. Dibeler and R. M. Reese, *J. Chem. Phys.* **40**:2034, 1964.
29. G. L. Weissler, J. A. R. Samson, M. Ogawa, and G. R. Cook, *J. Opt. Soc. Am.* **49**:338, 1959.
30. R. E. Fox and W. M. Hickam, *J. Chem. Phys.* **22**:2059, 1954.
31. J. D. Morrison, *J. Chem. Phys.* **22**:1219, 1954.
32. K. Watanabe, F. F. Marmo, and E. C. Y. Inn, *Phys. Rev.* **91**:1155, 1953.
33. K. Watanabe, T. Nakayama, and J. Mottl, "Final Report of Ionization Potentials of Molecules by a Photoionization Method," Department of Physics, University of Hawaii, December 1959.
34. H. Hurzeler, M. G. Inghram, and J. D. Morrison, *J. Chem. Phys.* **28**:76, 1958.
35. A. J. C. Nicholson, *J. Chem. Phys.* **39**:954, 1963.
36. J. D. Morrison, *Rev. Pure Appl. Chem.* **5**:22, 1955
37. K. P. Huber, *Helv. Phys. Acta* **34**:929, 1961.
38. Y. Tanaka, *Sci. Papers Inst. Phys. Chem. Res. (Tokyo)* **39**:456, 1942.
39. K. P. Huber, M. Huber, and E. Miescher, *Phys. Letters* **3**:315, 1963.
40. K. Watanabe and F. F. Marmo, *J. Chem. Phys.* **25**:965, 1956.
41. D. C. Frost and C. A. McDowell, *J. Am. Chem. Soc.* **80**:6183, 1958.
42. W. C. Price and G. Collins, *Phys. Rev.* **48**:714, 1935.
43. F. M. Matsunaga and K. Watanabe, Sci. Rept. No. 5, Contract No. Af 19(604)-4576, Geophysics Research Directorate, University of Hawaii, 1961.

44. H. M. Rosenstock, M. B. Wallenstein, A. L. Wahrhaftig, and H. Eyring, *Proc. Natl. Acad. Sci. U.S.* **38**:667, 1952.

45. J. T. Tate and W. W. Lozier, *Phys. Rev.* **39**:254, 1932.

46. R. E. Fox and J. A. Hipple, *Rev. Sci. Instr.* **19**:462, 1948.

47. H. D. Hagstrum, *Rev. Mod. Phys.* **23**:185, 1951.

48. R. J. Kandel, *Phys. Rev.* **91**:436, 1953.

49. R. J. Kandel, *J. Chem. Phys.* **22**:1496, 1954.

50. M. E. Wacks and V. H. Dibeler, *J. Chem. Phys.* **31**:1557, 1959.

51. M. E. Wacks, *J. Chem. Phys.* **41**:1661, 1964.

52. R. J. Van Brunt and M. E. Wacks, *J. Chem. Phys.* **41**:3195, 1964.

53. G. R. Lester, in: J. D. Waldron (ed.), *Advan. Mass Spec., Proc. Conf. Univ. London,* Pergamon Press Ltd., London, 1959, pp. 287–307.

54. R. M. Hedges and F. A. Matsen, *J. Chem. Phys.* **28**:950, 1958.

55. J. L. Franklin, *J. Chem. Phys.* **21**:2029, 1953.

56. G. Briegleb and J. Czekalla, *Z. Elektrochem.* **63**:6, 1959.

57. H. Kuroda, *Nature* **201**:1214, 1964.

58. K. Watanabe, *J. Chem. Phys.* **26**:542, 1957.

59. D. M. Speres and J. D. Rossini, *J. Phys. Chem.* **64**:1723, 1960.

60. E. Kovats, H. Guntherd, and P. A. Plattner, *Helv. Chim. Acta* **38**:1963, 1955; **40**:2008, 1957.

61. P. N. Rylander, S. Meyerson, and H. M. Grubb, *J. Am. Chem. Soc.* **79**:842, 1957; S. Meyerson and P. N. Rylander, *J. Chem. Phys.* **27**:901, 1957; *J. Phys. Chem.* **62**:2, 1958; S. Meyerson, *J. Am. Chem. Soc.* **85**:3340, 1963.

62. J. Momigny, L. Brakier, and L. D'Or, *Bull. Classe Sci., Acad. Roy. Belg.* **48**:1002, 1962.

63. H. D. Hagstrum and J. T. Tate, *Phys. Rev.* **59**:354, 1941.

64. W. M. Hickam and R. E. Fox, paper presented at 3rd Annual Meeting Am. Soc. Testing Materials, Committee E-14 on Mass Spectrometry, San Francisco, May 1955.

# MASS SPECTROMETRY DATA CENTER

## R. G. Ridley

*Atomic Weapons Research Establishment*
*Aldermaston, Berkshire, England*

The explosion in the volume of data and information in all fields of science makes it necessary to evolve special methods and to consider specialized data centers for particular topics.

An advisory committee (Fig. 1) was appointed by the United Kingdom Office for Scientific and Technical Information (O.S.T.I.), Department of Education and Science, in August 1965 to assess the need for a data center for mass spectrometry and to make recommendations. As a result, the O.S.T.I. is supporting the Mass Spectrometry Data Centre at Aldermaston, Berkshire.

The particular projects at present receiving attention are shown in Fig. 2.

## MASS SPECTROMETRY BULLETIN

There is a real need for a regular information service to the whole field of mass spectrometry. It was felt by the Committee that a classified guide to the current literature appearing monthly would best meet the requirement.

The *Mass Spectrometry Bulletin* is a guide to current literature, the main feature of which is a list of references. The center column of Fig. 3 shows how this information is presented. Each entry has a unique accession number, the original title, the authors' names, the journal reference, and up to ten terms describing the content of the reference. These index terms come from a standard list which will be regularly reproduced in the *Bulletin*.

References are grouped into eight broad sections. The contents page, reproduced to the left of the diagram, shows the groupings in each of the eight sections. This is a general guide to references of interest.

There are six indexes, which allow for detailed searching. Examples of these indexes are shown on the right of the diagram. It will be seen how they lead to references from a detailed subject classification, from selected classes of compounds, from a particular compound or ion of specified mass-to-charge ratio, and from an author's name. In addition there are indexes to elements and to materials.

As an aid to retrieval, the final issue of the *Bulletin* for the year will contain full indexes to the year's literature. As shown in Fig. 4, it is proposed also to experiment both with "peephole" cards and with a computer program for retrieval of information.

A sample edition of such a bulletin has been prepared at the Data Centre and a monthly production is starting in November this year. The *Mass Spectrometry Bulletin* can be obtained from the distributors, the U. K. Stationery Office (H.M.S.O.), at a subscription rate of £9. 9sh per year with postage additional.

ADVISORY COMMITTEE TO

U.K. OFFICE FOR SCIENTIFIC AND TECHNICAL INFORMATION

| Chairman: | Mr. A. Quayle | (Shell Research) |
|---|---|---|
| | Dr. J. H. Beynon | (ICI) |
| | Dr. P. F. Knewstubb | (Cambridge Univ.) |
| | Dr. N. R. Daly | (UKAEA) |
| | Dr. C. J. Danby | (Oxford Univ.) |
| | Mr. R. M. Elliott | (AEI) |
| | Dr. W. Kelly | (Unilever) |
| | Dr. I. Reed | (Glasgow Univ.) |

Fig. 1.   Advisory Committee to O.S.T.I. and Mass Spectrometry Data Centre.

PROJECTS

(1)   MASS SPECTROMETRY BULLETIN.

(2)   MASS SPECTRA LITERATURE – REFERENCE AND RETRIEVAL.

(3)   COLLECTION AND DISTRIBUTION OF LOW RESOLUTION MASS SPECTRA.

(4)   COMPOUND IDENTIFICATION.

(5)   N.B.S. DATA ON ION PROCESSES – ANSWERING SERVICE.

Fig. 2.   Mass Spectrometry Data Centre projects.

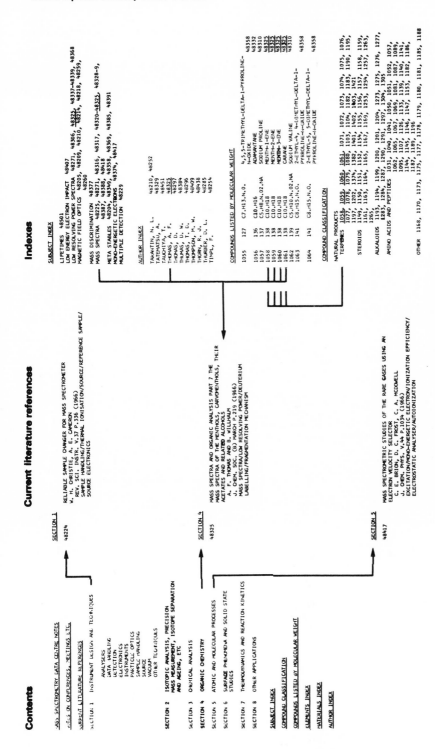

Fig. 3. The scope of the bulletin.

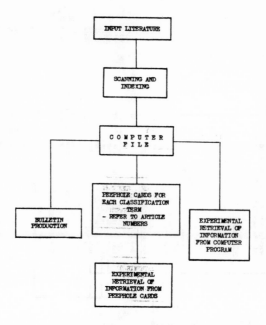

Fig. 4.    Information retrieval.

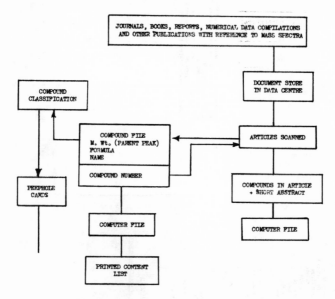

Fig. 5.    Mass spectra reference and retrieval.

## SURVEY OF THE LITERATURE REFERRING TO MASS SPECTRA

A complete survey of the past literature referring to mass spectra (Fig. 5) has been started with the object of providing a useful reference and retrieval service.

We would like to receive at the Centre copies of your past and future publications relevant to this topic as an aid to this survey. (Here we must thank those who have already responded to our appeal.) We would also like to have information on compounds that have been partly or completely mass analyzed in your laboratory but not yet published in the generally available literature.

It is hoped to get up to date next year when questions referring to the spectra of particular compounds will be answered (Fig. 6). Indexes to the main file will then be made available.

Consideration is also being given to a retrieval system involving particular types of compound.

## LOW-RESOLUTION MASS SPECTRA—COLLECTION AND DISTRIBUTION

We aim to provide a central organization for collecting and distributing low-resolution mass spectra that at present are not reaching established systems. Where necessary, the Centre is providing assistance in the measurement of spectra (Fig. 7).

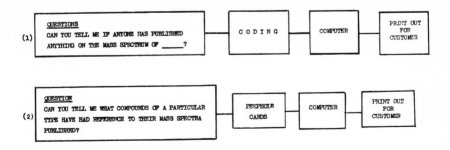

Fig. 6.   Mass spectra reference and retrieval — questions.

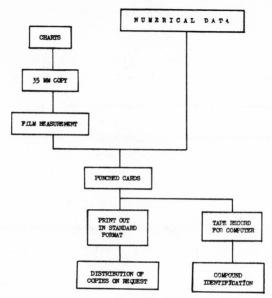

Fig. 7.   New low-resolution mass spectra.

## COMPOUND IDENTIFICATION

A study is being made, with the cooperation of Dr. W. Kelly of Unilever, of possible methods of using low-resolution mass spectra for compound identification.

Attempts are being made to assess the matching efficiency of several different methods using the complete spectrum in the computer file with particular attention being paid to instrumental effects.

## N.B.S. DATA ON ION PROCESSES—ANSWERING SERVICE

We have been fortunate in obtaining a copy of the *Data Collection on Ion Processes*, by Dr. H. M. Rosenstock at the National Bureau of Standards, Washington, D.C. We hope to be in a position shortly to answer questions on this in a form similar to that of the N.B.S. output, giving the ion, the appearance potentials, the methods used, and the article references.

## OTHER TOPICS

Other topics will be announced through the *Bulletin* as they arise.

# AUTHOR INDEX

Bold type denotes the citation of an entire paper in this volume. Italic type denotes a citation that is listed in a reference section.

Wallenstein, M. B., *359*
Walling, E., 229, *230*
Walter, G. R., *20*
Walters, W. D., *167*
Wankenne, H., 259, *269*
Wannier, G., 232, *270*, *358*
Wapstra, A. H., *111*
Warren, J. W., *358*
Watanabe, K., 232, 251, *270*, 342, 344,
    345, 346, 350, *358*, *359*
Watson, J. T., 11, *20*
Webster, B. R., *142*
Weissler, G. L., 341, 345, 346, *358*
Welti, D., *48*
Wexler, S., 254, 257, 259, *270*
Wheland, G. W., 307, *322*
Whitehead, J., 109, *111*, 208, *223*
Wijnen, M. H. J., *167*
Wilkins, T., *48*
Wilkinson, G., *322*
Wilkinson, P. G., *270*
Wilkstrom, S., *20*
Willhoft, E. M. A., 82, 83
Williams, A. E., *128*, *129*, *168*, *322*
Williams, D. H., *141*, *142*, *168*
Williams, E., *111*, 220, *223*
Williams, J. L., *224*
Wilmenius, P., *268*

Wilson, C. M., *223*
Wilson, H. W., **225**, 229, *230*
Winchell, P., *194*
Winters, H. F., *270*
Wittmaack, K., 248, *268*
Wolmer, R. L., *270*
Wolstenholme, W. A., 20, 109, *110*, *111*,
    207, 211, 213, 214, 215, 219, 220,
    *223*
Wong, S. K., *168*
Wood, D. R., *223*
Wood, M., *111*, *223*
Woolston, J. R., 94, *111*, 198, *223*
Wulfson, N. S., *141*

**Y**

York, D., 44, *48*

**Z**

Zahn von, V., *83*
Zelikoff, M., 251, *270*
Zellars, G. R., *194*
Zhemchuzhnui, S., *194*
Zyakoon, A. M., *141*

# SUBJECT INDEX

JTC 5081